D1214137

Looking Ahead

Looking

 McGRAW-HILL BOOK COMPANY

Ahead

The Papers of
David Sarnoff

NEW YORK   SAN FRANCISCO   TORONTO   LONDON   SYDNEY

Looking Ahead

Copyright © 1968 by David Sarnoff. All Rights Reserved.
Printed in the United States of America. No part of this
publication may be reproduced, stored in a retrieval system,
or transmitted, in any form or by any means, electronic,
mechanical, photocopying, recording, or otherwise, without
the prior written permission of the publisher or author.

Library of Congress Catalog Card Number 68–19491

54743

1234567890 HDBP 7543210698

Designer: Ernst Reichl

This book is gratefully dedicated to my associates and co-workers at RCA, and to all those whose contributions to the art and science of electronics and the industry of communications helped turn my dreams into reality.

A special characteristic of our time and of our modern technical industry is the great dynamism which marks them both. This dynamism is frequently the result of the genius of a small number of great individuals. A few names stand out in the history of electrical communications—Hertz, Marconi, Fleming, De Forest, Pupin, Bell, Edison, Armstrong, Zworykin, and Sarnoff.

Foreword

Dr. Jerome B. Wiesner

Provost
Massachusetts
Institute of Technology
Cambridge, Massachusetts

David Sarnoff's life has paralleled that of the communications industry. His career began about the time of Marconi's epoch-making experiments, and he actually participated in some of them—at first as a sixteen-year-old messenger and general handyman. What memories General Sarnoff must have and how proud he should be of his accomplishments. In any event, from the beginning, young David was exhibiting that intuitive grasp of where the future lay which has been the hallmark of his long and brilliant career.

Except for David Sarnoff, my list of heroes of the communications industry distinguished themselves primarily by their technical contributions to the communications field. David Sarnoff, though thoroughly competent technically, brought other rare gifts to his labors—unusual perception, organizational genius, an undaunted spirit, and especially, a love for his work. His prophetic visions of the enormous possibilities of wireless communications for commerce, public information, and entertainment, combined with his knowledge of the technical possibilities have provided the objectives and challenges of a major segment of the wireless-communications industry for more than half a century.

Our lifetime, our period in man's long history is different from any before because of the technology we have at our disposal. In effect, our technological creations have expanded by a factor of millions our human capabilities to do work and communicate and have, in principle, made it possible for the majority of our citizens to enjoy prosperity and a well-rounded life. The man whose papers are assembled here has played a key role in these developments.

When young Sarnoff adjusted a crystal receiver in search of faint dots and dashes from far-off ships at sea, his mind's eye saw radio broadcasting. In 1915 he wrote:

> I have in mind a plan of development which would make radio a "household utility" in the same sense as the piano or phonograph. The idea is to bring music into the house by wireless. . . . The receiver can be designed in the form of a simple "Radio Music Box" and arranged for several different wavelengths, which should be changeable with the throwing of a single switch or pressing of a single button.

And then he invented the system of providing programs for them by calling for ". . . a chain of national broadcasting stations . . . simultaneously radiating the same program, whatever it may be, to reach every city, every town, every village, every hamlet, every home in the United States and with an organization capable of measuring up to the responsibilities of that character of a national service." That last promise, a nontechnical one, has probably been the toughest one to fulfill.

While others still regarded the radio as an incomprehensible miracle, the General wrote:

> I believe that television, which is the technical name for seeing instead of hearing by radio, will come to pass in due course. It is not too much to expect that in the near future, when news is telegraphed by radio—say, to the United States—of important events in Europe, South America or the Orient, that a picture of the event will likewise be sent over by radio and both arrive simultaneously.

It took only twenty years of his life and untold millions of dollars of someone's money to realize that dream. Each time the path from idea to reality led through uncharted technical terrain and forced scientists and engineers to discover and develop new devices and systems, this leader forced us to invent and innovate. New fields had to be conquered—among them, electron optics, pulsed circuits, very high frequency broadcasting. These, in turn, have made possible many other technical accomplishments, such as radar, aerial navigation, the digital computer, and the electron microscope. The last is one of the truly great inventions of our time and has probably been the most important tool of modern-day life sciences. Modern science is only possible because of the electronic tools that flowed from communications research.

The uniqueness of David Sarnoff lies in his combination of a visionary and determined builder and hard-headed industrial leader. He was among the first to recognize the role that science could play in modern industry and to stake his future entirely on its promise. This is clear in the prototype of the contemporary executive which he put forward in 1927 when he wrote:

> The needs of the times will bring forth perhaps a new type of executive, trained in a manner not always associated with the requirements of business management. He will have to reckon with the constant changes in industry that scientific research is bringing. He will have to be able to approximate the value of technical development, to understand the significance of scientific research.

As teachers, our ambition is to get people to think, to act, to be creative, but we haven't really discovered how to do this. General Sarnoff taught himself this lesson. Thousands of people marveled at crystal sets; a few may have dimly understood where they would lead, but only one possessed, at the same time, the imagination, the courage, and the energy to make such fantasies become realities. David Sarnoff has persistently led the way. This collection of his speeches and writings is important historically not only for the insight it provides the communications industry; it also reflects the visions of an extraordinary human being whose insights and energies did so much to shape that industry. I am certain that it will have a wider influence, inspiring youngsters of successive generations and reminding us all of the great genius of America, the challenge it gives to us all to participate and create and grow as our talents permit.

Several years ago, Dr. Elmer W. Engstrom, then President of RCA, **Acknowledgments**
Dr. George H. Brown, Executive Vice President for Research and
Engineering, and Dr. James Hillier, Vice President, RCA Laboratories,
proposed the establishment of a library to house the documents and
mementos associated with my work in communications and electronics.
They chose a site adjacent to the RCA Laboratories in Princeton,
New Jersey, with the thought that the library would serve as a center
for students, scholars, and scientists doing research in these two basic
areas of modern technology.

Beginning in late 1966, some 1,000 volumes covering technical and
commercial activities, letters, public statements and speeches were
transferred from my New York residence and my office files to their
new home in Princeton. As this work was nearing completion,
Kenneth W. Bilby, an Executive Vice President of RCA and my
associate in the establishment of the library, suggested that excerpts
from the major documents be assembled in book form for the convenience of researchers and for young people interested in careers in electronics.

The idea was broached to McGraw-Hill, whose editors responded
favorably. The extensive job of selecting and presenting the material
was a year-long undertaking. I am indebted to Mr. Bilby and Harold
Queen, and also to Mrs. Zenith H. Gross and Mrs. Jean Ely for their
valuable suggestions.

I wish to express to them, and to all those who have helped in
the establishment of the David Sarnoff Library, my profound thanks
and appreciation.

David Sarnoff

Contents

xiii

6 Science, Technology, and Human Affairs 193

CONTENTS

CHAPTER 1

Wireless Communications

If the history of communications in the twentieth century could be said to begin at any one time and place, the most logical point to choose would probably be a small area of the English Channel, near Dover, on a stormy day in 1899. From this "locus," a ship in distress signaled for help in an entirely new and dramatic fashion, setting in motion the chain of events, possibilities, and prophecies that are the material of this book.

The captain of this ship had agreed, fortunately for himself and his shipmates, to carry aboard a piece of experimental equipment put together by the Wireless Telegraph and Signal Company, Ltd., a recently established firm dedicated to the development of wireless telegraphy by electromagnetic waves. The equipment was indeed experimental since the first patent for it had been issued just three years before. Its inventor was also young—in 1899, Guglielmo Marconi was only twenty-five years old. In the crisis, however, the equipment worked. Help did come, and the ship was saved.

The event was widely publicized. Here at last, perhaps, was the solution to a problem as old as civilization itself. Having no means of communicating with land or with other ships except by such short-range devices as lanterns, cannons, and flags, a ship at sea usually faced disaster totally alone and un-aided. With wireless, both the ship and its personnel would have a far greater chance of survival. It was in this application, therefore, that the immense importance of Marconi's invention was first recognized. In 1901, Marconi spanned the Atlantic with the letter "S" transmitted by wireless in Morse. The oceans ceased to be a barrier to communications; the air above them became a highway.

By 1906, only five years later, wireless had become an established part of the burgeoning technology. A number of companies had entered the field, and there were wireless stations all over the world. Hundreds of ships were equipped with wireless. The Marconi Wireless Telegraph Company of America, né Wireless Telegraph and Signal Company, opened an office in New York. This office had the good judgment to hire as its new office-boy a fifteen-year-old immigrant from Russia named **3**

David Sarnoff. The pay was $5.50 a week. In less than a year, young Sarnoff was promoted to junior wireless operator. The $7.50 a week he then received was almost enough to support his mother and younger brothers and sister in the bleak hardships of a Brooklyn slum.

Curiously enough, a second crucial event in the history of radio communications, and in the personal history of David Sarnoff, also involved a ship in distress. This time, however, the ship was not saved. On April 14, 1912, Sarnoff was on duty as wireless operator at the John Wanamaker installation in New York when a message came through from the S.S. Olympic, 1,400 miles away: "S.S. Titanic ran into iceberg. Sinking fast." For seventy-two sleepless hours, Sarnoff remained at his post, gathering and relaying the information that gradually unfolded into tragedy. "It seemed," he wrote, many years later, "as if the whole anxious world was attached to those phones." At the end of his "long tryst with the sea," both he and radio (the newer term for "wireless") were famous.

Sarnoff's career had received a powerful impetus. Within a few months he was made radio inspector for the American Marconi Company and soon after became chief radio inspector and assistant chief engineer. In 1914, at the age of twenty-three, he became contract manager of the Marconi Company, a position which ideally suited his particular genius. Now he was free to explore new techniques for improving services and building business, to analyze new inventions and investigate new applications, and, above all, to develop those insights, those "glimpses into the future," for which he was to become famous. It was during this period that he acquired the habit of expressing his opinions and proposals on paper. The first of the hundreds of memoranda, letters, articles, and speeches that trace his long association with the communications field is dated 1914. These materials are presented here in extracted form for brevity and convenience. The complete texts are available as indicated in the sources following each excerpt.

4

Letter to E. J. Nally, Vice-president and General Manager
Marconi Wireless Telegraph Company of America
January 26, 1914

The following is a report of our activities in the railroad field.

On the 22nd instant, a special train left Hoboken with about five hundred members of the American Society of Civil Engineers who were guests of the Lackawanna Railroad. A wireless demonstration was given, and the apparatus worked satisfactorily. The following day's edition of *The New York Times* was quite descriptive regarding the wireless demonstration and, in fact, devoted more space to that than to the construction of the new Lackawanna bridge, which was really the cause of the special trip. . . .

While on this trip, I had an opportunity of meeting most of the engineers of the various railroads of the country; all these men were very favorably impressed and almost unanimously expressed the opinion that wireless telegraphy would soon become an important feature of railroad operation. . . .

Report to F. M. Sammis, Chief Engineer
Marconi Wireless Telegraph Company of America
Subject: Interview with New York Central
January 3, 1914

During my interview, I learned that the chief traction engineer has been commissioned by the New York Central Railroad to look into the question of wireless as applied to the railroad, from the engineering and scientific standpoint. Mr. Schwartz is desirous of obtaining a system which would enable him to signal from the rear end of a long freight train (approximately 1 mile long) to the front of the train or to the engineer; in fact, he wishes more than merely signaling—he wants to operate a relay which will, in turn, close a local circuit. This circuit can, of course, be made to do whatever he may desire.

He wished to know whether this idea was possible or impossible. I told him of course that, so far as I knew, this had never been at- 5 tempted in railroad work but that I could see no reason for it being impossible.

. . . As I see it, the rear car could be equipped with an antenna and the front car with an antenna. An automatic device could be installed in the rear which, when desired, could be set into operation and affect the coherer in the front car or engine room, thereby closing the local circuit. This provided a suitable relay can be obtained.

The next question raised was the source of energy. Mr. Schwartz brought up another hypothetical question, viz., the design of a small generator. . . . The best scheme, of course, would be the use of a small spark coil, which, in view of the short distance required, would be perfectly feasible.

Summing up the situation, it appears to me that it is possible to develop a small portable set which can be made to do the work required by Mr. Schwartz. This would have many advantages for railroad work. . . .

Should you think the above impractical, I would submit for your consideration the advisability of making up a small buzzer set. The buzzer could be installed in the engine room, and the small spark coil in the rear of the train. A prearranged order of signals or combinations could be entered into between the brakeman or conductor and the engineer, and with the first and last cars equipped with an antenna, it seems perfectly feasible that the conductor, in the rear, and the engineer, at the front, could keep in communication. As I understand the matter, it is not possible—or at least it is impractical—to equip long freight trains with bell service or other direct-contact means of communication. Therefore, the arrangement such as I suggest herein may be of sufficient value to induce the railroad companies to adopt it, particularly in view of the fact that the apparatus is simple and inexpensive. . . .

(Mimeographed texts: David Sarnoff Library,
Princeton, N.J.)

A Notable Wireless Advance
Armstrong's Regenerative Circuit

Memorandum to F. M. Sammis, Chief Engineer
Marconi Wireless Telegraph Company of America
February 2, 1914

On January 30th, I met Mr. E. H. Armstrong, Professor Morecroft, and Mr. Roy Weagant, with whom I proceeded to our high-power station at Belmar, N.J., to test Mr. Armstrong's receiving system.

Two aerials were erected, one about 1,600 feet long and the other the entire length of the masts erected at Belmar.

Signals were heard from Clifden, Ireland, at about 4 P.M. (New York time), and from this time until we finished experimenting, which was about 5 A.M. (New York time), January 31st, no appreciable variation of intensity of Clifden signals was noticeable. . . .

There was no difficulty in reading Clifden signals when the telephone receivers were on the table, and I stood about 12 feet away from the telephone. With a loudspeaking telephone connected to the receiver, signals could be read in the adjoining room.

. . . Speaking relatively of received signals means, of course, very little, since the human ear is not to be depended upon, but an idea of the difference may be obtained when it is stated that signals from Clifden on Armstrong's receiver could be read with ease with telephones on the table when signals on our receiver were barely readable with the telephones on the ears.

. . . At about midnight (New York time), I heard "HU"— Poulsen station at Honolulu—trying to work with the Poulsen station at San Francisco. . . . Signals received from Honolulu were sufficiently strong to be read with the telephones on the table.

At 1:25 A.M., January 31st, I heard the Telefunken station at Nauen, Germany, calling "P.O.Z." . . . The text of the message and the beginnings and endings signified very clearly that it was the Nauen station transmitting. The signals from the Nauen station were very good and strong. . . .

I would state that the results obtained with Mr. Armstrong's receiver are sufficiently convincing to warrant our most careful investigation of his patents and circuits, etc., for I believe that his device has tremendous advantages, and unless there be other systems of equal merits, which are unknown to me, I am of the opinion that it is the most remarkable receiving system in existence.

(Book: *Radio and David Sarnoff*, by E. E. Bucher, part 1, p. 112.)

The Need for Skilled Wireless Operators

Paper presented to Institute of Radio Engineers
New York City, September, 1914

With the increased number of ship and shore stations, with the present government regulation of wavelengths, and with the constant increase in the volume of traffic, it is most desirable to so regulate the transmission of radiograms that they may be accurately received with maximum efficiency during a minimum of time. To accomplish this result, three factors must be given constant consideration:

1. Efficient operation, which, among other qualifications, calls for a competent telegraphist
2. Efficient apparatus
3. System and brevity in transmission and the elimination of all superfluous words and symbols

The importance of the human element in radio communications cannot be overestimated.

It seems to be an open question as to which of the following combinations is preferable: An older and, within reasonable limits, less efficient type of equipment in the hands of a skilled radio operator or a modern and more efficient set in the hands of a poor operator. My own observations and experiences in connection with the problem incline me to favor the skilled operator. However, I fully appreciate the necessity and desirability of having the ideal combination, namely, the good operator and the good set. . . .

An amusing feature of the present radio laws and regulations was recently brought to light when it was found that a vessel not required by law to carry wireless apparatus, but which was voluntarily equipped, sailed with a skilled operator in charge who, however, did not have a license. Had the vessel sailed without an operator, the law would have been fully complied with, but because the vessel sailed with an unlicensed operator on board, the owners became liable for a violation of the law. It would have been an interesting sequel had that operator been the means of saving the lives of several hundred people on some vessel in distress.

I do not, of course, mean to imply that licenses for radio operators are unnecessary; I simply cite an instance where the regulations might have defeated the very purpose for which they were designed.

In this connection, it should be noted that any wireless company which guarantees to furnish operators and equipments to fully comply with the requirements of the law must at all times be on the *qui vive* to see that all operators are in possession of the proper licenses before they are assigned for duty at any radio station. Companies furnishing operators endeavor to employ only those holding first-grade licenses, for unforeseen circumstances may arise and make it imperative to transfer an operator from a cargo ship to a passenger ship requiring a first-grade operator.

(RCA technical magazine: *Wireless Age*, October, 1914.)

THE ISSUE OF GOVERNMENT CONTROL

Editor's Note   *In November, 1916, a plan was placed before Congress for authorizing the Navy to operate radio stations in competition with private industry even in peacetime. Under this program, rates and traffic would be regulated by the government, which was apparently seeking control of the radio communications field. Sarnoff testified before the Committee in his capacity as Secretary of the Institute of Radio Engineers.*

Free Enterprise in Communications

Statement before Interdepartmental Committee on
Radio Legislation of Congress
Washington, D.C., November 21, 1916

Many important problems in radiotelegraphy and telephony are still unsolved—as, for example, the problems of long-range radiotelephony, adequate selective reliability, call systems, and the elimination of atmospheric strays.

The solution of these important problems calls for the highest engineering and inventive talent and research. Such inventive effort and research can only exist under free institutions and under the stimulus of healthy competition.

Certain foreign governments have assisted, and not opposed, individual initiative and private enterprise in developing the radio communications systems of their countries with great success.

Government competition, or confiscation by the government, would effectively stifle inventive efforts.

The military control of radio, or any public-service communications, in times of peace virtually constitutes a continuous military inquisition into private correspondence, an undemocratic and dangerous institution.

The reliability and superiority of our radio communications in times of sudden national peril are dependent upon the inventive

10

and engineering resources of the nation, which should, therefore, be kept at the highest pitch and the broadest scope.

The Board of Direction of the Institute of Radio Engineers is opposed to the competition by any department of the government, and particularly by any military or naval department, with existing organizations founded for radio communication.

BOARD OF DIRECTION, INSTITUTE OF RADIO ENGINEERS

by *David Sarnoff*, Secretary

(Book: *Radio and David Sarnoff*, by E. E. Bucher, part 1, pp. 148–149.)

Opposing a Navy Wireless Monopoly

Testimony before Congressional Committee on the
Merchant Marine and Fisheries
Hearings to regulate radio communications
Washington, D.C., December 12, 1918

The passage of this bill (H.R. 13,159) would stifle the development of the radio art. Those testifying on behalf of this bill apprehended that the opponents of the bill would contend that its passage and enactment in the law would stifle the growth and development of the radio art, and well were they justified in their apprehension.

Not only do we contend that such would be the case, but we honestly and firmly believe it to be true. It may be said of us that we are commercial men and, as such, our opinion on this subject is perhaps not an impartial one. But what can be said of the opinion of the technical man and the inventor—who, the naval officer asks us to believe, would fare better under a government ownership and naval monopoly of radio communication than he does at present? Why do not these technical men and inventors employed by commercial companies, here described as victims of the present system, come before you and urge the passage of this bill and the creation of a government monopoly? And more significant still, what are the views and opinions expressed by independent scientists and inventors, whose long experience in the fields of discovery and invention

11

have qualified them to speak authoritatively on this all-important phase of the question? . . .

It should also be recognized that most of the inventions and improvements . . . have been made by the practical and technical men employed by the various commercial interests concerned with the operation of radio stations. . . .

Actual operating conditions at the stations, and especially with the equipment employed, form in most cases the basis upon which new thought, new ideas, were founded which have resulted in invention and improvement. If the Navy Department is given a monopoly over the operation of all radio stations in this country, where will these outside technical experts obtain their further experience and knowledge of actual operating conditions?

(Book: *Radio and David Sarnoff*, by E. E. Bucher, part 1,
pp. 189–191A.)

Continuing Fight against Navy Wireless Monopoly

Statement before the Senate Committee on Naval Affairs
Hearings on government ownership of communications
Washington, D.C., October 9, 1919

I have had the privilege of attending all previous hearings of the Committee on this subject . . . but I have not come prepared to discuss this bill, which was only introduced yesterday.

However, it seems to me that the bill is so far-reaching in its scope and so all-important to the general subject of radio communication that a great deal of attention should be given to it before it is enacted into legislation, if it is to become a law.

Throughout the hearings before this Committee and before the committees of the House which have dealt with this subject, it was apparent that Congress is opposed to giving the Navy Department a monopoly of radio communication. In other words, government ownership is objectionable.

Now this bill, in my judgment, will result in time in precisely
12   the thing that Congress had evidenced its opposition to, and my

reasons for entertaining such opinion I shall be very glad to state.
In the first place, competition by the Navy Department without restriction, such as this bill proposes, is unnecessary and unwarranted.
In the second place, the government is not subject to the same conditions as govern the operation of private companies, and therefore
competition with the government is just as impracticable and just as
impossible in radio as it is in any other business.

No provision is made here as to rates, the authority for which is
vested in the Secretary of the Navy. So it is a comparatively simple
matter for the Navy Department to introduce rates for the service
which would result in private companies going out of business; and
thus instead of directly, we would indirectly come to government
ownership and government monopoly of radio communication. . . .

This bill (S-3177) would at once permit the Navy Department to
handle commercial business on the Atlantic Coast as well as on the
Pacific Coast and with South America—in fact, anywhere else where
the Navy is able to communicate. And it seems to me that if this bill
becomes a law, private enterprise would, and in my judgment
should, hesitate a long time before investing a dollar in a commercial wireless company.

. . . All the legislation which is now being proposed for wavelength control, or communication control, points in the same direction, namely, the greatest freedom and the greatest control to
government agencies and government stations. Therefore, if private
enterprise does not have the same freedom in the matter of operation and in the matter of wavelengths, it could not withstand the
competition from the government if rates were dropped to a point
where private operation would be unprofitable.

(Book: *Radio and David Sarnoff*, by E. E. Bucher, part 1,
pp. 223–223A.)

Congressional interest in government operation of radio communi- Editor's Note
cations declined in the fall of 1919, and the proposed legislation
was abandoned.

NEW APPLICATIONS FOR RADIO

Greater Use of Shortwaves

Letter to Edward J. Nally, President
Radio Corporation of America
January 10, 1920

While dealing with the subject of transmission and reception on shortwaves, I might record a hunch which I have held for some time and which I have discussed with a number of radio engineers, who, I should say in justification of their opinions, definitely disagree with me. I refer to the possibility of employing shortwaves for long-distance communications and, perhaps eventually, transoceanic communications. The obvious answer to this is that daylight absorption makes impractical the use of shortwaves over long distances, but I doubt whether a careful and exhaustive research has been made on this point. Perhaps extreme amplification, such as is possible with the Armstrong amplifier, or even greater amplification, which should be possible, may detect radio signals from shortwaves where present-day amplification fails to do so. The advantages of employing shortwaves over long distances are, of course, well known to engineers, who recognize that greater freedom from static and station interference is possible when employing shortwaves.

(Book: *Radio and David Sarnoff*, by E. E. Bucher, part 1, p. 251.)

RCA Business Prospects

Report to Owen D. Young, Chairman of Board of Directors
Radio Corporation of America
January 30, 1920

It is obvious that we must have suitable apparatus for sale before we can actually sell in large quantities. . . .

The design of radio apparatus should be treated as a special problem—accessibility, reliability, and low manufacturing costs are prerequisites. . . .

The problems involved in connection with the development, manufacture, and sales of radio devices are made more difficult by reason of the rapid changes of the art; no sooner has a particular device been developed than it is made obsolete by some improvement which has made the sale of the earlier device impractical. . . .

Because of this important fact, it is not feasible to order very large quantities of any one item unless there is a fair probability of the universal need for such an item. The design of any type of transmitter might be made obsolete at any time by an improved design.

. . . The question of high-power apparatus and sales has not been treated in this report. However, the same thought as expressed elsewhere in this report, namely, that every vessel afloat is a potential possibility for a radio equipment, equally applies to the question of a high-power radio station for every country in the world. Each country should—and, in my judgment, ultimately will—be equipped with a high-power radio station, capable of international communications. This will come about for national reasons if not for purely commercial reasons. The war has taught the nations of the world that communication is vital to national defense, and each nation will desire to be independent of the other so far as its communications with the rest of the world are concerned. **Worldwide Sales Possibility**

(Book: *Radio and David Sarnoff,* by E. E. Bucher, part 1, p. 299.)

Extending Radio Communications

Article in *The New York Herald*
Issue of May 14, 1922

As an internationalizing agency, radio broadcasting is an instrumentality which, if properly used, may well break down prejudices, help men to understand each other, and sway and even govern national **15** and international motives by bringing the personality, the intelligence, and the thought of the world's great men to millions and hundreds of millions of people everywhere. It is right to think of this wonderful invention in terms removed from mere amusement, to conceive it as leading to something more than the hearing of a sound.

Radio communication of the future obviously tends to include all moving vehicles; it is already beyond the experimental stage for installations on ships at sea, in submersibles, in aircraft, and on railroad trains. It is reasonable to expect its eventual application to automobiles and even, in some cases, to individuals.

In a competitive sense, the future of radio is equally bright. Its opportunities in long-distance communications are manifold, as evidenced by the fact that messages can be sent through the air at tremendous speeds of transmission, and commercially, more words per minute mean less cost per word. With lessened cost, there will naturally be created new classes of service, until the day may come when a businessman will look upon the writing of a letter to Europe on an urgent subject as an archaic practice.

The practical vision of the future of radio does not include, however, the scrapping of undersea cable systems; radio will supplement rather than supplant cables. In the first place, experience has shown that new inventions usually result in the improvement of existing methods. In the second place, communication facilities always have been inadequate—just as new subways never quite relieve congestion —and the increase in facilities will cause increase in new services. It is inconceivable that the development of the transmission of intelligence will go forward at a leisurely pace; everything points to a very great acceleration. In putting an end to the single point-to-point limitation imposed upon the cable, radio will become the dominating method of conducting long-distance communications and will hold that leadership.

Rich Field for Development

In some measure, the same considerations apply to the future prospects of radiotelephony over land. In the mobile services, in connecting up isolated communities, and in connecting the shore with the sea, there is a rich field for development. That radio will supplant the wire telephone is not to be contemplated. Wire-telephone communication, as we know it today, has the greatest utility for the type of service rendered. It is a wonderfully developed and complete system for seeking out for the user, through a wire network and central-exchange personnel, the particular individual wanted. This entire system, this entire service, would have to be duplicated to establish radiotelephony on a parity in usefulness; and even if this were technically practicable with radiotelephony—which it is not —there is no economic justification for such duplication. The radio-telephone, on the other hand, has a large sphere reserved for it in reaching locations where wires cannot be placed or maintained, in spanning inland waters or connecting up islands off the coast. As a supplement to wire telephony alone, radio is assured of a great future—which again directs me to the subject of broadcasting, a field that distinctly belongs to radio.

To those of us who watched every step in the onward march of radio, who saw scientific principles shaping themselves into business facts, who sensed the trend of research in the development of wireless, the instantaneous success of radiophone broadcasting does not come as a surprise. In 1915, from the possibilities that could be foreseen, I had worked out a plan for radio broadcasting in commercial detail and submitted it for consideration by my company.

The time was not ripe, however, for action on this project; we were in the midst of war activities, and the devices for radiophone transmission and reception had not been perfected to the point to which they have been brought at the present day. Broadcasting is a reality now. . . .

The hearthside circle is only a small part of the unmeasured sphere of its influence, however. Country schools cannot afford to employ the best teachers or the most able lecturers. Think of a system of rural education augmented through the setting up of a broadcasting station with a range of several hundred miles and connecting up within that radius a thousand country schools. Appraise the benefit of having one skilled lecturer in history or geography or hygiene, or whatever the subject may be, deliver his lesson as the children listen in their schoolrooms, possibly with the interspersing of

New Uses of Radio

17

appropriate items of entertainment and music to hold the children's interest.

And what may we expect when the telephone reaches across the ocean? Up to the present time, there has been no way for transoceanic transmission of the human voice because the cables lying on the bottom of the ocean are not suitable for speech transmission. They can carry feeble currents for telegraphy but not for telephony, because of the distortion of the speech and for other technical reasons. But with the radiotelephone, it may be predicted that within the next few years, and possibly sooner, we shall be talking across the Atlantic Ocean. It will be possible then for a man in New York to pick up his ordinary wire telephone, secure connection with the radiotelephone station which will carry his voice across the ocean, and connect up with his partner or business associate on the other side.

. . . Consider also one application of international broadcasting by radio: an international conference to make open covenants openly arrived at—and the whole world "listening in." Someday, and perhaps in the not very distant future, the dream will be a reality. When it is possible for the peoples of the world to listen to the deliberations of statesmen, to have firsthand knowledge of the functioning of their executives in power, then the voice of the people may literally be heard. . . .

(Book: *Radio and David Sarnoff*, by E. E. Bucher, part 2, p. 331; part 26, pp. 3581–3584.)

High-power Shortwave Broadcasting

Letter to E. J. Nally, President
Radio Corporation of America
August 2, 1922

. . . As you know, I have been a believer in the possibilities of shortwaves for a number of years, and I have had my faith more or less strengthened by what Senatore Marconi told us during his last

visit in America about his experiments and success with shortwaves.
I appreciate and have great respect for the views of our technical
experts, who have cautioned me not to hope for too much from
shortwaves because of the problems of reflection, refraction, and
dissipation; yet, no doubt because my knowledge is so little as compared with our technical experts, I am not so troubled by the difficulties which they with their greater knowledge can see, and I,
therefore, place no brakes on my imagination in this new field of
development.

Although it is purely a speculative statement and necessarily
based on incomplete knowledge and information, yet it would not
surprise me if in the next few years we find that a radio signal . . .
will travel around the world and be received through the highly sensitive and delicate receiving instruments which are rapidly projecting themselves into the radio art. . . .

It may well be that someday in the future we shall signal and
talk across the Atlantic and Pacific with short instead of long
waves. . . .

(*Early Reports in Radio*, by David Sarnoff, vol. 1, 1914–
1924, pp. 122–125; David Sarnoff Library, Princeton, N.J.)

Communications and Commerce

Address before New York Electrical Society
New York City, November 22, 1922

I think America may be justly proud of the fact that the center of
the world's most modern communication system has transferred
from London to New York. The center of the world's communications by radio is the United States, although London still retains
its preeminence as the cable center.

There is a very great relationship between communications and
commerce. When we speak of maritime service, we say that trade
follows the flag, but before trade can follow the flag, communications must precede it, and it may thus be said that trade follows
communications, as well as the flag. Therefore, a great commercial **19**

importance attaches to adequate and reliable communications, whether the method be by radio or by cable. Great Britain had the foresight to recognize the significance of this by developing a predominant position in the world's cable system. But the United States was quick to see the possibilities opened up by radio, and in the brief span of some two years, we have acquired unquestioned leadership in the more modern art of world communications. There are more commercial radio circuits in operation in the United States at present (1922) than there are in all the rest of the world combined.

An important aspect of radio communication, from a technical standpoint, is its great possibilities for high-speed transmission. Already it has been practicable to send and receive some 100 words per minute and to operate duplex, which means sending and receiving at the same time—in other words, a speed of 200 words per minute from each of these circuits. Higher speeds of operation already have been attained with radio than have been attained by transoceanic cables during the past forty years. The significance of high speed is cheaper communications, and cheaper communications mean greater intercourse among nations and peoples, with the commercial and social advantages that follow favorable international relationships and international understanding. . . .

(Book: *Radio and David Sarnoff*, by E. E. Bucher, part 2, p. 336.)

Power and Distance in Communications

Address before British Empire Chamber of Commerce
for the United States
New York City, December 16, 1924

Theoretically, there is no reason why, when we send out a radio signal, even with a feeble power, that power should not travel over the entire universe—why it should not be heard everywhere if one has a delicate enough instrument to receive it. Yet we have to use great power, 200 kilowatts and more, to transmit these messages regularly and commercially. It is our lack of knowledge rather than our possession of it which makes these great powers and forces necessary. We are dealing with Nature with brute force. We release sufficient energy into the atmosphere so as to overcome the "parasites of the air," as we call them—static and other forces that interfere with the signals. But as we become better informed on the forces of Nature in the air, so we shall be able to reduce the amount of energy necessary to negotiate distances; and with that reduction will come greater simplicity and more economy of operation, and of course, all that means cheaper rates. But you understand that I am speculating now about something concerning which we do not know much as yet.

(Book: Radio and David Sarnoff, by E. E. Bucher, part 2,
p. 419.)

Extending the Radio Spectrum

Article in New York Evening Post, issue of Feb. 7, 1925
Reprinted by permission of New York Post
Copyright 1925 New York Evening Post

The question has been asked, "Will shortwaves replace long waves in the operation of big commercial stations?" In answering the question, let me say first that I see no reason for confining long-distance or transoceanic radio communications to a single band of waves, whether they be long or short.

. . . There is no reason why the big commercial station should be constrained to operate within a small portion of the available "radio spectrum." On the contrary, I believe that our expanding knowledge will enable us sooner or later to make the whole radio spectrum available for this purpose. It may well be that under normal conditions, the longer wavelengths will give the most reliable communications over long distance but that under certain conditions, the very short waves may be found to be most desirable for communications over similar distances.

. . . Chiefly due to the development of the vacuum-tube transmitter, the shortwave end of the radio spectrum has become available for exploitation. The results now being obtained on shortwaves

21

indicate that their usefulness in the long-distance communications field will be considerable.

. . . It may be confidently expected that the use of shortwaves will immeasurably and in a practical way advance the art of radio communications in the field of wireless telegraphy as well as wireless telephony.

. . . To my mind, one of the greatest advantages which will result from experiments now being conducted with shortwaves is the increased knowledge we shall gain of the behavior of different wavelengths in the conducting medium between the sending and receiving stations. Much has already been accomplished in perfecting the radio sending and receiving instruments, but much more still remains to be learned about what actually occurs to the electromagnetic waves in the space which separates the receiver from the transmitter. The possibilities of radio development in all branches of the art, however, are too great and promising to permit any negative views that its advance will stop here or there.

(Book: *Radio and David Sarnoff*, by E. E. Bucher, part 2, pp. 447–449.)

The "Titanic" Disaster

Report in *The Saturday Evening Post*
Issue of Aug. 7, 1926

When John Wanamaker decided to equip his New York and Philadelphia stores with radio stations more powerful than any then installed in the commercial field, I applied for the place of operator because it would leave my evenings free to take a course in engineering at Pratt Institute. So it happened that I was on duty at the Wanamaker station in New York and got the first message from the *Olympic*, 1,400 miles out at sea, that the *Titanic* had gone down.

I have often been asked what were my emotions at that moment. I doubt if I felt at all during the seventy-two hours after the news came. I gave the information to the press associations and newspapers at once, and it was as if bedlam had been let loose.
22 Telephones were whirring, extras were being cried, crowds were

gathering around newspaper bulletin boards. The air was as disturbed as the earth. Everybody was trying to get and send messages. Some who owned sets had relatives or friends aboard the *Titanic*, and they made frantic efforts to learn something definite. Finally, President Taft ordered all stations in the vicinity except ours closed down so that we might have no interference in the reception of official news.

Word spread swiftly that a list of survivors was being received at Wanamaker's, and the station was quickly stormed by the grief-stricken and curious. Eventually, a police guard was called out and the curious held back, but some of those most interested in the fate of the doomed ship were allowed in the wireless room. Vincent Astor, whose father, John Jacob Astor, was drowned, and the sons of Isidor Straus were among those who looked over my shoulder as I copied the list of survivors. Straus and his wife went down, too.

I remember praying fervently that the names these men were hoping to see would soon come over the keys, but they never did.

Much of the time I sat with the earphones on my head and nothing coming in. It seemed as if the whole anxious world was attached to those phones during the seventy-two hours I crouched tense in that station.

I felt my responsibility keenly and, weary though I was, could not have slept. At the end of my first long tryst with the sea, I was whisked in a taxicab to the old Astor House on lower Broadway and given a Turkish rub. Then I was rushed in another taxicab to Sea Gate, where communication was being kept up with the *Carpathia*, the vessel which brought in the survivors of the ill-fated *Titanic*.

Here again, I sat for hours—listening. Now we began to get the names of some of those who were known to have gone down. This was worse than the other list had been—heartbreaking in its finality —a death knell to hope.

I passed the information on to a sorrowing world and, when messages ceased to come in, fell down like a log at my place and slept the clock around.

(Photostat of text: "Radio," by David Sarnoff, as told to
Mary Margaret McBride, *The Saturday Evening Post*,
Aug. 7, 1926; David Sarnoff Library, Princeton, N.J.) **23**

The Value of Ultrashort Waves

Letter to Guglielmo Marconi
New York City, September 4, 1930

I am highly interested in information which you gave me about the experiments you are now conducting with ultrashort waves, as I fully believe in the great possibilities which that spectrum offers. As you unlock the secrets of that part of the spectrum, you will bring forward enormous improvements in radio communication and in all radio applications. I am delighted to know that you are working along these lines and wish to reiterate the assurances that I have formerly given you that anything the Radio Corporation of America can do on its side to facilitate and assist you in your work will be gladly done. . . .

(Book: *Correspondence between Guglielmo Marconi and David Sarnoff*; one volume, unpaged.)

In Memory of Marconi

Remarks for broadcast on the death of Guglielmo Marconi
New York City, July 20, 1937

In the passing of Guglielmo Marconi, the world today has lost a great inventive genius—one whose name will live forever in the pages of history. On this sad occasion, it is a consolation to remember that the world did not wait until after Marconi's death to recognize and reward his great achievements. Both his own country and almost every other civilized nation have bestowed many honors upon him—and by doing so, have honored themselves. As long ago as 1909, he won the Nobel Prize for Physics, and the other awards, medals, degrees, and titles he received during his lifetime constitute a long and impressive list.

The widespread, international character of these symbols of recognition calls attention both to the universal nature of Marconi's immortal invention and to the fact that he himself was, in the finest sense, a true citizen of the world. The whole universe was the laboratory in which his mind and inspiration worked. Four centuries earlier, the great Italian explorer of geography, Christopher Columbus, had conquered an ocean and discovered a new continent. Marconi, the explorer of science, conquered space and united the whole world. He was the benefactor of all mankind.

The genius of Marconi was a gift to the people not of one nation but of all nations. His scientific achievements—like the radio waves themselves—transcended international boundaries. They benefit all men, everywhere, regardless of the man-made barriers of language, creed, and politics.

It was my great privilege to have known Guglielmo Marconi for more than thirty years, ever since I was a boy. He was always a source of inspiration to me, always a kind teacher and a loyal, helpful friend. It is impossible to put into words my deep sense of personal loss. I can only express my gratitude that my life should have been enriched by this friendship. . . .

(Book: Correspondence between Guglielmo Marconi and David Sarnoff; one volume, unpaged.)

RCA Progress: 1920 to 1947

Letter to Owen D. Young
New York City, August 4, 1947

In the first year of RCA's operations—1920—its gross income was $2 million, and for the same year, the gross income of the General Electric Company was $272 million.

I remember, and perhaps you will remember, too, that the first time we met, and you asked my views about the future possibilities of radio, I expressed to you, among other things, my belief that RCA would one day do as much business as the General Electric Company was doing at that time. I remember, too, saying to you that I believed you and I would like to see that day. You showed great pleasure at my youthful optimism and called my attention to the fact that the General Electric Company was doing business at the rate of almost $1 million for every working day of the year.

While that goal appeared high, I was not disturbed then because, as was said on another occasion, "It is wonderful to have an imagination unrestrained by the slightest knowledge of the facts." At that time, I had neither knowledge nor facts, but both of us had wholesome respect for enthusiasm and faith.

Now I have much pleasure in sending you the consolidated statement of RCA's operations for the first six months of the present year—a year of so-called "peace." You will note therefrom that the gross income of RCA is now running at the rate of $300 million a year!

I congratulate you on being here to see this happen, and I am glad to be here, too. Being twenty-seven years older and now encumbered by a little knowledge and many facts, I am reluctant to make predictions for the next quarter of a century. But I still retain the same enthusiasm for, and faith in, radio. And I know that you do, too.

(Original letter in bound volume: *Owen D. Young and David Sarnoff, 1923–1962*, David Sarnoff Library, Princeton, N.J.)

CHAPTER 2

Radio Broadcasting

"Ain't it a bully fight!" cried the announcer's water boy, and the nearly 400,000 lucky owners of crystal detector sets and one-tube receivers who heard in their earphones a blow-by-blow description of the Dempsey-Carpentier heavyweight championship fight agreed with him. Seated in distant theaters, ballrooms, and barns, they had a better idea of what was happening in the ring than the crowd that had made the hot and dusty trip to Jersey City to witness the event. Many of these wireless enthusiasts might have realized also the importance of what was taking place. For not only did Dempsey retain the heavyweight title on that hot July afternoon in 1921, but the first, great step in the development of radio broadcasting had been taken. And the young David Sarnoff saw his vision begin to take on the form of reality.

Six years earlier, when he was only twenty-four, Sarnoff had proposed to his employers at the Marconi Wireless Telegraph Company of America that a "Radio Music Box" could profitably be manufactured. With this, he said, music, lectures, and events of national importance could be brought into every American home, even those in the most remote areas. In the world of 1915, this was indeed a leap of the imagination!

The more immediate concerns of World War I prevented Sarnoff from pursuing this "visionary scheme," and it was not until 1920 that he again attempted to persuade his company (now RCA) to go into the radio business. Finally, the RCA board agreed to put up $2,000 to develop a receiver. The next year, with funds borrowed from other sources, Sarnoff financed the transmission of the Dempsey-Carpentier fight. The broadcast caused a sensation, and radio was on its way.

Those who are too young to remember radio before the advent of television may find it difficult to understand the tremendously important role that it played in shaping the cultural life of America during the decades that followed that historic broadcast. But the generation that listened to the daytime serials; the voices of newscasters Lowell Thomas, Elmer Davis, and Ed Murrow; the Hit Parade; and the President's Fireside Chats   **29** will know how deeply they affected the nation's tastes and thinking.

From the beginning, David Sarnoff realized that a potential power of vast influence existed in radio broadcasting, imposing great responsibilities on the broadcasters. Again and again during the early years of radio, he speaks and writes of these responsibilities. Thus, in 1922, he writes: ". . . broadcasting represents a job of entertaining, informing, and educating the nation and should, therefore, be distinctly regarded as a public service."

In 1924, the campaign for the Presidency was broadcast nationally for the first time—from the Republican and Democratic nominating conventions to the election returns and Coolidge's inaugural address. This new, political facet of radio made it apparent that some sort of regulation was essential to ensure the freedom of the airways. In testimony before a House committee, Sarnoff states, "So powerful an instrument for public good should be kept free from partisan manipulation."

To obtain the highest quality of broadcast material, he suggested that radio stations all over the country be linked through a broadcasting network and established as a public service. In 1926, under Sarnoff's guidance, the National Broadcasting Company was born.

By 1929, radio sales had reached $842 million a year in the United States. Broadcasting companies competed for advertisers, and advertisers competed for the rapidly increasing radio audience. The broadcast material in the 1930s often reflected the difficulties involved in appealing to mass audiences. To create programs for a whole population at once was an imposing problem, and to do this while maintaining standards of excellence required careful coordination and discipline in an industry that had grown immensely in a comparatively short period of time. That Sarnoff was deeply interested in this problem is apparent from his letter to Felix Frankfurter in 1934. Certainly, it must have been much in his mind when he organized the memorable NBC Symphony Orchestra and persuaded Arturo Toscanini to come to America as its conductor.

30

Since those first broadcasts in the early 1920s, one of the prime functions of radio has always been the coverage of important current happenings—from political speeches and debates to sporting events. Today, this function has been enlarged and extended. From the purely national scene, American radio now reaches out across the oceans. The Voice of America, proposed by Sarnoff in 1943, broadcasts all over the world, fighting "the battle between truth and falsehood . . . to make it possible for people everywhere to know the truth."

"Radio Music Box"

Memorandum to Edward J. Nally, Vice-president and General Manager
Marconi Wireless Telegraph Company of America
Sept. 30, 1915

I have in mind a plan of development which would make radio a "household utility" in the same sense as the piano or phonograph. The idea is to bring music into the house by wireless.

While this has been tried in the past by wires, it has been a failure because wires do not lend themselves to this scheme. With radio, however, it would seem to be entirely feasible. For example, a radiotelephone transmitter having a range of, say, 25 to 50 miles can be installed at a fixed point where instrumental or vocal music or both are produced. The problem of transmitting music has already been solved in principle, and therefore all the receivers attuned to the transmitting wavelength should be capable of receiving such music. The receiver can be designed in the form of a simple "Radio Music Box" and arranged for several different wavelengths, which should be changeable with the throwing of a single switch or pressing of a single button.

The "Radio Music Box" can be supplied with amplifying tubes and a loudspeaking telephone, all of which can be neatly mounted in one box. The box can be placed on a table in the parlor or living room, the switch set accordingly, and the transmitted music received. There should be no difficulty in receiving music perfectly **31** when transmitted within a radius of 25 to 50 miles. Within such a radius, there reside hundreds of thousands of families; and as all can simultaneously receive from a single transmitter, there would be no question of obtaining sufficiently loud signals to make the performance enjoyable. The power of the transmitter can be made 5 kilowatts, if necessary, to cover even a short radius of 25 to 50 miles, thereby giving extra-loud signals in the home if desired. The use of head telephones would be obviated by this method. The development of a small loop antenna to go with each "Radio Music Box" would likewise solve the antenna problem.

**News by Radio
Predicted**

The same principle can be extended to numerous other fields —as, for example, receiving lectures at home which can be made perfectly audible; also, events of national importance can be simultaneously announced and received. Baseball scores can be transmitted in the air by the use of one set installed at the Polo Grounds. The same would be true of other cities. This proposition would be especially interesting to farmers and others living in outlying districts removed from cities. By the purchase of a "Radio Music Box," they could enjoy concerts, lectures, music, recitals, etc., which might be going on in the nearest city within their radius. While I have indicated a few of the most probable fields of usefulness for such a device, yet there are numerous other fields to which the principle can be extended. . . .

The manufacture of the "Radio Music Box," including antenna, in large quantities would make possible their sale at a moderate figure of perhaps $75 per outfit. The main revenue to be derived would be from the sale of "Radio Music Boxes," which, if manufactured in quantities of a hundred thousand or so, could yield a handsome profit when sold at the price mentioned above. Secondary sources of revenue would be from the sale of transmitters. . . .

**$75 Million in Sales
Foreseen**

The company would have to undertake the arrangements, I am sure, for music recitals, lectures, etc., which arrangements can be satisfactorily worked out. It is not possible to estimate the total amount of business obtainable with this plan until it has been developed and actually tried out, but there are about 15 million families in the United States alone, and if only 1 million, or 7 percent of the total families, thought well of the idea, it would, at the figure mentioned, mean a gross business of about $75 million, which should yield considerable revenue.

Aside from the profit to be derived from this proposition, the possibilities for advertising for the company are tremendous, for its name would ultimately be brought into the household, and wireless would receive national and universal attention.

(Book: *Radio and David Sarnoff*, by E. E. Bucher, part 1, pp. 123–125.)

"RADIO MUSIC BOX"

Radio's Business Growth

Memorandum to E. W. Rice, Jr., President
General Electric Company
March 3, 1920

The "Radio Music Box" proposition (regarding which I reported to Mr. Nally in 1915 and to Mr. Owen D. Young on January 31, 1920) requires considerable experimentation and development, but having given the matter much thought, I feel confident in expressing the opinion that the problems involved can be met. With reasonable speed in design and development, a commercial product can be placed on the market within a year or so.

Should this plan materialize, it would seem reasonable to expect sales of 1 million "Radio Music Boxes" within a period of three years. Roughly estimating the selling price at $75 per set, $75 million can be expected. This may be divided approximately as follows:

1st year	100,000	Radio Music Boxes	$ 7,500,000
2nd year	300,000	Radio Music Boxes	22,500,000
3rd year	600,000	Radio Music Boxes	45,000,000
		Total	$75,000,000

33

Editor's Note   RCA's actual sales of Radio Music Boxes during the first three years
of its activities in this field were as follows:

1st year	1922:	$11,000,000
2nd year	1923:	22,500,000
3rd year	1924:	50,000,000
	Total	$83,500,000

(Book: *Radio and David Sarnoff*, by E. E. Bucher, part 1,
pp. 234–235.)

The First Major Sports Broadcast

Reports on radio broadcast of
Dempsey-Carpentier world's heavyweight championship fight
The Saturday Evening Post, Aug. 7, 1926
Reader's Digest, December, 1955

Editor's Note   *At the broadcast of the Dempsey-Carpentier championship match
in Jersey City on July 2, 1921, Major J. Andrew White, who was
then the editor of the RCA publication, Wireless Age, was the announcer. David Sarnoff was at his elbow to assist in the description
through the microphone of station WJY, temporarily installed by
RCA at Hoboken, N.J.*

*In later years, Sarnoff and White both published accounts in
popular magazines of that notable broadcasting event.*

*Following are excerpts from the reminiscences of J. Andrew
White, written for the Reader's Digest in December, 1955.*

A Crazy Experiment   . . . This experiment, frowned upon as "just plain crazy" by
financiers, had been built on the enthusiastic dream of young David
Sarnoff. To pull it off, Sarnoff and I had scrounged $1,500 from a
special account of the then new Radio Corporation of America.

The cheerfully stubborn Sarnoff first suggested sending entertainment and information over the air in 1915, when he was twenty-
four. The American Marconi Company, for which he was assistant
traffic manager, had been so skeptical that its board of directors
34   laughed heartily when it turned thumbs down on his idea.

. . . Each time Sarnoff brought up the subject—which he did
frequently—our company management (called, from 1919 onward,
the Radio Corporation of America) turned him down. Then in
1921, his luck turned. As it happened, a man named Tex Rickard
opened the door. While Sarnoff and I were talking about radio, pro-
moter Rickard had Europe and America talking about the coming
prizefight. . . .

Millions wanted to see the fight, but Rickard's arena seated only
91,000. If we could offer it on the air blow-by-blow while it was
happening, we would have a vast audience.

We lacked several things, however—including money. Then
Sarnoff, digging into his books as a general manager, discovered
$2,500 of RCA money in accumulated rentals of ship wireless equip-
ment. "Take it," he said to me. Then he added cautiously, "But
don't spend a nickel more than $1,500!". . .

Now we needed some public support in high places. If our
broadcast could be made a charity "benefit," that might turn the
trick. Anne Morgan, daughter of the banker J. P. Morgan, headed
the American Committee for Devastated France, and young Franklin Roosevelt was president of the Navy Club. Would they join
forces with us? Soon Sarnoff announced that these two organizations would get a share of the gate receipts wherever crowds paid
admissions to hear the radio broadcast. . . .

I was at ringside early on July 2, testing. From the railroad shack
at the other end of my telephone line, Owen Smith reported *all
well:* crowds were already gathering outside the theaters, and my
signal was coming in fine.

Finally, Dempsey, in his ragged red sweater, and the pale Car-
pentier, in a gray silk Japanese kimono, were in the ring. . . . That
was when I said, "Ladies and gentlemen, . . ." to begin the first big
radio broadcast.

. . . In the fourth round, Dempsey, bigger and more solidly
built, waded in to finish the fight. . . .

In a few minutes, Sarnoff and I were looking at a terse cable-
gram from RCA's president, who was vacationing in London. "You
have made history," it said.

We were tired and bleary-eyed, but in our minds' eyes, Sarnoff **35** and I were seeing the crowds that were pouring out of theaters and halls in Pittsburgh and St. Augustine, Boston and Washington, Albany, Philadelphia, and Akron, their ears full of a modern miracle. We knew then that the era of radio for the millions had begun.

(Photostat of text: "The First Big Radio Broadcast," by J. Andrew White, *Reader's Digest*, December, 1955; David Sarnoff Library, Princeton, N.J.)

Editor's Note   *In the August 7, 1926, issue of* The Saturday Evening Post, *David Sarnoff recalled his impressions of the Dempsey-Carpentier fight.*

A High-water Mark in Broadcasting

A feature of radio that early drew the man of the house toward what at first he was inclined to regard as a plaything was the prospect of hearing descriptions of his favorite athletic events broadcast by expert announcers. The pioneer in this field, so far as I know, was J. Andrew White, who, on July 2, 1921, announced the Dempsey-Carpentier fight from the ringside in Jersey City.

White worked out a scheme to equip theaters throughout the Middle Atlantic States to receive a blow-by-blow description of the battle, which he sent by way of a temporary station constructed at Hoboken. He had to use makeshift paraphernalia and trust to luck. Two nights before the fight, he called me up.

"Well, I'm in the soup," he announced cheerfully. "So far, we haven't been able to get a sound to register beyond Newark. We are averaging a complaint a minute just now."

That night, with White sick from worry, whatever was wrong with his transmission system—and he doesn't know to this day what that was—righted itself, and his patrons were able to assure those to whom they had sold tickets for listening in to the event that the show would come off as planned.

My remembrance of that fight is vivid. I went with White to his place at the ringside. It was a torrid day, and we all fried slowly in the sun. White was dripping with perspiration, and his throat was parched. In the excitement, a boy who had been brought along expressly to supply him with iced water forgot all about his duty, and when White, who could not speak except in his role of announcer, signaled for the vacuum bottle containing the precious fluid, the boy merely cried, "Yes, ain't it a bully fight!"

An exciting feature of the day for radio was that one news agency scooped the whole journalistic world by wireless. The reporter who had been listening to White at a downtown office flashed the word of Dempsey's victory by radio to Paris and, in spite of the many cables which had been leased by powerful newspapers, beat everybody by thirty-three seconds.

As a dramatic ending to the fight, the very instant that White finished pronouncing the words, "Dempsey remains the champion of the world," his transmitting set went smash. He could not have sent another syllable over it.

It was estimated that nearly 400,000 persons attended the Dempsey-Carpentier fight by proxy. This number seems infinitesimal in view of the millions who would listen in on a similar event now, but it was a high-water mark for those days and pointed the way to the prospective popularity of at least one kind of broadcasting.

(Photostat of text: "Radio," by David Sarnoff, as told to Mary Margaret McBride, *The Saturday Evening Post*, Aug. 7, 1926; David Sarnoff Library, Princeton, N.J.)

By the beginning of 1922, RCA was in the "Radio Music Box"   *Editor's Note*
business, and by the end of that year, their sales had totaled $11 million. Letting others settle into the profitable present, David Sarnoff continued to focus on the future. Perhaps more than anyone else, he saw the possibilities in this infant industry.

Union of Radio and Phonograph

Memorandum to RCA management
April 10, 1922

The radiotelephone, as a receiver of broadcast material, steps out of the role formerly played by a telephone instrument—namely, that of being part of a two-way communicating system, usually for tolls   **37**

—and enters the new field of being the important element of a one-way communication system.

The usefulness of such devices to the purchaser depends entirely on the character and continuity of the material broadcast by the radiotelephone sending station, or stations, within the range of the receiving instrument. Therefore, the extension of the radiotelephone to the home and the building up and maintenance of a large sales volume will depend on the organization of a broadcast sending service, designed to render a public service of an order which will be acceptable to the average, regarded as valuable by the public, and as such suitably protected by the government as to licenses, interferences, etc.

While it is possible to provide a variety of interesting material for broadcasting purposes, such as lectures, speeches, news, and educational items, yet in order to find popular appeal, the main features of the service will no doubt be musical and entertaining in character. Music, vocal and instrumental, must constitute the foundation of a broadcast service, and the brief experience to date has already demonstrated this fact.

Considering, then, that the radiotelephone, as a broadcast receiver, is (1) a product for the home, (2) primarily a musical instrument, and (3) dependent for its vitality and usefulness on a service which must meet the public taste, principally in music, we at once see the natural relationship between the radio instrument (which, for convenience, I shall refer to here as the Radiola) and the phonograph.

The Relationship between Radio and Phonograph

In addition to the natural relationship between the Radiola and the phonograph, there are also physical, structural, and economic elements which justify and, indeed, make advisable a happy association of the two instruments, which should live under the same roof. For one thing, they will take up less room in the home if they both stay in the same cabinet. Secondly, they will cost less when purchased as a combination radio and phonograph instrument in one cabinet than if purchased separately with two cabinets. Thirdly, some of the parts—as, for example, the horn or loudspeaker now used with each instrument—need not be duplicated where a combination instrument is used.

Technically, the Radiola and the phonograph are both trying to do the same kind of job, i.e., to reproduce, as faithfully as possible, speech or music. The phonograph employs mechanical means to accomplish this result; the Radiola, the electrical means. The former is old and has about reached the limits of its capabilities. The latter is new, in fact just begun, and the future holds for it untold possibilities. Fortunately, the electrical method of sound reproduction is applicable to the phonograph as well as to the Radiola, and any advance or improvement in the radio art of reproduction will be equally beneficial to phonograph-record reproduction, and the same device can be made to serve both purposes.

. . . Rapid and important advances in the art of sound reproduction are bound to follow now that the need for them is apparent and the field promising. Thus, radio may be expected, in the course of developing its own business, to produce inventions and improvements which not only will be applicable to the phonograph industry but may, indeed, technically govern or control the future of the phonograph.

(Book: *Radio and David Sarnoff*, by E. E. Bucher, part 2, pp. 310–312.)

Radio Is Here to Stay

Address before the Electrical Jobbers Convention
Hot Springs, Va., May 26, 1922

My belief is that radio broadcasting is here to stay—that regardless of the size of the problem, regardless of the difficulties that may beset our path, in radio broadcasting we have a force, an instrumentality greater than any that has yet come to mankind. Back of it is a philosophy, something more than a mere merchandising situation. When you transmit the human voice into the home, when you can make the home attuned to what is going on in the rest of the world, **39** you have tapped a new source of influence, a new source of pleasure and entertainment and culture that the world thus far has not been able to provide with any other known means of communication.

For these reasons, it is inconceivable to me, gentlemen, that mechanical limitations or economic limitations of the moment will stand in the way of making this a permanent industry. It may be that we are not wise enough ourselves to work out all these problems. It may be that we are not the fellows who will get permanent solutions to all of these problems. But certain it is, in my mind, that the day is coming, and perhaps not so far distant, when a man will be ashamed to admit that his home is not equipped with a radio broadcasting device, just as a man today would be ashamed to admit that his home is not equipped with a bathtub. I regard radio broadcasting as a sort of cleansing instrument for the mind, just as the bathtub is for the body. Hitherto, the home has been confined to four walls, and nothing in the home has been articulate except the telephone; but the telephone, wonderful as it is, is confined to a particular person, and no one thinks of the telephone except to accomplish a definite purpose. Now . . . the broadcasting station makes possible, for the first time in the history of civilization, communication with hundreds and thousands and, perhaps, millions of people, simultaneously. . . .

When you provide an institution of this kind, when you make it possible for men and women and children to sit in their homes and listen to opera and jazz, if you please, and lectures and political debates and market reports and all kinds of information of value, it seems to me that you have provided something which collectively represents a sufficient answer to the question of whether radio broadcasting is here to stay.

(Book: *Radio and David Sarnoff*, by E. E. Bucher, part 2, p. 314.)

National Broadcasting Envisaged

Letter to E. W. Rice, Jr., Honorary Chairman of the Board
General Electric Company
June 17, 1922

It seems to me that in seeking a solution to the broadcasting problem, we must recognize that the answer must be along national rather than local lines, for the problem is distinctly a national one.

Secondly, I think that the principal elements of broadcasting service are entertainment, information, and education, with emphasis on the first feature—entertainment—although not underestimating the importance of the other two elements. Expressed in other words, and considered from its broadest aspect, this means that broadcasting represents a job of entertaining, informing, and educating the nation and should, therefore, be distinctly regarded as a public service.

That this kind of job calls for specialists in the respective fields and that it requires expert knowledge of the public's taste and the manner in which to cater to the public's taste is apparent on the surface. That manufacturing companies or communications companies are not at present organized and equipped to do this kind of job in a consistent and successful way is to my mind also clear.

If the foregoing premises be correct, it would seem that the two fundamental problems calling for a solution are:

1. Who is to pay for broadcasting?
2. Who is to do the broadcasting job?

Many suggestions have been made by well-intentioned persons on the inside and outside in an endeavor to answer both the above problems, but to my mind none of the suggestions yet made with which I am acquainted is sufficiently comprehensive or capable of withstanding the test of real analysis, and this largely because the major portion of the suggestions thus far offered build a structure on a foundation which calls for voluntary payment by the public for the service rendered through the air.

41

With respect to problem No. 1: Attractive as the above suggestions are, I am of the opinion that the greatest advantages of radio —its universality and, generally speaking, its ability to reach everybody everywhere—in themselves limit, if not completely destroy, that element of control essential to any program calling for continued payment by the public. Stated differently, it seems to me where failure to make a payment does not enable a discontinuance of service—as, for example, in wire telephony, gas, electric light, or water supply—the temptation to discontinue payments on the ground of poor service, etc., is too great to make any system of voluntary public subscription sufficiently secure to justify large financial commitments or the creation of an administrative and collection organization necessary to deal with the general public. Therefore, if I am correct in assuming that such a foundation is insecure over a period of time, the superstructure built on this foundation is perforce equally weak.

For these reasons, I am led to the conclusion that the cost of broadcasting must be borne by those who derive profits directly or indirectly from the business resulting from radio broadcasting. This means the manufacturer, the national distributor (the Radio Corporation of America), the wholesale distributor, the retail dealer, the licensee, and others associated in one way or another with the business.

As to No. 2: When the novelty of radio has worn off and the public is no longer interested in the means by which it is able to receive but, rather, in the substance and quality of the material received, I think that the task of reasonably meeting the public's expectations and desires will be greater than any so far tackled by any newspaper, theater, opera, or other public information or entertainment agency. The newspaper, after all, caters to a limited list of subscribers. The theater presents its production to a literal handful of people, but the broadcasting station will ultimately be required to entertain a nation. No such audience has ever before graced the effort of even the most celebrated artist or the greatest orator produced by the ages.

The service to be rendered distinctly calls for a specialized organization with a competent staff capable of meeting the necessities of the situation.

The plan I have in mind and one which I respectfully suggest for your consideration and discussion . . . is as follows:

Let us organize a separate and distinct company, to be known as the Public Service Broadcasting Company or National Radio Broadcasting Company or American Radio Broadcasting Company, or some similar name.

This company to be controlled by the Radio Corporation of America, but its board of directors and officers to include members of the General Electric Company and the Westinghouse Electric Company and possibly also a few from the outside, prominent in national and civic affairs. The administrative and operating staff of this company to be composed of those considered best qualified to do the broadcasting job.

Such company to acquire the existing broadcasting stations of the Westinghouse Company and General Electric Company, as well as the three stations to be erected by the Radio Corporation; to operate such stations and build such additional broadcasting stations as may be determined upon in the future. . . .

**Formation of
Broadcasting Company**

Since the proposed company is to pay the cost of broadcasting as well as the cost of its own administrative operations, it is, of course, necessary to provide it with a source of income sufficient to defray all of its expenses.

As a means for providing such income, I tentatively suggest that the Radio Corporation pay over to the broadcasting company 2 percent of its gross radio sales, that the General Electric and Westinghouse Companies do likewise, and that our proposed licensees be required to do the same. . . .

While the total . . . may be regarded as inadequate to defray the whole of the expense of the broadcasting company, yet I think it should be sufficient to provide for a modest beginning. Once the structure is created, opportunities for providing additional sources of

Sources of Income

43

income to increase the "pot" will present themselves. For example, if the business expands, the income grows proportionately. Also, we may find it practicable to require our wholesale distributors to pay over to the broadcasting company a reasonable percentage of their gross radio sales, for it will be to their interest to support broadcasting. It is conceivable that the same principles may even be extended in time to the dealers.

Since the broadcasting company is to be organized on the basis of rendering a public service commensurate with its financial ability to do so, it is conceivable that plans may be devised by it whereby it will receive public support and, in fact, there may even appear on the horizon a public benefactor who will be willing to contribute a large sum in the form of an endowment. It will be noted that these additional possibilities of income are merely regarded as "possibilities" and do not in themselves form the foundation upon which the broadcasting company is to operate.

Once the broadcasting company is established as a public service and the general public educated to the idea that the sole function of the company is to provide the public with a service as good and extensive as its total income permits, I feel that with suitable publicity activities, such a company will ultimately be regarded as a public institution of great value, in the same sense that a library, for example, is regarded today. . . .

(Book: *Pioneering in Television: Prophecy and Fulfillment*, a compilation of speeches and statements by David Sarnoff, pp. 159–163.)

Portable Radio

Letter to Dr. A. N. Goldsmith, Director
RCA Research Department
August 2, 1922

In 1915, when I was faced with the problem of expanding the sales activities of the old Marconi Company, it seemed to me that radio as a sales proposition required the creation of new fields, for up to that time the communication end of radio was the predominating business and sales were confined to a few special classes of customers who were interested in the possibilities of communication between fixed points for their private or business purposes.

I well recall that the foregoing limitations and the necessity for expansion caused me to think that if a way could be found for making radio a household utility, the opportunity for sales would be tremendously extended and theoretically limited only by the number of homes.

. . . I have been thinking again along the same lines as in 1915 and also with the view of creating new fields so as to expand our sales activities. This line of thought has led me to the following analysis of radio:

1. That the first stage of radio operation was necessarily confined to radio men. That is to say, it required radio men at each end of the circuit to send and receive wireless telegraph messages.

2. That the second stage of radio operation was extended to the home, where nonradio persons could operate the receiving devices and, through the radiotelephone, listen to the human voice, musical instruments, etc. Nevertheless, this is still a confinement of radio since it extends to a home or a more or less fixed place.

3. That the third stage of radio now comes into view and can be extended not only to the home but to the individual, whether he be within or outside of a fixed place.

More specifically, my idea is to take advantage of recent technical improvements in shortwave communication and to develop a system of broadcasting communication between a radiotelephone transmitting station and the individual, wherever he may be.

News on the Quarter Hour

For the sake of illustration, let us suppose that a broadcast transmitter, operating on extremely short waves—say, somewhere between 5 and 25 meters—and with reasonable power, is located in New York City (presumably Aeolian Hall Building, where we are now erecting our main broadcasting station) and that this shortwave transmitter is made to send out, periodically or continuously, information of a character that will interest the individual, **45** not only at home but in the office, workshop, street, or elsewhere. Let us assume that every quarter of an hour or so, this broadcast transmitter would send out the time and would say, "It is now— o'clock," and give baseball scores, stock quotations, news items (perhaps in headline form), weather reports, railroad schedules or changes thereto, special entertainment announcements, accident or safety information, police information, burglary or fire alarms, criminal detection, and a variety of items which are too numerous to mention but all of which the average individual is normally interested in or vitally concerned with.

The "Radiolette"

As there is no question about the feasibility of transmitting on these shortwaves and of finding helpful and interesting material and service along the lines indicated, the problem of transmission may be left at this point, from which we approach the more important problem of developing a suitable receiver in such compact and efficient form as to enable an individual to conveniently carry it on his or her person and to satisfactorily receive such broadcasted material. The ideal to approach here is the watch carried by a lady or a gentleman, which is not only serviceable but ornamental as well. For the want of a better name, which does not suggest itself to me at this moment, I shall call the individual radio receiving set a "Radiolette."

The Radiolette should be designed to take advantage of the best known methods of reception, which include the best dry-battery type of receiving and amplifying tubes possible and the superregenerative circuits, and, in its first models, should strive at a receiving distance of, say, 10 to 25 miles with a minimum of apparatus.

Radiolette should first be developed with the utilitarian view in mind. For example, since the instrument must necessarily include a tube (lamp) and a source of energy (battery), the idea occurs to me that the lamp and battery might be used as a flashlight when not employed as a radio receiver. Here, you see, comes into view a device which not only may be able to tell one the time but may also show the way in dark places and give helpful and interesting information at other times. These combined uses and services would ultimately

46 create in the individual a real desire to possess a Radiolette. I have mentioned the flashlight as only one possibility but, no doubt, other possible uses will occur.

Next to being useful, the Radiolette should be beautiful, for people do not like to carry things about their person which do not look beautiful. Moreover, as the development is sure to be directed toward making the Radiolette smaller and smaller, just as has been the case with the watch, the day will undoubtedly come when a Radiolette will be made in pocket-watch or wristwatch form, and this would introduce the element of jewelry. It is not inconceivable that diamond-studded Radiolettes, mounted in platinum, will be the most hoped-for gift of the society lady but, at the same time, we must not neglect the Ingersoll purse of the average human.

I also think that if the scheme proves successful in practice—and I firmly believe it can be made successful—it will open up new fields of opportunities for manufacture and sales hitherto undreamed of in radio. It is also interesting to observe that, after radio demonstrated its utility in ship-to-shore communications (where no telegraph or telephone communication had been possible prior to the advent of the wireless), it moved in the direction of supplementing, competing with, or doing a better job than some of its predecessors. Thus, we find radio supplementing wire lines, competing with cables, and going forward either cooperatively or competitively (I do not yet know which) with the phonograph or music- and sound-reproducing devices; and now, with the Radiolette in view, we may associate radio and jewelry and pass them all on to the individual —for whom, after all is said and done, this world must have been created.

New Fields for Radio

(Book: *Pioneering in Television: Prophecy and Fulfillment*, a compilation of speeches and statements by David Sarnoff, pp. 169–172; original letter is in David Sarnoff Library, Princeton, N.J.)

BROADCASTING BECOMES AN INDUSTRY

Editor's Note   *By 1923, radio stations had begun to multiply. An entire new world of entertainment and instruction was being discovered. Singers, pianists, violinists, ministers, lecturers, and actors were performing before the microphone and were being heard not only in their own but in surrounding cities.*

A new mass medium was emerging, one that was to become more potent in its ability to form men's minds than even the newspaper. It was time for broadcasters to consider their responsibilities.

The Future of Broadcasting

Address before Atlantic City Chamber of Commerce
Atlantic City, N.J., January 23, 1923

I am frequently asked about the future of broadcasting. My questioners no doubt expect me to visualize for them unknown or revolutionary uses of radio. To these questions I must give the somewhat paradoxical answer that the things of the future are with us today. In other words, we do not need to look to the unknown for radio possibilities. The art is here and ready to serve. It remains for us to solve the problems which up to now have been retarding the development of radio and to place into practical operation the wonderful possibilities which radio holds for the people of this country.

First, I might say, we require suitable government regulations of a nature that will divide the United States into radio-broadcasting zones, each of these zones having the necessary number of stations to effectively serve that territory and employing such bands of wavelengths as will eliminate interference. The elimination of interference is most important, and I believe that the well-organized station, charged with the responsibility of disseminating information, instruction, and entertainment to the masses, should enjoy the greatest protection which it is possible for the government to provide.

In culture, in music, in art, in religion, in political betterment, in international relationships, in a happier home life, in the better understanding of the languages of different countries, broadcasting takes a stand in the front line. Isolation is today a word almost without meaning.

. . . The time is coming, and very soon, too, when the country's leaders in music, science, and politics will no longer be content to give their best to, literally speaking, a mere handful of people within the confines of four walls. Indeed, they will demand, and rightly so, that they be heard by the people of every state, every city, and every town and hamlet, in railway trains and vessels on the high seas—in short, by millions instead of hundreds. . . . Radio can do this very thing. Its future is here.

(Book: *Radio and David Sarnoff*, by E. E. Bucher, part 2, pp. 350–352.)

Application of Radio to Agriculture

Memorandum by David Sarnoff
April 5, 1923

I also believe that radio is destined to be used extensively in the remote control of various forms of industrial and agricultural mechanisms.

It is possible to set mechanisms into motion at a distance by means of radio and to control their functioning.

Under present-day conditions, agricultural implements, such as plows, are largely pulled by horses or gasoline-engine tractors and directed by men. It is possible to control by radio a gasoline-driven tractor without requiring the operator to be seated in the machine and to follow it tediously around the fields. In this way, the need for the horse and man will be eliminated, and a considerable number of purely mechanical agricultural implements can be simultaneously controlled by radio by one man or woman at a radio watchtower suitably located.

(*Early Reports in Radio*, by David Sarnoff, vol. 1, 1914–1934, p. 149; David Sarnoff Library, Princeton, N.J.) **49**

When Radio Reaches Half a Billion

Address before the Electrical Supply Jobbers Association
Buffalo, N.Y., November 15, 1923

It is estimated that the American public spent in 1922 between $75 million and $100 million on radio. . . .

On the same basis, it is estimated that the American public will spend during the present year at least $150 million on radio. . . .

I believe that this industry will go on for the next few years virtually doubling in volume each year.

Two years ago, I made the prediction that the radio industry would be equal in a few years to the phonograph industry, which in normal times reaches $400 million a year.

Today, I say that the radio industry will be worth within the next few years a half billion dollars a year in consumers' prices . . . .

Now, as to the public—the ultimate consumer—it is very difficult to obtain accurate figures on the number of sets in use because there are a good many homemade sets that cannot be recorded. But I regard as a very conservative estimate the statement that 2 million sets are in use in the United States. Multiplying this figure by the size of the average American family, you have a radio audience totaling approximately 8 million, and if it be true, as I have indicated earlier, that this business is to double itself each year for the next few years until it reaches a certain level, we may expect within a period of three to five years to be speaking to practically 50 million people in the United States through the agency of radio. . . .

The Purpose of the Broadcast Station

More and more, it is evident that the purpose of the broadcast station is to do those things which other agencies cannot do as well or at all. No other agency can speak with a single voice to 10 million people. It is an instrumentality for national events, for high-grade talent, for good music, for good lectures, and the like, and therefore it means, in my judgment, that there will be erected in time a number of high-powered broadcast stations . . . joined together either by wire or by radio, preferably the latter.

These may constitute a chain of national broadcasting stations or a national broadcast service, each of these stations simultaneously radiating the same program, whatever it may be, with a power sufficient to reach every home in the United States, and with power sufficient to give enjoyable loudspeaker operation, and with an organization capable of measuring up to the responsibilities of that character of a national service. . . .

Fortunately for this country, America leads and has led in radio development, not only in broadcasting but alike in the matter of transoceanic and long-distance communication, and since it is possible to take a high-power station in New York and reradiate its output in California by radio, it is likewise possible to take a high-power station in London and reradiate its output in New York. In other words, radio can link these superpower stations until the whole world is covered by this new agency of transmission, which I think for simple reference may be called a one-way communication system. It is the only one-way communication system in the world.

Now, how about supporting these broadcasting stations? . . . It has been said by a great many people and a great many corporations, some very large and able, that broadcasting depends upon a solution of the problem whereby the consumer will pay for the entertainment which he receives. In other words, it has been said that unless some means is created for collecting revenue from the user of a broadcast machine, the whole industry is founded on sand and is bound to collapse in time because there will be no means of supporting it.

In Defense of Free Listening

I want to go on record very definitely this morning, and for the first time, in saying to you that it is my firm conviction that that sort of solution to the problem is not necessary, that broadcasting can be made commercially practicable without any means being found for collecting from the consumer, and that the greatest advantage of broadcasting lies in its universality—in its ability to reach everybody, everywhere, anywhere, in giving free entertainment, culture, instruction, and all the items which constitute a program, in doing that which no other agency has yet been able to do—and it is up to us, **51** with intelligence and technique and broadness of spirit and vision as to the future, to preserve that most delightful element in the whole situation, the freedom of radio. . . .

Editor's Note *Available records of radio industry sales at consumer prices indicate the following:*

1924	$358,000,000
1925	$430,000,000
1926	$506,000,000
1927	$425,000,000
1928	$690,000,000
1929	$842,000,000

(Mimeographed text: David Sarnoff Library, Princeton, N.J.; Book: *Radio and David Sarnoff*, by E. E. Bucher, part 2, p. 354.)

Radio and the Farmer

Address at the University of Missouri
January 7, 1924

Radio's greatest contribution to civilization lies not so much in what it does for the city dweller but upon the signal influence it can bring upon the life and action of our farm population. True enough, to the city dweller radio is a valuable medium of obtaining news, information, and entertainment, but to the farmer and the farmer's family it will become a vital necessity of their economic, social, spiritual, and intellectual life if it realizes the possibilities foreseen by the educators who devote themselves to agricultural betterment. These possibilities may be summarized in one sentence: Radio will do for the farmer what it will do for anybody else and more. It will help:

1. To relieve the farmer and his family of the sense of isolation which is, perhaps, the harshest handicap of agricultural life.

2. To broaden their social, spiritual, and religious life.

52 3. To cope with class and sectional differences and develop greater national unity as between the farmer and other elements of our citizenship.

4. To make possible a system of agricultural colleges which will be open to all the 30 million Americans who live on farms.

5. To aid in keeping the boys and girls on the farm, thus preserving for agricultural developments the energies of the thousands of ambitious young men and women who are drawn away each year to urban pursuits.

6. Radio can be employed to furnish accurate time signals and weather reports to the farmer and townsman. It can broadcast warning of approaching storms, and flood warnings received through radio will be of priceless value to the farmer.

7. Radio can furnish accurate news of prices and trade conditions of farm products at all principal markets within the hour and make it available to every farm home.

8. Radio, in my judgment, is destined to become one of the most effective elements in the business equipment of the farm, comparable perhaps to the great utility of the automobile.

Above and beyond its utilitarian uses, the message that radio brings to the farmer is the message of human contact, human sympathy, and culture. If men and women of the farm are not to continue to drift away from the land, to herd themselves in great cities, to swell the ranks of industrial labor and leave the farms unmanned, agricultural life must be made more attractive. The farmer deserves to share and should share in many of the educational opportunities now enjoyed only by the city dweller; his family deserves and will have the entertainment and cultural influences which the cities have created; his children should not be without the educational advantages which sparsely populated communities cannot afford at present.

No movement to bring the young man or woman back to the farm could fully succeed without the vital, human touch that is the gift of radio. Radio, I believe, is destined to bring the city to the **53**

farm, without the crowding, the dependence, and the fierce competition which are the risks imposed upon those who would live in the
cities.

. . . The results to be accomplished by radio in connection with
the life of the farmer may prove of importance second only to the
vast developments brought about by the evolution of printing.

(Printed booklet: "The Message That Radio Brings to
the Farmer," speech by David Sarnoff.)

Freedom of the Airways

Testimony before a government Legislative Committee
Washington, D.C., March 7, 1924

I cannot help feeling not only that the public should be left free
from the payment of any license fee to the government or others for
the privilege of listening on a broadcast receiver but that it should
also be free from fees or tolls of any kind in the field of broadcasting
through space. Furthermore, I believe that the expressions of educators and statesmen should reach them uncensored and uncontrolled.
The air belongs to the people. It should be regulated by the will of a
majority of the people. Its main highways should be maintained for
the main travel. To collect a tax from the radio audience would be a
reversion to the days of toll roads and bridges, to the days when
schools were not public or free and when public libraries were unknown.

In the same way, the drawing of political, racial, or religious lines
would be a flareback to the day of intolerance and persecution.

Broadcasting stations, in my conception, are indeed the bar at
which causes can be pleaded for the verdicts of public opinion. The
public is well aware that radio broadcasting is not confined to the influence of the lone speaker in the broadcast studio, that speeches
from public halls even now are constantly heard by a million listeners, and that eventually it will be practicable, if Congress is willing,
to turn on the debates in the Federal legislative bodies so that the

radio world may form its own impressions of laws and how they are made.

So powerful an instrument for public good should be kept free from partisan manipulations. America today may justly be proud of the freedom of its press. In no country in the world has this freedom been preserved more steadfastly. It is the newspapers which have forwarded the movements to expose wrongdoing and to establish justice, and it is my hope that the freedom of broadcasting will be maintained in the same American spirit. Not only do I believe that no artificial means should be evolved to restrict or tax the radio listeners, but I believe that the radio audience alone should be the final judge of interest in every radio program.

Superpower Stations

A few superpower stations located at suitable points in the country and interconnected by radio itself would enable all units to send out the same program simultaneously. But such a system would no more replace the smaller, more individual broadcasting stations than the national magazines of large circulation replace the local newspapers. Indeed, the smaller broadcasting stations might supplement the work of the superstations by automatically and mechanically repeating the national programs sent out by the superstations, so that every city, town, village, and hamlet in this country might have the benefits of such a program. On the other hand, these smaller stations could continue to send out their individual programs, as at present, when they so desired.

(Book: *Radio and David Sarnoff*, by E. E. Bucher, part 2,
pp. 380–382.)

Radio and Politics

Address before Chicago Association of Commerce
Chicago, Ill., April 23, 1924

For the first time in the history of an American Presidential election, rival Presidential candidates will appeal through the forum of the air to the American electorate. For the first time in the history of national conventions, America's millions will be able to follow word by word every dramatic phase in the battle of "favorite sons" for the distinction of being nominated for the Presidency of the United States. The enthusiasm and tumult of a great political convention will no longer be a show for the fortunate few; radio has made it possible for millions to follow every move in the convention hall. No other event will so serve to focus the minds of the American people on the great destiny and power of radio.

. . . The radio audience, while it is the largest audience ever addressed by a single human voice, nevertheless has become one of the most concrete, responsive forces in America. The speaker who is dull or rasping or unintelligent is immediately labeled as such by the preponderance of the letters and postcards and even telegrams which arrive at the broadcasting station the next morning. The speaker who is forceful, brief, honest, and instructive is likewise labeled by the preponderance of commendation that comes in the next mail.

(Book: *Radio and David Sarnoff*, by E. E. Bucher, part 2, pp. 283–284.)

TWO ASPECTS OF THE NEW MEDIUM

International Radio

Address before the annual convention of the
National Electric Light Association
Atlantic City, N.J., May 21, 1924

The ability of radio to deposit its message directly into the country of its destination is a matter of great significance. International radio overcomes the necessity of relaying messages through the government land lines of any country other than that to which the messages are routed. The advantage which this gives to every nation, in times either of peace or of war, is very great, for it eliminates completely the opportunity formerly afforded to hostile censors of the intervening countries to stop relayed messages in transit or to interfere with them.

"Plug-in" Radio

My conception of the future type of receiving set is one where some device of simple design can be interposed between the lighting circuit and the vacuum tubes of the radio receiver, thus energizing these tubes directly from the power mains. A further requirement would be that the device be of a character calling for infrequent attention, adaptable to existing and future types of receiving sets without necessitating changes in design of the vacuum tube or in the set itself. . . .

To my mind, the perfection of such a device is the next forward step in broadcast reception. And I am in a position to state that our engineers are making considerable progress in this direction. . . . For the sake of convenience and for lack of better designation, I shall refer to it here as the "current-supply device." To the general public, such a device would mean a simplicity of operation now exemplified, **57** let us say, in the lighting of an electric lamp by the turning of a switch.

The commercial and technical advantages of the current-supply device would be very great indeed. It would provide a steady and uniform voltage to the vacuum tube. It would require practically no attention on the part of the user except as it may be necessary to replace parts after extended periods of use. It would make the installation and use of the radio receiver as simple and convenient as the operation of a lamp or vacuum cleaner, for when the receiver is installed, it would merely be necessary to plug the usual form of extension cord into a base receptable in the home to start operation of the radio set.

(Book: *Radio and David Sarnoff*, by E. E. Bucher, part 2, pp. 387–388.)

Radio Requires a World Outlook

Statement to the press en route to Europe
July 12, 1924

A great stride is now being made in the development of broadcasting in some of the European countries, following the impetus given to the art in the United States, and the problems affecting international communications, which a constantly developing art may forecast, require a world outlook if the complete picture is to be envisaged.

Radio is becoming increasingly a world problem. When a concert broadcast in Pittsburgh is received in Argentina and rebroadcast by the local stations to thousands of listeners in that republic, the day when we in America may have a regular service of international broadcasting comes nearer to realization. Equally important developments may be forecast in the field of transoceanic commercial communications.

(Book: *Radio and David Sarnoff*, by E. E. Bucher, part 2, p. 394.)

Transoceanic Broadcasting

Statement to the press on return from Europe
August 30, 1924

I investigated the broadcasting systems of England, France, and
Germany and met the principal persons, both in governmental and
private circles, responsible for the development of radio in Europe.
. . . I endeavored to interest the British, French, and German
broadcasters in the idea of increasing the power of their sending stations so that the programs of London, Paris, and Berlin might be
easily heard by the American listening public. At the same time, I
suggested the possibility of American stations sending over their programs, which could be regularly heard abroad. Much interest was
shown in these proposals, and I believe that an era of transoceanic
broadcasting is near at hand. Realization of such a plan would
greatly enhance the value of broadcasting to the public on this side
as well as on the other side of the Atlantic Ocean and would help to
bring the Old and New Worlds a little closer together.

(Book: *Radio and David Sarnoff*, by E. E. Bucher, part 2,
p. 396.)

A National Broadcasting Service

Statement at third annual Radio Conference
Washington, D.C., October 6, 1924

In order adequately to fulfill the broadcasting mission, radio must
develop into a national service. By a national broadcasting service, I
mean a service that will make every home in the country resonant
with the music, entertainment, and culture that radio can bring, that
will enable every man and woman in the United States to receive the
word-of-mouth messages broadcast by our great public men, that
will create a vast forum of the air for the discussion and consideration of vital problems, and that will keep the remotest home in the   **59**

land attuned to the thought and the doings of the great world outside.

. . . Nor would I stop with national broadcasting. The voices
echoed by American radio stations already have been hurled across
the oceans, and messages broadcast by our public men have been
heard in other hemispheres. The day is not far when technical developments in the broadcasting art will enable our country, through
superpower stations, to reflect its culture and to speak its best
thought to other nations of the world, and at that time the United
States will take the same position of leadership in worldwide broadcasting that it occupies today in worldwide radiotelegraphic communications.

**Plans for National
Programming**

Our plans are to add vastly to the facilities which now exist in
order that any national broadcast program yet to be organized might
reach ultimately to every home in the United States and even make
our voice heard in countries beyond the seas. . . .

It is my pleasure to inform you today that the Radio Corporation
of America is ready to begin the immediate erection of a great superpower broadcasting station at some point outside of the City of New
York, located with due regard to the minimum of interference with
listeners and with local stations maintained by other interests and
capable of serving directly millions of people within the range of its
voice. We might go for the moment as high as 50 kilowatts if no reg-
ulatory proposals are adopted that would limit the art.

When the range and usefulness of this station have been proved
experimentally, the Radio Corporation of America would begin the
construction of another superpower station at some point where the
limit of reliable effectiveness had been reached by the first station.
Thereafter, in close technical and practical cooperation with its associates, the system would be extended to cover every nook and corner of the United States.

Our purpose would be to equalize the broadcasting service received in every part of the country. In order, also, to add to the
effectiveness of the great superpower broadcasting station to be established by us, means will be provided at the station for the purpose
60 of relaying programs to other points in the United States and abroad.

Not only is it proposed eventually to interconnect this great group of superbroadcasting stations, but interconnection could also be made with local stations in various parts of the country.

. . . Nor will superbroadcasting give control of the air to any one interest or any one element. Every effort, from whatever direction, to give the country a national service by radio should be encouraged. For I do not believe that the American public will ever accept a single standardized program broadcast on the air. I do not believe that any one agency should or could undertake to tell the American people *en masse* just what proportion of entertainment or music or news they should receive through the air, to whom they should listen, or what they should hear. The air must be kept a free forum for the public to take what it desires and reject what it will. The primary purpose of the Radio Corporation of America in establishing a system of superpower broadcasting is to create the facilities for a really national service. . . .

"Air Must Be Kept a Free Forum"

The factors, in my opinion, that will shape the solution of how a permanent broadcasting program is to be organized and paid for are as follows:

Radio Support and Financing

1. Truly national broadcasting facilities must first be created, and broadcasting transmission as well as reception must be developed to a point where the art will meet every requirement made upon it. The radio industry, the wire-communication interests, and other elements are now developing such facilities. The permanent operation and maintenance of such facilities are assured by the fact of self-interest, if for no other reasons. The radio industry, on its own account, must support the broadcasting facilities it has created if the industry is to survive; the local station will continue in every instance where its establishment is based upon the fundamental fact of community self-expression; and it is not unlikely that other elements will develop revenue-producing methods for radio-broadcasting facilities.

2. The radio industry must secure the cooperation of the established elements that have long served our national culture in order that **61**

the air may carry the supreme music, education, and entertainment of the country. In other words, I do not believe that the radio and broadcasting interests of the United States should attempt to develop an operatic organization comparable to the one or two national institutions that already exist. I do not believe that it is either practically or economically sound to organize for exclusive use through the air such supreme musical achievements as are now represented in the Philharmonic, the Boston, the Philadelphia, the San Francisco, and other great orchestras. I believe that the great colleges of the country should direct the educational programs broadcast by radio and that the cooperation of established news organizations should be sought for the broadcasting under suitable conditions of such facts as will heighten the interest in current events fully treated in the newspapers.

3. It should be the self-imposed duty of the radio industry not only to support financially the distribution upon a national scale of those elements of the radio program that are contributed by public and educational interests but to organize a system of payment for such talent as may be necessary to secure a well-balanced program. The problem, I recognize, may involve a distinction between commercial and noncommercial broadcasting stations, between broadcasters representing the industry and broadcasters representing the community or private interests.

(Mimeographed text: "Statement by David Sarnoff"; David Sarnoff Library, Princeton, N.J.)

Radio and the Newspaper

Address before The Sphinx Club
New York City, January 13, 1925

What I particularly desire to discuss tonight is the relationship of radio to the newspaper.

Printer's ink has been the greatest friend that radio has had. In turn, I believe that radio has been, and will continue to be, one of

the greatest accelerants, from the standpoint both of circulation
and of advertising, that newspapers and magazines have ever
known. . . .

It is quite true that seeming miracles are being wrought by radio. The day will come, I believe, when a message written by a newspaper correspondent in London will be flashed photographically by radio into the newspaper office—when a photographic copy of an editorial in a French newspaper can be transmitted the whole length of the ocean in a fraction of the time it now takes to send a summary.

Perhaps we may carry our imaginations further and translate the recent scientific achievement that resulted in sending a photograph over the ocean, through the ether, into a system that might permit photographic reproductions of distant scenes right in the home, through the same agency that now carries the human voice and music.

But in whatever direction radio may develop, it will be, I believe, toward supplementation, not substitution. The truth is that printer's ink achieves something that radio cannot achieve; conversely, the security of radio and its assured permanence lie in the fact that it provides a different service than the printed word ever rendered, or ever could render. . . .

Insofar as radio may attempt to serve the listening public with a digest of current news, *it is the herald of the newspaper.* It announces in "headlines," as it were, that which impels millions of listeners to seek in the press the necessary details or the raw material of public opinion. In the broadcasting of public events, radio makes every listener a participant.

The man who has "attended" a political convention by radio reads the newspaper accounts of the convention with added zest, just as those who have been present at a premiere performance at a theater are keen to compare their own observations with the reactions of the drama critics who review the play for the newspapers. The same is true in the field of sports, as in the broadcasting of a major prizefight or a World Series baseball game.

. . . The limitations of radio broadcasting in relation to the functions of the newspapers are not less evident than the advantages. Radio, it is clear, has a great cultural and educational destiny, but it **63**

can never replace the newspaper in giving a historical record of the
news of the day. Radio can broadcast briefly stated facts at fixed hours
of the day or night or make initial emergency announcements as
news may develop.

But beyond this, there is no more likelihood that the broadcasting station will displace the newspaper as the chronicler of the news
than that the public will ever be willing to abandon written history
for the word-of-mouth records of times gone by, or that it will desert
the classroom for a radio lecture course or abandon the opera for a
general musical program broadcast through the air.

(Book: *Radio and David Sarnoff*, by E. E. Bucher, part 2,
pp. 437–445.)

Radio and Industry

Introduction to "The Radio Industry"
Harvard University lectures
Cambridge, Mass., 1928

We are now at the beginning of the era of television in the home,
when radio will bring the panorama of life as well as the sounds of
music and speech to the world's multitudes. Again inventive genius
is called upon to develop a new art. Industry once more must organize to supply the mechanisms of a new service. Business again finds
itself with new problems to solve.

Radio makes a particularly effective appeal to the student of
business and to the business executive. Wireless communication has
added enormously to the range of business and trade activity by
opening up direct communication between countries hitherto connected only through intermediate wire services. Insofar as radio thus
insured the independence of communications, it served largely to
insure the independence of world trade.

As a factor in the industrial growth of the United States, the
greatest significance of radio lies in its effects upon, and in the relations it has established with, other industries. The record of the industry is therefore a fitting subject for study.

The implications which may be drawn from modern radio development are not merely industrial. Radio communication presents a world problem to the statesman. For international communication requires harmonious cooperation between the transmitting and receiving ends, each under the control of a different nation. It presents many legal problems to the lawyer because the air is still largely an undefined domain.

To the scientist and the engineer, radio still sends forth a challenge. There is yet to be defined the medium through which the electric wave is propagated from the transmitting station; there are yet to be discovered many of the laws that govern the movement of electromagnetic waves through space; there are still to be unlocked many secrets of radio transmission that will infinitely enlarge the scope of the radio art and the opportunities of the radio industry.

(Book: *Radio and David Sarnoff*, by E. E. Bucher, part 26, pp. 3585–3589.)

PROBLEMS AND
OPPORTUNITIES OF A MASS MEDIUM

Editor's Note By the 1930s, radio had become the most powerful single force in shaping the cultural patterns of American society. Virtually the whole population tuned in, and finding a continuous supply of material to offer so large an audience was no easy task. After the initial enthusiasm of the twenties, some people were beginning to probe more deeply into the value of radio as an instrument for educating and enlightening the public.

It was inevitable that radio would arouse criticism as well as praise. In a widely quoted article in 1927, H. G. Wells characterized radio as an "inferior substitute for better systems of transmitting news or evoking sound." He called it of little consequence to civilization, asserting that before long, radio stations would be talking to a "phantom army of nonexistent listeners."

Response to H. G. Wells's Attack on Radio

Address at Syracuse University
Syracuse, N.Y., April 28, 1927

It is difficult to understand how a brilliant mind that could foresee so many modern inventions could have reached such extraordinary conclusions about radio. The fundamental basis of broadcasting is a service to the many, not to the few. Broadcasting is, and must be, a thoroughly democratic institution, dedicated to the service of the general listening public. Its cultural and educational influence is constantly increasing.

. . . Through what other medium of communications could a musical, cultural, and entertainment service have been rendered to many millions of homes throughout the world? What other instrumentality developed by man bears a greater unifying force? By what means of communication could we have hoped to reach, simulta-

66

neously and effectively, unnumbered thousands of isolated homes throughout the country with the same message of education, information, or service as that now rendered by radio broadcasting? . . .

Any service transmitted to millions of homes must necessarily be based upon the greatest common denominator of public good. Broadcasting cannot hope to thrill the intellectually overfed or the spiritually jaded, but it can and does fulfill a splendid destiny in the field of mass entertainment and edification.

It is more important to the progress of mankind that 10 million men, through the slow process of general education, should rise in intellectual stature, even though a fraction of an inch, than that a few should be able to leap to the heights of Olympus; it is of greater consequence to the happiness of a nation that a million isolated homes throughout the country should be made vibrant with music transmitted by broadcasting stations than that a few should be thrilled by an exotic star on the concert stage.

The critics who fix their thought upon the immediate limitations of the radio art are taking their places with those who guffawed at the possibilities of the "horseless carriage," who considered the telephone as a mere toy and the steam engine as merely a dangerous "contraption."

(Book: Radio and David Sarnoff, by E. E. Bucher, part 3, pp. 647B–647D.)

The Uses of Broadcasting

Letter to Prof. Felix Frankfurter
February 10, 1934

When I received your letter of December 10, 1933, to which you attached the interesting article from the *Literary Supplement* of the London *Times* on the subject of broadcasting, I was anxious to write to you and to comment thereon. But I could not do justice to the subject without making a statement as long as the article, and to do so seemed to me to be penalizing you for an act which deserved gratitude. . . .

To return to the article on broadcasting—the best thing about it is
the reference in your letter which says:

> From my point of view, the use we make of the radio and the
> other instruments of mass suggestion cuts across all the other
> forces of political society.

This view justifies the statement that radio must be regarded as
a force rather than an instrumentality. It is not the ability of radio to
be used as a means of mass communication that is important, but
the use made of it will determine its ultimate value.

While various commentators praise or condemn radio, few of
them establish, even in their own minds, the difference between the
machine and its use, and they often charge the mechanic with the responsibility for the use made of his machine. Personally, I do not
even belong to the class who would assume that because man may
know how to produce a good machine, he necessarily also knows how
best to use it.

The radio machine might well be likened to the printing press.
Suppose the inventors of the latter were charged with the responsibility for the material printed or to be printed by their press. What
could be said of printing that could not be also said of radio?

Again, imagine the inventors and owners of the telephone instruments being held responsible for the things which are said over their
system. Likewise the telegraph, and perhaps even the force of electricity itself.

Of course, I realize that, having accepted the responsibility for
operating broadcasting stations and rendering a service to the public,
I am not privileged so easily to dispose of the subject.

Nevertheless, it is more true of broadcasting than of almost any
other service I know that those who have something of value to contribute to the public have greater opportunity to utilize the instrumentality of radio than they possess in practically any other field.
Certainly it is easier, at least in the United States, for a speaker to
secure the use of the microphone than it is for a writer to obtain
space in a newspaper. And the audience which his voice can reach is
vastly greater than the number of eyes which would meet his pen.

68 And right here is one of the real difficulties. Few voices can do more than make a noise and rattle the microphone. The very size of the potential audience makes it more necessary than ever that speakers have something to say instead of merely saying something.

Alongside this difficulty is another and perhaps even greater one. It is the fact that the new agencies of distribution in the field of mass communication and mass entertainment, such as are provided by radio and the talking pictures, devour worthwhile material with a speed that exhausts creative effort and leaves a yawning gap.

Added to all the foregoing is the important factor of *mass* versus *class* information and entertainment. I know the old argument about not lowering standards to meet the uncultured taste of the masses and about the more elevating effort of raising the taste of the masses to the pitch of the masters. But in a world of reality . . . it would be hard to convince not only the prospective advertiser seeking mass consumption of his product but even the statesman, the educator, and the artist that a small audience of selective taste might suit their purpose better than a large and indiscriminate audience with a popular appetite.

. . . The answer must ultimately be that both kinds of information and entertainment—mass and class—must be provided by stations catering to both tastes. In fact, this is being done to a larger extent by broadcasting than by any other medium. Every known artist of quality, every orchestra of value, opera, and many other cultural programs of high artistic value are heard over the air time and time again. The trend of broadcast programs is constantly upward, and trends, as you know, are most important.

I have often tried the experiment, in talking with well-intentioned critics of broadcasting programs, of asking them how many of the outstanding broadcasts of the week they have heard. Almost invariably, they have heard none of them and did not know they were on the air although their existence was advertised in the daily press. What these people want is, at the moment when it suits their fancy to turn on the radio, to have the loudspeaker pour forth the particular kind of music or information in which they happen to be interested. They would not expect this in a theater or an opera house because they would have to select the date, pay for a ticket, and take their person to the place of entertainment. In radio, however, entertain- **69** ment comes to the place where the person is, and there being no work to do and no payment to make, it is natural and understandable that the listener should be even more demanding.

Now all this may sound like an *apologia* for the bad pipes of my plumbing trade, but I assure you it is not so intended. I am conscious of the present inadequacies of radio broadcasting but not disheartened, because the very limitations of today are the opportunities of tomorrow. However, I would call upon the creators of thought and artistry to do their part and help the mechanic and the plumber.

(Mimeographed text: David Sarnoff Library, Princeton, N.J.)

Radio as a New Public-opinion Force

Address before the fifth annual Current Events Forum
Conducted by the *New York Herald Tribune*
New York City, October 17, 1935

To promote the prosperity of our heterogeneous world and to lighten its burdens, a comprehensive system of intercommunications by which peoples may discover their common bonds is indispensable.

. . . It is only natural that a system of communications as vast as radio broadcasting should have a definite and growing place among agencies that contribute to the molding of public opinion. But the problem of radio and public opinion cannot be viewed from a single dimension. Three leading elements demand consideration.

The first element, radio broadcasting, performs a unique function in relation to public opinion. It supplies a comprehensive system of electrical conduits through which education, entertainment, information, and opinion constantly flow to the public. On its waves, the leader of a movement, the advocate of a cause, the spokesman of a party, or the proponent of an educational theory may present his case directly to the people. Radio broadcasting now brings the speaker's living voice, with its inflections and emphases, its overtones of sincerity or hypocrisy, into two-thirds of the homes of our country.

70 Day after day and night after night, the radio waves transport music,

science, and social and political discussions to all parts of the nation.
On its waves, truth can circle the globe with the speed of light. So
may a lie. The voice of the statesman can be heard from pole to pole.
So may the voice of the demagogue. The music of great masters and
artists can fill the air. So may a mere jumble of sound.

Open Channels for Information

In the use of this new medium, the second element, the broadcasters of the nation, are impelled by the very nature of this service
to ensure that the channels of radio shall be open to all matters of
public interest, regardless of race, creed, color, or political party.
Other media of public information and entertainment may key their
appeal to specific audiences they seek to reach. But radio, a universal
medium, must serve a universal audience. Upon the management of
radio-broadcasting facilities, therefore, falls the duty of maintaining
freedom of the air with no less faith and firmness than must be used
to preserve freedom of speech and press in our country. Broadcasters
must strive to maintain a balance which will ensure listeners a fair
opportunity to hear both sides of an important question. That they
will sometimes fall short of this goal is inevitable. That they should
ever lose their steadfastness of purpose is unthinkable.

The third element in the relation of radio to public opinion is, of
course, the public itself. Since the birth of our country, the right to
form their own opinions, reach their own conclusions, and set their
own standards of taste has been the zealously guarded prerogative of
the American people. Those who have no faith in the capacity of the
public to distinguish between good and bad, sound and unsound,
true and false when full information has been made available will be
without hope for any democratic form of society.

Public opinion may not always be infallible, but happily the
records of democracy show that on great national issues it has risen
triumphant over sophistry and demagogy. Where politics or government have temporarily swerved a nation from its true course, an
aroused public opinion has ultimately expressed itself and pointed
the way to the right road. Without such freedom of expression there
can be no democracy.

The interests of the public impose distinct obligations on those
concerned in the relationship of radio to public opinion. Upon the **71**

speaker before the microphone rests the responsibility for a fair and sincere statement of the subject in the light of his convictions. Upon the management of broadcast stations rests the responsibility to see that both sides of a matter affecting the national welfare are given a fair opportunity to discriminate between statesmanship and partisanship, between faith and prejudice, between sincerity and hypocrisy, between heated argument and cold fact.

(Book: *Radio and David Sarnoff*, by E. E. Bucher, part 3, pp. 856–863; part 4, pp. 1019–1020.)

Staffing the NBC Symphony Orchestra

Letter to David Sarnoff from Arturo Toscanini
Milan, Italy, February 8, 1937

It is useless to repeat once more my great happiness to have accepted your invitation [to conduct in America]. Now I begin to realize how difficult it must be to put together a fine orchestra worthy to rival those of New York, Philadelphia, and Boston. Your undertaking is not a commercial but an artistic one, and only from this point of view must it proceed. Every attempt must be made to select the best musicians among the many good ones who are living in the United States.

My good friend Chotzinoff will be happy to join you in this difficult task, and I beg you to do your utmost to realize all that is now hoped for. This will be a happy event for you to add to the many which have occurred in your life.

Very cordially
yours   *Arturo Toscanini*

The string quintet must be at least:

12 first violins	8 cellos
12 second violins	7 basses
10 violas	2 flutes

1 piccolo (playing third flute)
2 oboes
1 English horn
2 clarinets
1 bass clarinet
2 bassoons
1 contrabassoon

4 French horns
3 trumpets
3 trombones
1 bass tuba
1 or 2 harps
1 timpani
1 cymbal
1 bass drum and triangle

(Original letter: David Sarnoff Library, Princeton, N.J.)

Toscanini and the NBC Symphony

Exchange of correspondence:
Arturo Toscanini to David Sarnoff, March 25, 1954
Sarnoff reply, March 29, 1954

My very dear David:

Maestro Toscanini's Letter

At this season of the year seventeen years ago, you sent me an invitation to become the musical director of an orchestra to be created especially for me for the purpose of broadcasting symphonic music throughout the United States.

You will remember how reluctant I was to accept your invitation because I felt at that time that I was too old to start a new venture. However, you persuaded me, and all of my doubts were dispelled as soon as I began rehearsing for the first broadcast of Christmas night in 1937 with the group of fine musicians whom you had chosen.

Year after year it has been a joy for me to know that the music played by the NBC Symphony Orchestra has been acclaimed by the vast radio audiences all over the United States and abroad.

And now the sad time has come when I must reluctantly lay aside my baton and say goodbye to my orchestra, and in leaving I want you to know that I shall carry with me rich memories of these years of music making and heartfelt gratitude to you and the National Broadcasting Company for having made them possible.

I know that I can rely on you to express to everyone at the Na-

73

tional Broadcasting Company who has worked with me all these years my cordial and sincere thanks.

Your friend,
Arturo Toscanini

Reply to the Maestro   Dear Maestro:

Your letter, significantly written on your birthday, touched me deeply. I realize that after more than sixty-five years of absolute dedication to the art of music you have fully earned the right to lay down your baton. Yet I am saddened, along with millions of people in America, indeed, all over the civilized world, at the thought that we shall no longer be privileged to look forward to your broadcasts and concerts, which for so many years ennobled our lives. That you have made your decision at a time that finds you at the height of your artistic powers only adds poignancy to our deprivation.

As you know, my own life has been chiefly devoted to the development of instruments of communication. But however important these may be, they are at best only instrumentalities. Their function is only to transmit. In the final analysis, they will be judged by what they transmit.

For the last seventeen years, radio, television, and the phonograph have done their best to transmit with the utmost fidelity your self-effacing, incomparable re-creations of the great music of the past and present. And those of us who have striven to perfect these instruments feel in the highest degree rewarded for our labors. Happily, these instruments have recorded and preserved for us, and for posterity, the great music you have interpreted so faithfully and magnificently.

During these seventeen years of our intimate and happy association I have learned from you much that is as vital in industry as it is in music. Your attitude toward your art and especially toward that human instrument—the orchestra—which realized your musical ideals became an inspiration to me from the very first time I watched you at work. You proved so convincingly that, in striving to attain perfection, the leader who seeks to obtain the maximum from those he leads must demand the utmost not only from them but also from

74   himself.

I know, dear Maestro, you will carry with you the love and gratitude of our many friends and the great multitude, unknown to you, whose lives have been enriched.

> Your friend,
> *David Sarnoff*

(Original letters in bound volume: *Toscanini Correspondence*; David Sarnoff Library, Princeton, N.J.)

Remarks on the 100th anniversary of Arturo Toscanini's birth
New York City, March 12, 1967

**Reminiscences of
Toscanini**

In 1937, I tried to induce Maestro Toscanini to return to America and enlisted in this effort the help of the late Samuel Chotzinoff. However, the Maestro rebuffed our initial approaches, and he appeared determined not to come back.

Then we offered to create a radio symphony orchestra especially for Toscanini. He began to show more interest, and finally we reached an agreement. I believe that he was principally won over by the opportunity to have his music heard by millions of people who had never before listened to a live symphony orchestra.

From 1937 to 1954, Toscanini directed the NBC Symphony. It proved to be the most productive period in his long career.

He was 70 when he first raised his baton over the NBC Symphony, 87 when he retired. And his artistry, his vitality, his dedication to truth and beauty never wavered.

The genius of Toscanini gave music its richest endowment. And through radio, millions of people around the world shared in that magnificent gift.

(Transcript of Bell Telephone Hour broadcast over NBC.)

Proposal for "Voice of America"

Memorandum to Cordell Hull, Secretary of State
Washington, D.C., January 9, 1943

With the victory of the United Nations, the United States will have to play an increasingly important part in world affairs.

The likelihood is that the United States will emerge as a more vigorous entity than any other. Our production capacity will be at a new peak, our resources will be greater than those of any other nation, our technology will have produced many synthetic substitutes to add to the sum total.

. . . We shall be called upon, doubtless, to help feed, clothe, and shelter war-torn Europe and Asia. We shall be called upon to assist in reestablishing law and order. Many countries in the world will, perhaps, be seething with rebellion as a result of the disestablishment of Axis control and the impoverishment and disillusionment of people who have lost all in the war.

. . . Doubtless, new ideologies will develop, yet there will be a continuing struggle of democracy against totalitarianism. Our aid will be given to some peoples and denied to others, and it will be necessary that we cause all peoples to understand the reasons for our aid as provided or withheld.

Mass Communications Needed

In order to help the peoples of the world understand the reasons for our policies, it will be necessary to utilize a mass means of communication. . . . This, therefore, means that we shall be necessarily closely linking our foreign broadcasting to our foreign policy.

. . . It is inconceivable that the international voice of the United States should be silent or remain weak in the postwar world. . . . Our interests will require no less an effort than the present one, and quite probably even a greater one.

. . . Here would seem to be a field offering the greatest opportunity for government and industry to cooperate on a public-service basis. Government is needed to expose, on a world basis, the nation's foreign policy and to provide the financial means commensurate with the task; industry is needed to provide initiative and ingenuity for making this exposition effective.

Toward this end, it is proposed that a new corporation be organized that might be jointly owned by private industry and government and that would be charged with the responsibility for doing the job discussed.

76

Such a corporation might derive its legal authority from Congress through enactment of a bill that would define specifically the purposes and scope of such an organization, representing, as it would, to the rest of the world the "Voice of America."

While the government should have the ultimate control, the organization should be removed as far as possible from political influence and domination. Its board of directors might be composed of representatives of the radio industry, of the public, and of governmental departments most directly concerned with our foreign policy and with other phases of our relations with other countries.

Since the Department of State is the organ of our government specifically charged with the overall formulation of foreign policy and conduct of foreign affairs, it should occupy the place of paramount authority in general supervision of the policies and activities of the corporation.

. . . It would seem reasonable to go to work on this situation now because, in the changed atmosphere which is bound to exist at the conclusion of the war, there would be a natural desire on the part of Congress and large sections of the public to liquidate war agencies, built to serve war purposes only.

(Mimeographed text: David Sarnoff Library, Princeton, N.J.)

Freedom to Listen—A Plan for the United Nations

Plan for international broadcasting submitted to the United Nations
New York City, April 4, 1946

If it is to be effective, the principle of "Freedom to Listen" must be established for all peoples of the world. This is as important as "Freedom of Speech" and "Freedom of the Press." People everywhere must be able to listen without restriction or fear. In the light of present-day world developments, it would seem highly important that the UN should be able to reach directly everyone, everywhere, so that they, in turn, may impress their thoughts and desires upon their leaders. In this way, the danger of the people's being kept uninformed or misinformed by their leaders would be overcome.

77

One way to achieve this is for the UN to provide a worldwide system of broadcasting that can reach all peoples freely and simultaneously. That system would supplement the plan I have outlined for international broadcasting by the United States.

To further this idea, I submit the following plan for international broadcasting by the UN:

1. Establish the principle of "Freedom to Listen" for all peoples of the world. This is as important as "Freedom of Speech" and "Freedom of the Press."

2. Establish an independent international broadcasting system, to be known as "The Voice of UN." This system should be owned and operated by the UN. It should have a worldwide range and be used for broadcasting the public proceedings of the United Nations, for disseminating its information to listeners everywhere, and for spreading knowledge and understanding among the peoples of the world. "The Voice of UN" should broadcast in the principal languages employed throughout the world. The UN should continue to afford to other broadcasters and the press the privilege of broadcasting and publishing its proceedings and information.

The practical problems involved in adopting and executing this plan are both technical and political. The technical problems can be solved. The political problems require for their solution the consent of the member nations of the UN and their united will to make the plan work.

(Printed booklet: "The Voice of America," proposals dealing with problems of international broadcasting.)

Freedom to Listen and Freedom to Look

Address before the United States National Commission for UNESCO
Chicago, Ill., September 12, 1947

Since the fighting war ended . . . another global conflict has started—a battle for the minds of men. Forces of totalitarianism and aggression still are attempting to mislead the masses. Fully aware of the power of radio, they are using it to spread propaganda that runs contrary to peace, freedom, and democracy.

Our American concept of radio is that it is of the people and for the people. Its essence is freedom—liberty of thought and of speech. Our purpose in fostering international broadcasting is to help make the spectrum of radio truly a spectrum of peace.

By its very nature, radio is a medium of mass communication; it is a carrier of intelligence. It delivers ideas with an impact that is powerful. In the preservation of peace, the electron, which is the heartbeat of radio, may prove more powerful than the atom. In a forum for international discussion and education, the voice of radio can carry knowledge of public issues around the earth and mold public opinion far more quickly and far more effectively than any other means.

But if radio is to achieve its destiny in the interest of peace, it must have listeners. Merely to broadcast into unlistening space is a waste of energy. It is not the kilowatts of the transmitter that are important but the message which the listener, rich or poor, great or humble, plucks from space.

Therefore, the vital question is: How is the United Nations to acquire listeners? The answer is simple. Powerful shortwave transmitters located at strategic points around the globe can make it easy for people everywhere to receive strong, clear broadcasts of programs aimed to captivate their interest and to win and hold their confidence.

Radio should make a prisoner of no man, and it should make no man its slave. No one should be forced to listen, and no one compelled to refrain from listening. Always and everywhere, it should be the prerogative of every listener to turn his receiver on or off of his own free will.

It is of paramount importance that the principle of "Freedom to Listen" be established. It should be the inalienable right of people to listen anywhere and at any time to the voices on the wavelengths that come to them from home or abroad. They have the right to know the truth in the news, and it is the duty of international broadcasting to provide them with the truth. That is the precept which the **79**

United Nations must follow if they are to succeed in their plan to increase the knowledge and understanding of the people everywhere
about the problems of the world. The question is not financial or
technical. It is political. To answer it, every nation must be willing
to cooperate so that radio's great power for goodwill can be effectively achieved throughout the world.

Every nation, large and small, must be afforded opportunity to
play its individual part in this greatest of international communication projects. But, in addition, I believe that the independent efforts
of individual nations should be supplemented by a united voice
speaking through the United Nations over a worldwide system of
broadcasting, maintained and operated by the UN and reaching all
people everywhere, regardless of race, creed, or political philosophy.

Freedom to Look   . . . Television fires the imagination, and I can foresee the day
when we shall look around the earth from city to city and from na-
tion to nation as easily as we now listen to global broadcasts. Therefore, "Freedom to Look" is as important as "Freedom to Listen," for
the combination of these will be the radio of the future. This is no
idle dream, and no one need doubt that we shall have international
television. . . .

May I point out that, when I speak of international television, I
do not think of it only as between the United States and Europe,
Asia, or South America but as intracontinental also; for London may
look in on Paris, Berlin, Rome, or Moscow, while their citizens in
turn will look in on London or on other cities of their choice. Such
television has broad possibilities in portraying the way of life of one
nation to another. For example, discussion in the press or on the radio of a food shortage is one way of imparting information, but to be
able to see hungry men, women, and children in breadlines would
help more fortunate people to visualize instantly the dire circumstances and basic needs of their fellowman. . . .

Indeed, the radio of today will not be the radio of tomorrow. The
opportunities of radio as we now see them on the international horizon will change with even greater speed than they did when the first
feeble transatlantic wireless signal in 1901 served as the thread out of
80   which a global communication system has been woven.

Today, science makes it possible for radio to serve all parts of the world instantly and simultaneously. Therein lies the greater responsibility for the leaders of all nations to encourage its proper use and to serve the peoples of the world, whose yearning is for peace.

Voice of Peace

This, then, is no time for whispering or for mere lip service. The "Voice of Peace" must be made strong—strong enough to be heard above the tumult that would stifle freedom or kindle the fires of atomic war. It behooves the United Nations to speak out in all tongues, clear enough to be heard on land and sea, on deserts, farms, and steppes. Its broadcasts should carry not only information and news but entertainment and melody as well, for music is a universal language.

It is the use to which radio is put that is all-important. Broadcasting and television may function free and unfettered, or they may be muzzled and restricted to the use of a few. Radio can spread truth and untruth with the same speed and over the same range. The choice must be made by man. . . .

Voice of America

. . . In my view, the maintenance of international shortwave broadcasting from the United States is as important today as it was at any time during the war. It is just as essential in the case of broadcasts to friendly, democratic nations as to those whose governments may be unfriendly and undemocratic.

. . . There is a war in the air today—a battle between truth and falsehood—a battle for the minds of men! American radio must not be silent in its fight for the truth; we must not retreat on the battlefield in space! In the interest of world peace we must help to make it possible for people everywhere to know the truth. Only then can they judge the words and acts of their own governments and leaders.

Our prestige as a defender of truth must be expanded, not curtailed. It is vital that private enterprise and government alike recognize the challenge to cooperate with each other in the national interest, for international broadcasting does not belong exclusively in the domain of either. It is a task that calls for the brains and facilities of both industry and government, functioning in harmony to make the "Voice of Peace" heard effectively around the world.

81

Let us not measure our opportunities merely by the radioelec-
tronic facilities presently at our command. We must look ahead.
Science is setting a swift pace. The world that appears small today
will be even smaller tomorrow.

The "Voice of America" is a "Voice of Peace." Let it be strong
and clear. Let it ring out to cultivate faith and understanding. Let
its invisible waves sweep across the sky as a symbol of liberty!

(Printed booklet: "The Voice of America," proposals
dealing with problems of international broadcasting.)

CHAPTER 3

Black-and-White Television

In November, 1929, at a convention of the Institute of Radio Engineers, the inventor Vladimir Zworykin introduced his iconoscope, an "electric eye" for scanning pictures. This was the first public demonstration of an electronic TV camera tube, and instead of an immediate stir of excited speculation, which in view of subsequent events would certainly have been appropriate, the response was, amazingly, a slight collective shrug. The industrial representatives were not particularly impressed. The tube was interesting, but there were too many unsolved problems and its application was too limited. For any practical purpose, what good was it? "What good," Benjamin Franklin once remarked in a similar situation, "is a newborn baby?"

One industrial leader had the vision to recognize that this "baby" would grow. Earlier that year, David Sarnoff had arranged to place RCA facilities and staff at Zworykin's disposal so that the inventor could develop and perfect his brainchild. The venture was to cost RCA $10 million before television became commercially practical and another $40 million before it became profitable. But the "baby" did grow, and once started, it grew with phenomenal rapidity. According to the latest industry figures, of the 59 million dwellings in the United States, over 55 million have television sets and more than 15 million of these have two or more sets!

The history of television actually begins before that of radio. As early as 1880, several patents were filed for devices designed to transmit pictures over wires. These devices used whirling disks or spinning drums to scan the image and convert it into electrical impulses, which were sent by wire and reassembled at the receiving end. By the 1920s, the technique of mechanical scanning had been perfected to the point that moving pictures—somewhat blurry but still identifiable—were being sent over radio waves. A few receivers were even put on the market. But the vague images which wavered across these tiny, 3-inch screens were not what Sarnoff had envisioned when he referred to television, in 1924, as the means by which we would someday "see the world in action."

85

Long before his decision to back Zworykin and thus launch RCA on yet another uncharted enterprise, Sarnoff had foreseen the vast potentialities of the medium. In 1923, in a memorandum comparable to his famous "Radio Music Box" memorandum of 1915, he described to the RCA Board of Directors the important future of "seeing . . . by radio." It is characteristic of him that his faith in this future was in no way diminished by the technical difficulties surrounding it. He was aware that the kind of picture transmission he was talking about could not be achieved by mechanical disks. Television, he was convinced, would be brought to fulfillment through an all-electric system. And he believed that where the need existed, American technology would find a means to satisfy it.

By 1932, Zworykin's iconoscope was ready to start operational tests. An experimental station began telecasting from the top of the Empire State Building. The original range was 50 miles. Gradually, the range was extended, and picture definition steadily sharpened. Each improvement involved the redesigning and rebuilding of the sending equipment, which, in turn, required that all receiving sets be redesigned and rebuilt. Costs increased rapidly; million followed million at a frightening rate —"down the drain," in the opinion of many, including, of course, RCA's competitors. One of Sarnoff's principal tasks during this period was to imbue his shareholders with some of the confidence which he himself felt. Outlining an expanded research program at the shareholders' annual meeting in 1935, he pointed out that the problems of television "call for courage and initiative without which a new art cannot be created or a new industry established."

Television came before the American public as a commercial reality at the opening of the New York World's Fair in 1939. RCA began telecasting programs on a regular basis from its Empire State Building installation, and a small number of receivers were placed on sale, at $625 apiece. The radio industry was alarmed. Many of RCA's competitors felt that Sarnoff was "jumping the gun" and thereby threatening the whole industry. The reaction, in some cases, was bitter—and personal. One corporation, for example, placed an advertisement which pictured Sarnoff, the "Televisionary," smashing the radio industry.

The fight was carried to the FCC, which withheld authorization of commercial telecasting pending an agreement on industrywide standards. The standards proposed by RCA, which had originally been supported by other members of the infant industry, were now set aside. In testimony before the FCC in 1940, the underlying principle of RCA's operation was clearly stated by Sarnoff: "Substantial progress in the art can come only after its introduction on a commercial basis. . . . [Then] the practical standards prevailing in any given period will represent the best that the art has attained."

In spite of this dispute, some 10,000 people in New York City watched the mounting excitement of the Republican National Convention in Philadelphia. When you could see as well as hear the young people in the galleries and when you were virtually on the floor with the Michigan delegation as it swung its votes to Willkie on the sixth ballot, it was almost as good as being there. Sarnoff's prophecies were beginning to come true.

Just as World War I had postponed the development of radio broadcasting, World War II brought television operations to a temporary halt. By 1946, however, RCA was back in the television business, producing transmitters and receivers in limited quantities. Industry opposition faded only gradually. Many felt that Sarnoff was still being "premature." Furthermore, the costs involved in equipment and programming seemed astronomical to advertisers and station owners accustomed to the relatively modest expenses of radio. For the next few years, Sarnoff was television's chief salesman—not to the public, which was overwhelmingly in favor of the new medium, but to industry —and RCA was almost alone in the field.

The boom did come at last, and when it came, it justified Sarnoff's "wildest" predictions. RCA sold 3 million sets in 1949 and 7 million in 1950. Television was no longer "around the corner"; it was about to become one of America's leading industries.

87

First Television Prophecy

Memorandum, "Radio Broadcasting Activities," to RCA Board of Directors
April 5, 1923

I believe that television, which is the technical name for seeing instead of hearing by radio, will come to pass in due course. . . . It is not too much to expect that in the near future, when news is telegraphed by radio—say, to the United States—of important events in Europe, South America, or the Orient, a picture of the event will likewise be sent over by radio and both will arrive simultaneously. Thus, it may well be expected that radio development will provide a situation whereby we shall be able actually to see as well as read in New York, within an hour or so, the event taking place in London, Buenos Aires, or Tokyo.

I also believe that transmission and reception of motion pictures by radio will be worked out within the next decade. This would result in important events or interesting dramatic presentations being literally broadcast by radio through the use of appropriate transmitters and, thereafter, received in individual homes or auditoriums, where the original scene will be reenacted on a screen with much the appearance of present-day motion pictures. . . .

(Mimeographed text: David Sarnoff Library, Princeton, N.J.; Book: *Pioneering in Television: Prophecy and Fulfillment*, a compilation of speeches and statements by David Sarnoff, pp. 165–166.)

Seeing the World through Television

Article in *The Saturday Evening Post*
Issue of Aug. 14, 1926

What will be the language of broadcasting? I do not know. Assuredly, with international broadcasting, there must for convenience arise a dominant language. I believe this language will be one already in use, perhaps English. . . .

88   The greatest day of all will be reached when not only the human

voice but the image of the speaker can be flashed through space in every direction. On that day, the whole country will join in every national procession. The backwoodsman will be able to follow the play of expression on the face of a leading artist. Mothers will attend child-welfare clinics in their own homes. Workers may go to night school in the same way. A scientist can demonstrate his latest discoveries to those of his profession even though they be scattered all over the world.

An explorer may use television to reveal the wonders of desert and wilderness. His lecture room will come to be whatever spot he finds most appropriate as an illustrative setting for what he is about to say. . . . Certainly such agencies as these cannot fail to supplement the classroom to everybody's satisfaction.

Will the radio oust the newspaper? An average big-city newspaper prints 100,000 words of news a day. To speak the same amount of material over the radio would require eight to ten hours.

News Pictures in the Home

The impracticability of this is seen at a glance. To get the news fresh off the tap, the subscriber to a radio newspaper would be compelled to listen in all day, and all night, too. It is possible, of course, that the radio will be able eventually to bring news pictures of what is happening in the world into the home, but even here the service will only be supplementing and will not supplant the picture sections of the newspapers.

I do not think it is fantastic to see in the future great radio universities broadcasting certain courses, perhaps all courses, and granting degrees on the basis of written examinations. When I speak of these things, of course, I do not mean that the plan of action is already worked out. It is only possible to sketch the highlights and to depend upon time to take care of the rest. . . .

What I see then for the future of radio is a steady development of the resources already known. I have not the imagination of a Jules Verne and must stick to probabilities. Perhaps the possibilities, and even what seem improbabilities to me, will become facts of the future. At least it is safe to conclude that seated by our own firesides, we shall someday see the world in action, as well as hear it. It is to be

expected that our scientists will find new and better ways of bringing
to our fireside retreats information, entertainment, and instruction
from the remote corners of the earth. What those ways will be and
what new wonders they will open we must leave to a Verne or to
time to reveal.

(Book: *Radio and David Sarnoff*, by E. E. Bucher, part 4,
p. 928; part 12, p. 33; part 23, pp. 2951–2952. Photostat
of text: "Radio," by David Sarnoff, as told to Mary
Margaret McBride, *The Saturday Evening Post*, Aug. 7,
1926; David Sarnoff Library, Princeton, N.J.)

A Look at Television's Future

Address before Chicago Association of Commerce
Chicago, Ill., June 8, 1927

It is an interesting reflection that, after thousands of years of communications experience, mankind will probably go back, in the not
too far future, to picture transmission—pictures of words as well as
photographic reproductions of images—for the basis of his written
communication system. We are just entering upon the era of communications by the square inch.

. . . The new principles developed in radio technique have not
found their sole application to wireless communications. Where it
has not definitely contributed to progress in other lines of communication or to technical improvements in other industries, radio, at
least, has quickened every industry with which it has come into contact. The greatest modern achievements of the phonograph industry,
in recording as well as in reproduction, have come from the electrical
arts associated in the development of radio. Transcontinental tele-
phonic service was made possible largely by the vacuum tube. The
new transatlantic telephone service rests upon radio communications. And now the latest of the electrical arts has come to solve the
problem of synchronizing the spoken word with the moving picture.

. . . Nevertheless, the truly fundamental relationships between
the spoken word and the pictured action lie somewhat behind devel-

opments thus far demonstrated. Insofar as the present tendency in radio communications is toward sight as well as sound, both radio and the moving-picture industry are working in the same medium—light.

. . . With the inspiring demonstrations recently made of television, or the art of distant seeing, we have passed the point of conjecture as to its scientific practicability. It is an accomplished fact. Not only by wire but by radio can an image be instantly flashed from point to point so that it appears as an animated or moving picture of the subject thus photographed. True, tremendous technical facilities were required for the feat of bringing to a group of spectators in New York the voice and movements of Secretary Hoover as he sat at his desk in Washington. But this is only the laboratory stage.

The possibilities of the new art are as boundless as the imagination. But this much is certain: In the sphere of communications, man will forever seek a medium of transmission in pace with his thoughts and desires. . . . It is the glory of man that he has never quailed before the apparently insurmountable obstacles of space and time. In the circumstances, it is inconceivable that he will not make the fullest possible use of a medium of communications which bridges the distance between himself and the objects of his interest.

(Original typed manuscript of address: David Sarnoff Library, Princeton, N.J.)

Theater of the Home

Article in *The New York Times*, issue of July 13, 1930
Copyright 1930 by The New York Times Company
Reprinted by permission

With great motion-picture theaters forming huge centers of entertainment, with neighborhood picture houses in every city, with radio and the "movies" at every crossroad, it might seem at first thought an extraordinary effort of the imagination to envisage virtually millions of "little theaters" added to the constellation of entertainment made possible by radio, talking pictures, and the modern phonograph. And yet the progress of the electrical arts inevitably points in this direction. A separate theater for every home, although the stage may be only a cabinet and the curtain a screen—that, I believe, is the distinct promise of this era of electrical entertainment. . . .

Progress, I am convinced, in both the educational and the entertainment arts will be stimulated by the home. . . . The forces of sound and sight, through the medium of broadcasting, talking pictures, and electrical recording, are gradually converging upon the home to open a new phase of electrical entertainment—selective communication, selective entertainment, and selective educational programs. This, with organized forms of mass entertainment, I believe, will unite in a new era of entertainment and educational service that will far eclipse the achievements of today.

Foundations for the Home Theater

. . . Already the foundations for countless new theaters of the home are being laid. Millions of homes are now resonant with sound. Portable motion-picture projectors, which would establish miniature sound theaters in the home, are being sold upon a commercial basis. Facsimile transmission—telegraph transmissions of reproductions of photographs and documents—is making continuous progress, and there is no technical reason why it should not reach the home eventually.

Television, now in the laboratory stage, still requires the solution of many technical problems before it can be established as a service to the home, although much of the pioneering work already done holds great promise for the future. Many elements that go to make up the electrical ear and the electrical eye are already established in the home through the instrumentalities of sound reception and motion-picture reproduction. The theater of the home, it is probable, will be built and ready long before many of the services that can be rendered through it will have been established.

It is interesting to consider the extent to which the foundations of the home theater already have been built. Approximately 10 million homes in the United States are now equipped with the instrumentalities of radio reception. Every one of these homes draws nightly upon the programs of the air for their family entertainment. The great events of the day are brought graphically to the fireside by radio announcers, and constant progress is being made in the development of educational features. Broadcasting is essentially a system of mass communication, although the instrumentalities of radio reception include some of the facilities necessary for selective entertainment and educational programs. . . .

In the meantime, equipment for recorded music and speech has been made available to the home through the electric phonograph, born of the association of the phonograph and radio industries. It is the immediate means of selective entertainment now offered to the home. By it, every music lover can make his own program and suit his own taste in musical culture. . . .

In the organization of a broadcasting service by television, the question immediately arises how a spontaneous event may be placed before the greatest possible number of spectators, allowing for the fact that such events are apt to occur in the daytime, that there are differences in time in various parts of the country, and that the family gathering hours are in the evening.

**Recording TV
Programs**

Nevertheless, the opportunities for entertainment and education which television brings into view are much greater than its service problems. Television could be harnessed to the motion-picture screen so that a great event might be simultaneously recorded in a number of key cities throughout the nation and the talking motion-picture film distributed again by television to millions of homes some hours after the actual occurrence. Television, when it does come upon a practical service basis, promises to supply a vast invisible channel of distribution for motion pictures in the home.

There is little in the field of cultural education that cannot be envisaged for the home through the new facilities of electrical communications.

(Printed booklet: "The Theater of the Home," by David
Sarnoff.)

93

Television—Today and Tomorrow

Statement at Hollywood, Calif.
May 18, 1931

In the city of Hollywood . . . it seems appropriate to discuss the most recent development in the field of electrical entertainment—television.

Where is television? When will it be ready for the home? What form will it assume? How about the necessary television transmitting stations? What are its likely effects upon the established radio and motion-picture industries? . . .

The present status of television might be likened to the condition of radio in the immediate prebroadcasting era, when amateurs were beginning to hear faint sounds through the air. Voices and music were passing through space in those early days of radio; comparably, there are actually some images passing through the air today. They are being received by established experimental stations and by amateur operators in various sections of the United States. In this connection, it should be observed that the early success of radio broadcasting was stimulated in no small measure by the amateur wireless operators of that day. Similarly, the amateur operator in television is now playing his part in the development of this new service.

The next stage—and I anticipate its realization by the end of next year—should find television comparable to the earphone stage of radio. At this point, the public may well be invited to share in its further unfolding.

By that time, television should attain the same degree of development as did radio sound broadcasting in the early period of the crystal set. This does not mean that the actual physical structure of the first television receiver will be similar in any way to the crystal receiver; the similarity will lie in the class and condition of the service. The visions which first come through the air to the public will be of the same embryonic quality as the first faint sounds which sent Mother hurrying to the earphone of the boy's crystal set in the attic.

When television reaches this stage, rapid strides may be expected, comparable perhaps to the growth and development of broadcasting

94

of sound. The progress to follow should make possible the projection of moving images on a screen on the wall. Reception of sight by radio then will be comparable to the loudspeaker stage of sound reception. . . .

Television Will Help the Radio Industry

There will be no interference between the broadcasting of sound and of sight. These services will supplement each other and complete the impression upon the human mind by reaching it through both the ear and the eye. Television-broadcasting stations will operate on wavelengths different from those now used for the broadcasting of sound. An entirely different receiver will be necessary; radio sets now used for sound reception are not equipped to receive television.

In the practical sense of the term, television must develop to the stage where broadcasting stations will be able regularly to broadcast visual objects in the studio or scenes occurring at other places through remote control; where reception devices are developed that will make these objects and scenes clearly discernible in millions of homes; where such devices can be built upon a principle that will eliminate rotary scanning disks, delicate hand controls, and other movable parts; and where research has made possible the utilization of wavelengths for sight transmission that will not interfere with the use of the already overcrowded channels in space.

Television Will Not Interfere with Motion Pictures in the Theater

There will be no conflict between television in the home and motion pictures in the theater. Each is a separate and distinct service. History confirms the fact that the creation of a new service for the public does not result in the elimination of an older service, provided each has something of its own to give. On the contrary, many examples might be cited to prove that the reverse is true. The telephone did not displace the telegraph. The radio did not displace the cable. The incandescent lamp did not displace the candle; more candles are being sold today than before the creation of the incandescent lamp. And television in the home will not displace the motion picture in the theater.

Man is a gregarious creature. Granting that we can develop 26 million potential theaters in the homes of America, public theaters **95** will continue to operate because people will go there in response to the instinct for group emotions and to see artists in the flesh. These are human demands which television in the home cannot satisfy.

**Television Will
Expand the Artists'
Field**

. . . In reflecting upon the entertainment arts in general, and the motion-picture industry in particular, one is impressed by two essential elements which must be regarded as their lifeblood. The mechanical age, with its new instrumentalities, only serves to emphasize the importance of and to increase the necessity for these two vital elements.

First, the creative element—the domain of the author, the playwright, the composer. The man or woman who has a story to tell or a song to compose will be in demand so long as the art of entertainment endures.

Second, the human interpretation of the creator's work. Someone must speak the playwright's words before they can be placed upon the screen, the radio, or the phonograph record; someone must interpret the composer's music before it can come to life through any of the mechanical devices of the electrical era.

. . . Television, when it arrives as a factor in the field of entertainment, will create a fresh market for this fuel; it will give new wings to the talents of creative and interpretive genius and will furnish a new and greater outlet for artistic expression. All this will stimulate and further advance the art of motion-picture production.

**Television's Potential
Audience**

The potential audience of television in its ultimate development may reasonably be expected to be limited only by the population of the earth itself.

Since the dawn of the new era of electrical entertainment, untold millions have been added to our audiences. . . . This vast increase in the entertainment audience has been made possible by the introduction of modern science into the older arts. And now television will come to open new channels, to provide new opportunities for art and the artist, and to create new services for the audiences of all the world.

The instantaneous projection through space of light images produced directly from objects in the studio or in the scene brought to the studio by remote control involves many problems. Special types of distribution networks, new forms of stagecraft, and a development of studio equipment and technique will be required. With these must come a new and greater service of broadcasting, both of sight and of sound. A new world of educational and cultural opportunities will be opened to the home. New forms of artistry will be encouraged and developed. Variety and more variety will be the demand of the day. . . . The service will demand, therefore, a constant succession of personalities, a vast array of talent, a tremendous store of material, a great variety of scene and background. . . .

But even more appealing to the individual is the hope that television may, at least in a measure, enable man to keep pace with his thoughts. The human being has been created with a mind that can encompass the whole world within the fraction of a second; yet his physical senses lag woefully behind. With his feet, he can walk only a limited distance. With his hands, he can touch only what is within reach. His eyes can see within a limited range, and his ears are useful for short distances only.

When television has fulfilled its ultimate destiny, man's sense of physical limitation will be swept away and his boundaries of sight and hearing will be the limits of the earth itself. With this may come a new horizon, a new philosophy, a new sense of freedom, and greatest of all, perhaps, a finer and broader understanding between all the peoples of the world.

(Photocopy of text: David Sarnoff Library, Princeton, N.J.)

What May the Public Expect from Television?

A Plan for Television's Growth

Statement at annual meeting of RCA shareholders
New York City, May 7, 1935

Television service requires the creation of a system, not merely the commercial development of apparatus. The Radio Corporation of America, with its coordinated units engaged in related phases of

97

radio-communication services, is outstandingly equipped to supply the experience, research, and technique for the pioneering work which is necessary for the ultimate creation of a complete television system. Because of the technical and commercial problems which the art faces, this system must be built in progressive and evolutionary stages.

Considering these factors and the progress already made by your company, the management of RCA has formulated and adopted the following three-point plan:

1. Establish the first modern television transmitting station in the United States, incorporating the highest standards of the art. This station will be located in a suitable center of population, with due thought to its proximity to RCA's research laboratories, manufacturing facilities, and broadcasting center in Radio City.
2. Manufacture a limited number of television receiving sets. These will be placed at strategic points of observation in order that the RCA television system may be tested, modified, and improved under actual service conditions.
3. Develop an experimental program service with the necessary studio technique to determine the most acceptable form of television programs.

Through this three-point plan of field demonstration, we shall seek to determine from the practical experience thus obtained the technical and program requirements of a regular television service for the home.

It will take from twelve to fifteen months to build and erect the experimental television transmitter, to manufacture the observation receivers, and to commence the transmission of test programs.

. . . In announcing this plan, I wish to emphasize the clear distinction that must be made between the coming field-demonstration stages of television and the ultimate fulfillment of the promise of worldwide transmission of sight through space—an achievement which will be second only to the worldwide transmission of sound

through space. . . .

While the magnitude and nature of the problems of television call for prudence, they also call for courage and initiative, without which a new art cannot be created or a new industry established. Your Corporation has faith in the progress which is being made by its scientists and its engineers, and the management of the Radio Corporation of America is exploring every path that may lead to an increasing business for the radio industry and to a new and useful service to the public.

(Printed booklet: "Television," a statement by David Sarnoff.)

THE INFANT
INDUSTRY: PREWAR TELEVISION

Editor's Note *The RCA Exhibit Building at the 1939 New York World's Fair featured television in operation. When David Sarnoff dedicated the building, on April 20, he spoke before a television camera. Several hundred people watched him on the receivers inside the building at the Fair and on receivers in the RCA Building in Manhattan.*

The Birth of Television

Address at New York World's Fair
Flushing Meadows, April 20, 1939

Today we are on the eve of launching a new industry based on imagination, on scientific research and accomplishment. We are now ready to fulfill the promise made to the public last October, when after years of research, laboratory experiments, and tests in the field costing millions of dollars, the Radio Corporation of America announced that television-program service and commercial-television receivers would be made available to the public with the opening of the New York World's Fair.

Ten days from now, this will be an accomplished fact. The long years of patient experimenting and ingenious invention which the scientists of the RCA Research Laboratories have put into television development have been crowned with success. I salute their accomplishments and those of other scientists, both here and abroad, whose efforts have contributed to the progress of this new art.

On April 30th, the National Broadcasting Company will begin the first regular public television-program service in the history of our country; and television receiving sets will be in the hands of merchants in the New York area for public purchase. A new art and a new industry, which eventually will provide entertainment and information for millions and new employment for large numbers of men and women, are here.

100

. . . And now we add radio sight to sound. It is with a feeling of humbleness that I come to this moment of announcing the birth in this country of a new art so important in its implications that it is bound to affect all society. It is an art which shines like a torch of hope in a troubled world. It is a creative force which we must learn to utilize for the benefit of all mankind.

This miracle of engineering skill, which one day will bring the world to the home, also brings a new American industry to serve man's material welfare. In less than two decades, sound broadcasting provided new work for hundreds of thousands of men and women, added work in mines and forests and factories for thousands more, and aided the country and its citizens economically by causing the flow of hundreds of millions of dollars annually. Television bids fair to follow in its youthful parent's footsteps and to inherit its vigor and initiative. When it does, it will become an important factor in American economic life. Also, as an entertainment adjunct, television will supplement sound broadcasting by bringing into the home the visual images of scenes and events which up to now have come there as mind pictures conjured up by the human voice.

(Printed booklet: "The Birth of an Industry," address by
David Sarnoff.)

A New Force in Society

Article in *Journal of Applied Physics*
Issue of July, 1939

With the advent of television, a new force is being given to the world. Who can tell what the power to extend vision will mean ultimately in the stream of human life?

Television will finally bring to people in their homes, for the first time in history, a complete means of instantaneous participation in the sights and sounds of the entire outer world. It will be more realistic than a motion picture because it will project the present instead of the past. Aural radio already has demonstrated the greatly **101** heightened psychological significance, to the listener, of feeling that he is present at the radio performance, as a member of an audience listening to living performers. The sensation that one is participating in an event actually taking place at the precise moment of hearing it is quite different and much more intense than the sensation one has in witnessing a sound picture or hearing a record of the same event, later on. With the advent of television, the combined emotional results of both seeing and hearing an event or a performance at the instant of its occurrence become new forces to be reckoned with, and they will be much greater forces than those aroused by audition only. The emotional appeal of pictures to the mass of people is everywhere apparent. We have only to regard the success of motion pictures, tabloid newspapers, and modern picture magazines to be convinced of this.

(Printed booklet: "Probable Influences on Society," by David Sarnoff.)

Opportunities of Television

Testimony before Federal Communications Commission
Washington, D.C., April 10, 1940

The Board of Directors and the Management of the Radio Corporation of America are of the considered opinion that television offers the opportunity for the creation of a new industry, new employment, and new services; that its introduction now is not only timely but important; and that substantial progress in the art can come only after its introduction upon a commercial basis.

. . . The Radio Corporation of America believes that in an art such as television there can be no shorter cut from promise to performance than through the process of laboratory development, field test, and service to the public.

If the industry is left free to determine, through experimentation and test, the competitive advantages of every system, the practical standards prevailing in any given period will represent the best that the art has attained.

The Radio Corporation has never proposed or urged the freezing of standards. Nor is such action necessary to create the television industry and the new public services that would flow from it.

It is a fallacy to assume that the commercial introduction of television, on any standard now conceivable, would affect the continuance of research in this art or prevent the adoption of higher standards of service and performance.

The triumph of television lies in the fact that science, research, and experimentation have made possible the addition of the electrical eye to the electrical ear in radio.

Because it recognized this as a fundamental development, the Radio Corporation of America has invested more than $10 million in television research, development, experimentation, patents, field tests, and actual program service.

Mounting Television Investment

. . . But these expenditures are only a drop in the bucket to what will be required for further research and development in the next twenty years. Almost two decades have elapsed since the introduction of sound broadcasting on a commercial basis, but improvement still continues; and I can safely say there is little we have achieved today that will survive the next ten years.

. . . And while on the subject of research, let me refer to the importance of increasing the size not merely of the television picture but of the television audience—in other words, to give more people in more communities the opportunity to enjoy television and to participate in its activities. I submit that a greater public interest will be served at this time by research toward the methods that would extend television service to as many homes as possible than by improvements that would merely add to the size or the definition of the picture now enjoyed by the few.

To meet this need, the Radio Corporation of America has developed a radio relay system designed to extend the service of television to the public on a nationwide basis.

The Radio Corporation of America is ready, if commercial television is authorized, to ask for a license from the Federal Communications Commission for the construction of such a radio relay system, using higher frequencies than have ever before been utilized. **103**

Such facilities could serve broadcasters with programs moving simultaneously in both directions.

**RCA Welcomes
Competition**

The Radio Corporation of America welcomes the keen competition promised in the industry in the development of the television art. The promise of this competition is increased, not lessened, by the present disagreement among a few engineers as to standards of transmission and reception and methods by which the highest standards may best be achieved.

. . . It is the firm belief of the Radio Corporation of America that a truly new industry and new service and new employment could be created, on a scale that would affect our whole economy, through the development of television that would give our own country leadership in this new art. I believe that, given the opportunity, American ingenuity and enterprise can, in a reasonable time, develop a new industry in television amounting to a billion dollars annually. It is our opinion that this could be done without undue disturbance to the present broadcasting structure. But this achievement is impossible unless we show the courage that has made this country the radio center of the world.

(Book: *Radio and David Sarnoff*, by E. E. Bucher, part 4, pp. 980G–981; part 12, pp. 211–243; part 23, pp. 2964–2965.)

Milestone in Human Affairs

Article in *The Annals of the American Academy of Political and Social Science*
Issue of January, 1941

On June 27, 1940, a social and political event took place which may well be regarded in the future as a milestone in human affairs. On that day, for the first time in history, a spellbound audience of ten thousand or more people in New York City and its vicinity witnessed the nomination of a candidate for President of the United States at the Republican National Convention in Philadelphia, nearly one hundred miles away. The members of this audience, seated comfortably in their homes and in restaurants or other public places, were aurally, visually, and immediately transported to the distant scene by the modern miracle of television. The time was a critical one in the history of the nation, the event one of traditional significance, and its outcome a subject of the greatest interest to millions of people. Many of those in the television audience saw a substantial part of the entire Convention proceedings, which were broadcast by television for more than thirty-three hours, over a period of five days; and they were so absorbed that it was given one of the highest audience program ratings of the year.

This was one of a series of programs of the television broadcasting service inaugurated by the National Broadcasting Company. . . . Considered as an extension of the already existing radio sound broadcasting system, this new service marks an important development in mass communications. Considered more fundamentally, however, as an extension of the power of human vision, it assumes a social significance of an entirely different order of magnitude. It is a major milestone in the long struggle of humanity to triumph over its physical limitations. . . .

Political addresses are certain to be more effective when the candidate is both seen and heard and when he is able to supplement his address with charts or pictures. Showmanship in presenting a political appeal by television will become more important than mere skill in talking or the possession of a good radio voice, while appearance and sincerity will prove decisive factors with an audience which observes the candidate in closeup views.

An outstanding contribution of television is its ability to bring to the listener news and sporting events while they are occurring— while the outcome is still in doubt. The widespread public interest in sound broadcasts of such events is well known. It may readily be imagined what the results are when television adds to the effect of reality by projecting the vision as well as the hearing of the audience to the scene of action. In experimental television broadcasting, news events have proved among the most popular features with the audience. . . .

(Book: Radio and David Sarnoff, by E. E. Bucher, part 13,
pp. 275–281; part 23, p. 2967.)

POSTWAR GROWTH

Editor's Note   *General Sarnoff had been a general for only five days and was still in his colonel's uniform when he came up from Washington to attend the first annual convention of the Television Broadcasters Association. He was guest of honor, and the special award that he received was the title "Father of Television." Television stood just then in need of a strong "father." Powerful elements in the industry were still stubbornly opposed to it, and nonparticipation by the industry could be a body blow both to television and to RCA, which had invested and was continuing to invest so heavily in its future.*

Worldwide Television Interest

Address at the first annual conference of
the Television Broadcasters Association
New York City, December 12, 1944

We enter now a new phase in the development of television. Whatever its possibilities or whatever its limitations, one thing you may be certain of: there is not only national but worldwide interest in the great promise of television as a postwar art and a postwar industry. That nation which establishes television first will undoubtedly have the first great advantage in establishing its designs, its patterns, and its standards in the rest of the world and will thus gain a great advantage in the export markets.

It is of vital importance to America, not only from the standpoint of rendering a new service made possible by television but also from the standpoint of not being outdistanced in the important export fields, that we be ready at least as soon as any other exporting nation of the world may be ready, and I should hope sooner. . . .

(Book: *Radio and David Sarnoff*, by E. E. Bucher, part 8, pp. 1789–1797; part 12, pp. 1–2; part 13, pp. 298–305; part 23, pp. 2969–2970.)

Statement in RCA booklet,
"Radio in 1945–1946, Review . . . and a Preview"
Released December 13, 1945

Television networks are in prospect as automatic radio relay stations are being built to relay television from city to city. At the same time, the coaxial cable, another artery of television, is being extended; already, New York is linked with Washington by means of this new cable, and it is moving into the South toward Dallas, Texas. Gradually, radio relays and coaxial cables will grow out across the country to link coast with coast—and to provide a nationwide service of sight and sound.

Before nationwide television is possible, however, there must be hundreds of transmitters to supplement the nine commercial stations now on the air. These transmitters will begin to be generally available late in 1946, and by the end of 1947 considerable activity in television broadcasting may be expected.

Television will be widely utilized throughout commerce and industry. Department stores will use it so that the public can shop by television; through intrastore television, merchandise will be displayed throughout the stores at "telesite" salons. . . .

The miracle of radar and the advent of postwar television make 1945 a year to be remembered as beginning the third cycle in the evolution of radio: First, there was wireless telegraphy; second, broadcasting of the human voice and music; and now the world enters the third cycle—the era of radio sight. . . .

(Book: *Radio and David Sarnoff*, by E. E. Bucher, part 8, pp. 1848–1850; part 13, pp. 341–347; part 15, pp. 902–906; part 23, p. 2972.)

Airborne Television

Remarks at Navy–RCA demonstration of airborne television
Anacostia, D.C., March 21, 1946

Airborne television represents monumental progress in widening television's scope of service. I foresee it as a revolutionary means of television news coverage over long and short distances from cars, boats, and planes.

It opens the way for coverage of events with instantaneous transmissions of eye-witness views at the scene and at the exact time of the occurrence. This can cover fires, floods, train wrecks, or happier events of public interest.

I believe the way also is opened for development of the "walkie-lookie"—a lightweight, portable television camera with which a reporter might cover street scenes as readily as he does now with a news camera.

Further Possibilities for Service

There are additional possibilities—and I mention only a few:

1. *Safeguarding the lives of test pilots.* This may be achieved by replacing pilots with remote-control apparatus, including airborne television, in experimental planes of supersonic speeds or in any plane in which there is an element of risk. The television equipment not only can give "eyes" to planes but can transmit to control headquarters up-to-the-second readings of instruments and testing gear.

2. *Use in aircraft navigation.* Television reports of terrain surrounding airports, as well as of the layout and activity of the airports themselves, might be flashed to incoming pilots in time to avert landing difficulties. This form of sight transmission also may be valuable in marine navigation, particularly in port and docking operations.

3. *Widespread applications in industry.* Adaptations destined to become the "eyes" in factories and large-scale production enterprises are envisaged. This type of television can be a new means of coordinating manufacturing activities and may enable watch-

108

ing and controlling from a distance processes and operations that might otherwise be inaccessible or perilous to man.

4. *Use as a visual stimulus to tour enterprises.* This is another possibility. Airborne television can bring prospective travelers firsthand views of the scenic attractions and popular appeal of distant resorts and playgrounds.

5. *Use in police traffic control.* This may prove especially useful at the approaches to large cities where vehicular congestion ofttimes occurs because of sudden fluctuations of traffic. A television-equipped police plane could keep traffic headquarters posted on exact conditions in such areas, and arrangements could be completed quickly to remedy congestion by rerouting or other traffic-control means.

6. *Increased safety for hazardous exploration and scientific expeditions.* This may be achieved by airborne television under circumstances where it is necessary to undertake preliminary investigations from a point of safety. Television pictures transmitted from the plane could provide vivid clues as to the dangers involved. Adaptations of this type of television equipment might likewise be used to probe areas far beneath the surface of the ocean to locate sunken treasures or to survey regions of the deep heretofore inaccessible due to great sea pressure.

These are some of the peacetime possibilities opened by airborne television. Others may soon be discovered, because American scientists and engineers are constantly striving to develop instruments holding promise of benefit to mankind. In the next few years, this new form of sight transmission may be translated into uses undreamed of at this historic demonstration today.

(Book: *Radio and David Sarnoff,* by E. E. Bucher, part 8, pp. 1879–1886; part 13, pp. 362–368; part 23, pp. 2974–2975.)

Industrial Television

Address before Radio Manufacturers Association
Chicago, Ill., June 12, 1947

Television, as I see it, not only is a service designed for the home but also is destined to have great implications for the theater, for the motion-picture studio, for the entertainment film, and last but not least, in the manifold processes of industrial life. Industrial television promises to be a great field in itself. . . .

Television, therefore, offers the radio industry a combination of opportunities: first, to make transmitters and receiving sets; second, to equip theaters; and third, to manufacture for industrial applications. We do not need to wait for the coming development of television on a national scale to receive the benefits it already affords on a smaller scale.

. . . Modern industry has become a complex, expansive world in which processes and operations often must be carried out over large areas or in locations inaccessible or dangerous to human attendants.

The television eye makes it possible to see anything, almost anywhere. It can be used to observe dangerous chemical processes. It can be put into blast furnaces to permit the study of the flame. Television brings a camera eye into mines and tunnels. It can be lowered into tank cars as well as into the depths of the sea. Fishermen may drop a television eye over the side to locate schools of fish and oyster beds. Explorers will scan marine life and the geology of the ocean floor. Wrecks at any depth will be observed from the decks of ships without endangering divers.

Television presents a panoramic view. I envisage factory superintendents at their desks overlooking their outlying plants, even those in distant cities, through television. Centralization of inspection is made possible; the assembly line can be observed at one or at many points, thus facilitating visual control of all operations. Coordination along the line is made possible; the delivery of parts can be watched and properly timed; movement of the belt can be regu-

110

lated for utmost efficiency; and work performance can be surveyed and time-studied. . . .

The industrial applications of television are endless. . . .

> [Book: *Radio and David Sarnoff*, by E. E. Bucher (address titled "The Outlook for the Radio Industry"), part 8, pp. 1974–1988; part 13, pp. 386–398; part 23, pp. 2980–2983.]

Television Progress

Address before NBC convention
Atlantic City, N.J., September 13, 1947

In speaking of television, for the past twenty-five years or so, we have been accustomed to say that "television is around the corner." In my observations today I should like to bury that phrase. Television is no longer around the corner. It is beyond the doorstep; it has pushed its way through the door into the home!

. . . Programs limited to sound and prepared through the techniques of sound broadcasting alone will continue to serve millions of people through many hours of the broadcasting period when the eye cannot be concentrated on the television picture. We must expect that these services will continue to grow and to supplement each other.

. . . Like the many independent local broadcasting stations which are successful and profitable, television stations also can thrive upon local talent and community service. There is no end to local program possibilities, for the small town is a natural television stage. People like to see their friends and neighbors on the screen. I can foresee many uses for television in religious and educational activities. Television can be a great aid to good government in city, town, and country by making citizens better acquainted with their local leaders and their work.

Local merchants will find television an effective means of advertising. Dramatic groups, county fairs, and community sports events will enlarge their audiences. Often, a local baseball or football game or a prizefight is as interesting to a community as a professional sport event in a distant city. Civic and fraternal organizations and women's clubs also are sources of programs for local television stations. . . .

Automatic relay stations, either alone or in combination with the coaxial cable, show great promise for speeding extension of television-program service throughout the nation. Radio relay stations are now in operation between a number of cities, and others are being erected. Eventually, these microwave channels will reach out further to connect additional communities in television network service, especially cities not reached by coaxial cables.

**New Techniques
Required**

. . . The telecaster will, of course, have the problem of talent. He cannot depend solely upon the radio, motion pictures, and other established sources of entertainment for his performers. Television is a new art form that calls for new techniques and for the development and encouragement of new talent to supplement present radio entertainers. Many well-known radio artists will adapt themselves to television as successfully as the artists of the silent screen adapted themselves to the talkies.

News and sports already have proved natural drawing features for television. Films also will play an important part in the flexibility of television programming. But timeliness is the great advantage which television has over all other forms of visual entertainment. Those who recently watched the American Legion Parade in New York, the Davis Cup tennis matches, and big-league baseball games throughout this summer can attest to this. News associations are studying methods of television news service to supplement the service they now perform for sound broadcasting. The Presidential nominations and election in 1948, with political candidates competing for public attention, will stimulate public interest in television on a widening scale. . . .

Recently, there have been several extraordinary demonstrations —one this week, which you perhaps read about in the press. Several surgical operations at the New York Hospital were televised by RCA, enabling those attending the American College of Surgeons

Congress to view the operations on television screens in the Wal-
dorf-Astoria. Television may prove to be the medical lecture hall of
the future.

In still another field, the U.S. Navy recently announced success
in underwater television experiments in which RCA equipment was
used. This opens an entirely new field in deepwater investigations
and novel television programs. . . . Explorers can scan marine life
on the ocean floor, as well as wrecks, by lowering television cameras
into the sea. Submarines may yet be equipped with television
eyes. . . .

Today, international television may seem far off. But let us recall that five years after sound broadcasting started as a nationwide
service, we had international broadcasting. While the technical
problems of international television are more difficult to solve,
nevertheless I believe we shall achieve international television in
about the same period of time. The scientific knowledge for doing
the job exists. In fact, I know of no problem in international television that money cannot solve.

**International
Television**

. . . Television is moving forward rapidly and is destined to become one of the major industries of the United States. In addition to
serving the home, television has application to the theater, the motion-picture studio, and the entertainment film. In the manifold
processes of industrial life, television also is destined to play an important role.

. . . Television will be supported by advertising, both local and
national, for it is an ideal advertising medium—unsurpassed in its
simultaneous appeal to the eyes and ears of many millions of people.
Studies indicate that the pulling power of advertising on television is
many times that obtainable by sound broadcasting alone.

**Television as an
Advertising Medium**

Television is setting a much faster pace as an advertising medium than broadcasting did in its pioneering days of the early
twenties. It is apparent that sound broadcasting soon will face keen
competition from television. As television expands on a national
scale, this competition is certain to increase.

113

It seems to me that broadcasters should not consider television solely from the standpoint of profits or losses during the pioneering period. We must look to the opportunities ahead and weigh the obligation which all of us share to render maximum service to the public.

**A Message to
Broadcasters**

There are other important economic considerations which must not be overlooked. . . . As the television audience increases and programs improve—and both results are sure to be achieved—many listeners are bound to switch from sound broadcast to television programs. I do not mean that they will switch permanently from sound broadcasting to television, but they will be switching back and forth between these two services. They cannot enjoy both at the same time unless sight and sound are combined in all programs. . . . As the switching goes on, it will reduce the audience of sound-broadcasting stations and increase the audience of television-broadcasting stations. Those who are not in television will find their sound-broadcasting revenue, which is based on circulation, diminished. That fact is self-evident.

To maintain their present position in their local communities, to render the greatest possible service, and to safeguard the capital investments and earning capacities of established sound-broadcasting stations, prudent owners will consider television as an added new service, vitally necessary to insure their existing business against reduction of audience, loss of profits, and depreciation of investments. . . .

I lived through the day when the Victor Talking Machine Company—and those who founded it did a great job in their day—could not understand how people would sit at home and listen to music that someone else decided they should hear. And so they felt that the "Radio Music Box" and radio broadcasting were a toy and would be a passing fancy. What was the result? Not many years after their fatal dream, RCA acquired the Victor Talking Machine Company, and the little dog changed its master.

I saw the same thing happen in the field of talking motion pictures. It was argued by many that people would not go to a movie that made a lot of noise and bellowed through an amplifier and disturbed the slumber of those who enjoyed the silent movie. That,

they said, was a preposterous idea! The very virtue of the silent
movie, they contended, was its silence! And then in 1927 came
Warner Brothers with *The Jazz Singer* and Al Jolson. Almost overnight a new industry was born. The silent actor became vocal, and
the silent picture was given an electronic tongue. Today, who goes
to a silent movie?

Now, I should like to impress upon those of you engaged in radio that, for the first time in its history, radio itself has a stake in the
present. It must be careful not to act like the cable company, the
phonograph company, and the silent-motion-picture company,
which looked upon the new children of science as ghosts of obsolescence that might adversely affect their established businesses. In
their desire to perpetuate and to protect their existing businesses,
some of them stubbornly resisted change and progress. Finally, they
suffered the penalty of extinction or were acquired by the progressive
newcomers.

Let me assure you, after more than forty years of experience in
this field of communications and entertainment, I have never seen
any protection in merely standing still. There is no protection except through progress. Nor have I seen these new scientific developments affect older businesses, except favorably, where those who
were progressive gave careful thought and study to the possibilities
of new inventions and developments for use in their own business. . . .

Therefore, may I leave you with this final thought: I am not here
to urge you to enter the field of television beyond the point where
you yourselves think it is good business for you to do so or to propose
that you plunge all at one time. Rather, I would suggest that you reflect carefully and thoughtfully upon the possible ultimate effects
of television upon your established business if you do nothing and
of the great opportunities for your present and future business if
you do the right thing!

(Book: *Radio and David Sarnoff*, by E. E. Bucher, part 8,
pp. 1992–2002; part 13, pp. 405–420; part 23, pp. 2984–
2986.)

ASPECTS OF TELEVISION'S FUTURE

Global Television

Article in *Popular Mechanics*
Issue of December, 1951

The television screen in your living room promises to be far more than just a fascinating stage for domestic events and entertainment. It may well be a picture window with an instantaneous view of the whole world.

We know the scientific principles for sending TV signals soaring across oceans and linking continents. Only details and economics must still be worked out. . . . At the flick of a dial, you'll be able to bring the sound and sight of exciting events in distant lands to your armchair side. They will be the events going on at the instant—not yesterday's or last week's.

. . . How can these wonders be achieved? Although the range of television signals is limited today, several specific ways of beaming programs around the world are known. One is to set up chains of microwave relay towers that would march across the countries of the globe like rows of pins on a battle map, each one picking up, boosting, and sending signals along to the next.

Such a network of towers, spaced about 20 to 50 miles apart, would have to girdle the world by land routes. If you look at your map, you'll see it's possible. From Patagonia to Alaska, one tower chain would link the west coasts of the Americas, with tie-in chains to major cities. Across the Bering Strait from Alaska to Asia is only 40 miles—a normal hop between towers. You can actually *walk* to Russia in the wintertime when the channel is frozen over.

From here, the tower chain might trail down across Siberia, China, India, Iran, and Iraq, where it would split—one branch heading out across the deserts and the velds of Africa, the other probing up into the countries of Europe. Thus the world would be encompassed by one communications net. . . .

I have no doubt of the ultimate practicality of transoceanic television. The idea of putting this new means of communication on an international scale is exciting. Think how television beamed abroad could *show* democracy at work to the rest of the world. To see democracy at work is to believe it, and that's one of television's big jobs of the future. Indeed, international television offers us a great opportunity to promote real understanding among people and to build a lasting peace among men.

> [Book: *Radio and David Sarnoff*, by E. E. Bucher (article titled "Let's Send Television around the World"), part 14, pp. 815–823. Photostat of text: David Sarnoff Library, Princeton, N.J.]

Electronic Advances and Television

Address at annual banquet of the
Institute of Radio Engineers
New York City, March 25, 1953

Between now and 1960—and that is only seven years away—great changes in industry will take place as a result of developments in solid-state electronics. Indeed, the vacuum tube is approaching its fiftieth anniversary confronted by a mighty competitor—the transistor.

Present-day electronic devices, instruments, and systems will be transistorized. This new tool of science will widen the usefulness of electronics. It will spread its applications into many fields which the electron tube has not been able to serve. . . .

Industrial electronics offers many opportunities for development and expansion. It will revolutionize many phases of business, especially within large organizations. For example, electronic computers can translate, process, compute, store, and print pertinent facts and information. They simplify the task, greatly increase the efficiency, and perform the functions of an accounting system with utmost speed and accuracy.

Electronics will change clerical operations, relieve men of routine and drudgery and effect enormous savings in time, money, and materials. The world of business machines is ripe for electronics.

117

Growing Uses of Electronics

Electronics can also serve in other directions. It promises new aids to health, safety, and better living. There are countless applications for the development of inspection methods to insure the highest purity in liquids, vaccines, drugs, and all bottled beverages, including milk. Electronics becomes the foe of impurity and contamination in all bottled, packaged, or canned products.

Another important area for further development and expansion of electronics is aviation, especially in communications and radar. Electronics is the pilot of the robot plane and the hand that guides the missile. Recently, the Army exhibited a new rapid-fire radar-controlled antiaircraft gun, which is an electronically guided artillery weapon that searches out and hits with deadly accuracy a hostile aircraft in any weather and destroys it at altitudes up to 4 miles.

In a few short years, we have seen television develop into a major factor in American life. Its extraordinary potentialities for political education, cultural instruction, and entertainment have been amply demonstrated. However, many other applications of television's basic function—extension of human sight—are ready for practical use.

Thus far, the phenomenal growth of broadcast television has overshadowed these other applications, which operate over closed-circuit systems and constitute the growing field of industrial television. The opportunities for expansion of television in this field are wide.

Wherever danger, remoteness, or discomfort preclude the presence of a human observer, the industrial television camera can take his place. Handling of explosives, pouring of castings, watching the operations of furnaces and remote power substations are examples of television's usefulness to industry.

Closed-circuit Potential

As yet, only a negligible fraction of the potential of industrial television has been tapped. The major obstacle has been cost. That obstacle is being overcome by lightweight equipment using the vidicon camera tube. The dimensions of industrial television may surpass the growth in broadcast television we are now witnessing. . . .

118

Schools, in which television sets are becoming more and more a standard classroom fixture, may employ their TV sets to bring talks and demonstrations to the entire school or to selected classes, without the loss of time or the confusion attendant upon a call to assembly. On college campuses, the linking of the lecture halls by television will permit exchange of instruction between departments, adding to the variety and interest of the courses. In biological research and technical education, this form of television has proved a valuable tool.

The availability of a simple closed-circuit system will put the television microscope as a new instrument for instruction within reach of every high school and college in the country.

Until now, industrial television has been utilized mainly by larger business and industrial organizations, but the reduction in cost brings it within reach of thousands of small businesses.

Many uses are also foreseen for closed-circuit TV in hotels, department stores, and other business establishments. A visual intercommunication system between offices, for checking papers and documents, or between office, factory, and warehouse can now be realized economically.

One of the largest fields ahead for the use of closed-circuit television is the home itself. Closed-circuit sound systems are familiar to Americans. We think nothing of voice communication between rooms in the same house, between offices in the same building, between upstairs and downstairs. We are destined, I believe, to become equally familiar with closed-circuit systems of sight transmission.

When the cost of the camera attachments is sufficiently low to permit their use in the average home, they may make the television receiver truly the control center of the home. The snap of a switch will turn the receiver from the broadcast program to view the children asleep in the nursery or at play in the yard or to check the cooking on the kitchen range. The housewife will not only hear but see the caller at the door before she opens it.

As the science of electronics continues to unfold, new discoveries will be made, new inventions will be created, and new products and services will be developed. This will steadily increase the size **119** of the electronics industry, its importance for national defense, and its value to the public.

(Book: *Radio and David Sarnoff*, by E. E. Bucher, part 24, pp. 3377–3379; part 27, pp. 3884–3899; part 29, pp. 42–56.)

Television for Police Work

Address at graduation exercises
FBI National Academy
Washington, D.C., June 11, 1954

Today almost 6,000 law-enforcement agencies use two-way radio, and a total of 100,000 vehicles are licensed by police units to operate mobile equipment. The New York Police Department alone uses more than 1,700 radio-equipped vehicles. Virtually all cities with over 10,000 population have a municipally operated two-way radio system, and every state police force is radio-equipped.

You men are aware of the importance of communications on highways. In Pennsylvania and New Jersey, where turnpikes are in operation, highly efficient microwave radio-communication systems have been installed. They provide instantaneous contact between mobile patrols as well as point-to-point communications between tollgates, service facilities, patrol headquarters, and other installations. In many other states, where turnpikes are planned or under construction, radio will have this opportunity to serve.

Eventually, we may be sure, these expressways will be interconnected not only by radio but by television. It is only a matter of time, moreover, before a coast-to-coast radio-television network will transmit teletype messages, weather reports, photographs, fingerprints, and other documents. Law enforcement will have at its disposal an all-seeing eye that scans the country at a glance. . . .

I should like to allude to another significant aspect of radio and

television which can play a great role in your success as law-enforcement officers. No matter where you live, you are aware of how closely radio is woven into the fabric of your community's life. And television, though a newcomer, already has 400 stations on the air. This dual service of sight-and-sound broadcasting gives America the greatest medium of mass communication in the world.

What you make of it depends in large measure upon your own energy and imagination as a citizen and as an officer of the law. It enables you to help shape the ideas and attitudes of both young and old, to expose the futility of crime and the perils of delinquency. Broadcasters have been brought up in a spirit of public service; they know that their own success will be gauged by their contribution to the best interests of the community. I know them well, and I do not hesitate to assure you of their cooperation.

(Book: *Radio and David Sarnoff*, by E. E. Bucher, part 31, pp. 4517–4524.)

Future of Military Television

Statement at U.S. Signal Corps and RCA television demonstration
Fort Meade, Md., August 11, 1954

Twenty years have passed since we began to develop our concept of military television. During those years, our scientists and engineers have worked hand in hand with the armed services to develop the most effective uses for television in a variety of military operations in the air, at sea, and on land.

Today, we see concrete evidence that a new era in tactical communications has opened.

In the continuing development of modern communications, the Signal Corps and the electronics industry look toward the future as well as the present. The demonstration we are witnessing today indicates that combat television units consisting of miniature color cameras and transmitters can be carried in action by one man or fixed in positions that will enable a constant eye to be kept on criti-   **121** cal areas. Television will enable a commander to keep a watchful eye on every section of the battlefront.

The use of television in military operations will provide increased combat efficiency and make possible a substantial saving of lives.

The results already achieved through Army-industry cooperation give us good reason to believe that further achievements are within our reach. This teamwork is continuing in the laboratories and in the field. The goal is to provide the armed forces of the United States with the most effective communications by sight, as well as by sound.

I foresee the extensive use of military television not only as a tactical system for use in combat but also for communications between the center of command in Washington or elsewhere and the theaters of operation across the seas. . . .

(Original typed text: David Sarnoff Library, Princeton, N.J.)

Television Sets without Tubes

Address at NBC television affiliates meeting
Chicago, Ill., August 31, 1954

I believe that at some time in the future . . . no tubes will be needed in a television set—not even the picture tube. Then all the debates about one-gun and three-gun tubes, rectangular and round, glass and metal, shadow-mask and focus-mask, and other kinds of masks will belong to the language of the past.

By electroluminescence we shall have a screen on the wall of whatever size you wish to make it—small or large—and that screen will be connected directly by a small cable to a little television box, about the size of an average cigar box, that can be placed anywhere in the room. No cabinet will be required, and if desired, screens can be placed in every room of the house.

The television box will contain the tuning and volume controls and the station selector. It will also have a remote-control knob enabling one to make the picture of any desired size, to have it either in black and white or in color, and to make it brighter or dimmer. All these features will be easily adjustable by the viewer to suit his individual taste.

(Book: *Radio and David Sarnoff*, by E. E. Bucher, part 32, pp. 4562–4599.)

CHAPTER 4

Color Television

As early as 1932, some of the major electronics companies, including RCA, began experimenting with sending color images using the old mechanical-disk process. When Sarnoff refers, in 1934, to a "dream of television in faithful colors," he has this mechanical process in mind. But by the early 1940s, RCA had discarded the mechanical system and had oriented its research in a totally different direction. What changed Sarnoff's mind was the perfection of black-and-white television on an all-electronic basis. Why not develop color television on the same basis? The advantages were undeniable: Not only would all-electronic color apparatus have the capability of producing better pictures on larger screens than those produced by whirling disks, but (even more important) the system would be compatible with existing black-and-white facilities. The question of compatibility was to become crucial. If people could receive programs broadcast in color on their black-and-white sets, even though they would be seeing the programs in black and white, there would be no loss of audience during the probably long transition period from monochrome to color. What advertiser would be willing to venture his budget on a color program that only reached the few who had been able to afford the converters necessary to receive it? Using an incompatible system would involve giving up the vast audience already available for monochrome programs.

Few in the industry disagreed with Sarnoff's assessment of the color-television situation. An all-electronic, compatible system would, indeed, be better than a mechanical, incompatible system. But there was one overwhelming, seemingly unanswerable argument against it: No one had yet begun to develop such a system, and because of difficulties inherent in the process, it seemed likely that no one ever would—at least not in the foreseeable future. If RCA wanted to squander its shareholders' money on a project that could only result in its being left far behind in the color-television competition, RCA was welcome to do so. This, apparently, was the attitude that underlay the decision by CBS to concentrate its research efforts on the mechanical system.

Thus the color battle was joined. Sarnoff, as anyone who **127** knew him could have predicted, was not to be dissuaded by arguments like these. "The word 'impossible'," he writes, some years later, "is not to be found in the vocabulary of the scientist."

By 1946, RCA scientists were able to show considerable progress in the development of the all-electronic process. In a private demonstration, two sets, placed side by side, received the same program—one in black and white and the other in color. The color reception was far from perfect. Flickering across the images, blotches of color turned bathing beauties a startling green and dissolved baseball players in mysterious bursts of yellow and red. But it was color, nevertheless, and compatible at that. Sarnoff decided to risk a public demonstration, although he wisely restricted it to still pictures.

CBS, in the meantime, applied to the government for authority to market its incompatible, mechanical process. The response of the FCC, in 1947, was that no available system was good enough to approve. Two and a half years later, CBS again petitioned the FCC, and this time the Commission was clearly going to have to make a decision. The hearings lasted for eight months—until May, 1950—and they aroused widespread interest. Unfortunately for RCA, when the two systems were demonstrated before the Commission, the CBS disk-scanning transmitters offered better reception. Sarnoff himself admitted, years later, that in RCA color, "the monkeys were green, the bananas were blue, and everyone had a good laugh." Logic, however, was on the side of RCA; its system was potentially much the better of the two. With the RCA color tube, color programs could ultimately be received on a 21-inch screen, while the whirling-disk process limited the size of the screen to 12½ inches. RCA color programs could be transmitted over existing coaxial cables. Furthermore, the RCA design enabled the three primary colors to be overlaid, or simultaneous, instead of sequential, as in disk scanning. Despite all this, the Commission concluded by ruling in favor of the mechanical, incompatible standards.

RCA had already invested $20 million in its color system, and Sarnoff was now faced with a terrible decision. Should he scrap the program, should he slow it down and wait for the rest

of the industry to catch up, or should he go ahead? Characteristically, he decided to go ahead. Instead of administering the
coup de grâce, the FCC verdict for CBS marked the beginning
of a new and more intensive phase of the color battle. Sarnoff
placed the RCA Laboratories in Princeton on a crash program.
He took his case to the courts. And, in a series of public demonstrations of his rapidly improving color tube, he brought the issue
before the people. Significantly, while RCA was continuing so
energetically to promote its "loser," CBS was exhibiting a curious lassitude with regard to its "winner." It had received a
go-ahead to manufacture color sets, but no color sets were forth-
coming. Plainly, even CBS had finally realized that the incompatible system was just not economically feasible.

The FCC was thus placed in the embarrassing position of
having decided in favor of a system nobody wanted. It took the
Commission over three years to find its way out of that position,
but at last, in late 1953, it reversed itself and approved the all-
electronic, compatible apparatus. Sarnoff could not resist crow-
ing just a little. "In 1939," he pointed out to the press, ". . . we
added sight to sound. Now we add color to sight."

RCA marketed its first color set in 1954, and for five years
thereafter, it was literally the only company in the field. Since it
had to carry the entire burden of color programming and sales
promotion, each color set sold represented a financial loss to the
company. The situation began to change, however, when sales
of black-and-white sets sharply declined in 1958. The market in
ordinary sets was becoming saturated, and manufacturers and
TV stations turned to color as a means of reviving the flagging
industry. By the early 1960s, as Sarnoff had predicted, color television was a booming industry.

Color-television Prophecy

Article in *The New York Times*, issue of July 13, 1930
Copyright 1930 by The New York Times Company
Reprinted by permission

Assume sufficient progress in the television art, and every home equipped for radio reception may, at certain times, become an art gallery. The great works of painting and sculpture in the art galleries of Europe and America lie buried there, insofar as the vast majority of the world's population is concerned.

Television, *advanced to the stage when color as well as shadow would be faithfully transmitted,* could bring these treasures vividly to the home. The Louvre and the Metropolitan could then extend their cultural influence to millions of homes.

Conceive the exhibition of such works of art in the home, accompanied by comments and explanations by the proper authorities. Just as sound broadcasting has brought a new sense of musical appreciation to millions of people, so could television open a new era of art appreciation.

. . . The inspiration and opportunity for creative talent will be multiplied many times by the enlarged cultural conception of entertainment which selective programs will make possible. There is no saturation point to the vast public interest in everything that entertains, amuses, informs, or instructs. The new age of electrical entertainment, which will bring the artist to the public, the lecturer to his audience, and the educator to his student body, offers a vast field of opportunity to creative talent.

(Printed booklet: "The Theater of the Home," by David Sarnoff.)

Broadcasting and Color

Address before New York University, College of Fine Arts
New York City, December 3, 1934

The vision of the artist and his ability to transmit that vision to others make of art a living thing. . . . Until the dawn of the radio age, it was the artist's fate that his influence should be ever restricted by the limitations of communications. Neither the Golden Age nor the Renaissance could provide the artist with a medium by which enjoyment of his creations might be extended beyond the intimate circle of his fellows and patrons. In his entire lifetime, Demosthenes could not convey his spoken words to more than a small fraction of the persons who today can hear a speaker in a single appearance before the microphone. . . .

Radio, perhaps more than any other industrial art, can claim kinship with the fine arts. On its wings, the messages of music and education speed to uncounted millions. It brings the symphony orchestra to the lonely farmhouse. It carries poetry and drama to the most isolated hamlet. With the speed of light, the ether wave carries art's treasures to all who may wish to receive them.

Television in Color

The arts sprang from the people and, through mass distribution, radio is giving the cultural arts back to the people. . . . Among the thrilling possibilities which radio has in store is television. Think what an impetus to the cultural influence of broadcasting, as well as to its entertainment possibilities, will be produced by that event. Talks on architecture, which are now broadcast by sound alone, will then be supplemented by television pictures, so that the audience may see the famous buildings of which they are being told. Listeners will be able to watch the performance of the opera they are hearing. A play on Broadway may be seen by an audience in Arizona.

If we let our imaginations plunge ahead, we may also dream of television in faithful colors. I believe that dream will come true one day. . . . We may then be shown reproductions of art treasures . . . and have them interpreted to us as we sit by our firesides and see them through the air. A new art appreciation will thus be awakened. . . .

(Printed booklet: "Art in the Radio Age," an address by
David Sarnoff.)

All-electronic Color Television

Statement at first public demonstration of
all-electronic color television
RCA Laboratories, Princeton, N.J., October 30, 1946

Electronic color-television pictures, produced by all-electronic means, are being demonstrated publicly for the first time today by Radio Corporation of America. . . . The realization of this universal system of television, which transmits and receives both color and black-and-white pictures with equal quality, is as far-reaching as was the creation of an all-electronic television system, which supplanted the mechanical disks used in black-and-white television when it first began. The realization of all-electronic color is as significant an advance in television as electronic recording was over mechanical recording of phonograph records or as the present color movies are over the early mechanical color on the screen.

It is with great pride and satisfaction that I congratulate the men who have created all-electronic color television in our laboratories. They have enabled RCA—the creator of all-electronic black-and-white television—also to create all-electronic color television, which has been the dream of radio scientists from the beginning.

The new RCA electronic color-television system will be available to the entire radio industry. The development is so important in contributing to television leadership for our country that we have decided to demonstrate it publicly as apparatus becomes available for each successive step. We begin with the current demonstration, in which still pictures are used but which sufficiently establishes the basic principle; it will be followed by the transmission and reception of color pictures in motion, then outdoor scenes, and finally electronic color television on large-size theater screens. . . .

(Book: *Radio and David Sarnoff*, by E. E. Bucher, part 13, pp. 372–373; part 15, pp. 916–919; part 23, p. 2977. Printed booklet: "All-electronic Color Television Created by RCA," a compilation of statements by David Sarnoff and other RCA, NBC officials.)

The RCA Color-television Picture Tube

Statement at first demonstration of
RCA color-television picture tube
Washington, D.C., March 29, 1950

Measured in comparison with every major development in radio and television over the past fifty years, this color tube will take its place in the annals of television as a revolutionary and epoch-making invention. When historians at the close of the twentieth century evaluate the most important scientific developments, I will predict that this tube will be among the great inventions of the second half of this century. As the master key to practical color television, it is an outstanding development of our time.

We are on the threshold of a new era in television—the era of color. We can see ahead to the commercial development of practical and simplified color receivers. Our generation is assured of clear and natural-color television programs. Generations yet to come will see around the world in color because this tube, which will go down in history as the father of future color-television picture tubes, is the key to greater achievements destined to come.

. . . The scientists, research men, and engineers of RCA whose skills have achieved this great success . . . have made a tremendous contribution to the art and industry and have greatly intensified television's effectiveness not only in entertainment but in education. By learning to harness electrons to "paint" with perfection in natural colors, these men of science and engineering have added to the preeminence of the United States in television.

As Dr. V. K. Zworykin's invention of the iconoscope and development of the kinescope revealed to experimenters in the twenties that the old mechanical scanning disk was a crude and impractical device for the sending and receiving of black-and-white television pictures, so this color tube reveals the superiority of electronics in color television. . . . The mechanical scanning disk in television now belongs to the ages. As an expedient, it merely gave laboratory technicians something to play with while the proponents of electronics applied the modern and practical methods to develop **133** an all-electronic, high-definition, completely compatible system of color television for the American public.

(Book: *Radio and David Sarnoff*, by E. E. Bucher, part 17, pp. 1466–1471; part 22, pp. 2923–2936.)

Color-television Progress

Statement before 31st annual meeting of RCA shareholders
New York City, May 2, 1950

During the past year, RCA scientists and engineers have achieved remarkable results in the continued development of the RCA all-electronic, high-definition, completely compatible color-television system. Field tests and demonstrations have been conducted in Washington, D.C., since September, 1949, and major advances have been made.

On March 29, 1950, in Washington, the new RCA electronic direct-view color picture tube was demonstrated publicly for the first time. It has been acclaimed in engineering circles and in the press as a triumph of science. . . . It is an outstanding development of our time and the master key to practical color television for the home. It provides a color-television receiver unencumbered by any mechanical parts or revolving disks. As a result, there is no flicker, no color breakup, no whir of disks in the RCA all-electronic color-television receiver. . . .

The new RCA color tube has enabled our engineers to develop receiving sets of the same size and appearance as the present standard RCA Victor television sets. The face of the direct-view tube appears to the observer exactly the same as that of a black-and-white receiver, except, of course, that the picture is in natural colors.

Another electronic development was demonstrated by RCA to the Federal Communications Commission in Washington on April 6, 1950, when our engineers revealed a new and significant method that makes possible the transmission of color-television programs

134 produced by RCA color-television system over existing coaxial cables. This special equipment makes it possible, at the very start of color-television service, for all existing network facilities, whether coaxial cable or radio relays, to transmit RCA color-television programs. . . .

(Printed booklet: "Statement by David Sarnoff at 31st Annual Meeting of RCA Shareholders." Mimeographed text: David Sarnoff Library, Princeton, N.J.)

COLOR TELEVISION PROGRESS

The FCC hearings on color television had lasted for almost eight months when Sarnoff appeared before the Commission. He testified through two days and one evening session. It was not only a "marathon performance," as one leading trade publication put it, but a brilliant summary of the philosophy which underlay RCA's decision to direct its research toward an all-electronic color system. At the heart of the matter was the "unlimited scope for future development" which such a system offered. The color system RCA had earlier demonstrated to the Commission was by no means the "finished product"; significant improvements had taken place since then, and the potentialities of the system were each month becoming more apparent. The CBS system, on the other hand, was "confined by the limitations of a mechanical disk," and its "obsolescence" was "already foreshadowed in this fast-developing electronic art." Although the FCC ruled against RCA, subsequent events were to prove that Sarnoff's analysis had been entirely accurate.

Editor's Note

For Compatible Color Standards

Testimony before Federal Communications Commission
Washington, D.C., May 3, 1950

There is no doubt about the desirability of color television, and . . . the fundamental question in this case is crystal clear.

The question is: "Shall American television move forward or backward?"

The importance of reaching the right answer to this question **135** cannot be overestimated. The consequences of a wrong answer could be disastrous for the public and the industry.

On the one hand, the Federal Communications Commission is asked by CBS to adopt color-television standards based upon a mechanical, incompatible system which gives a degraded picture and has additional defects.

On the other hand, the Commission is asked by RCA to adopt color-television standards which will permit the utilization of an all-electronic, compatible color-television system which does not have those defects and which has picture quality at least equal to that provided by existing black-and-white standards.

To my mind, the right answer is clear.

. . . Color is a further step along the television road which has been blazed by RCA. RCA was for television when that was a solo effort. The 100 successful manufacturers of today, the more than 5 million set owners, the many additional millions who are daily enjoying television programs, all bear witness to the fruitfulness of RCA's original concept and pioneering in this art.

We are for color just as we have been for every other advance in television.

**Electronic vs.
Mechanical Color
System**

CBS has asked this Commission to adopt a system which would saddle an all-electronic art with a mechanical harness. You are being urged by CBS to build a highway to accommodate the horse and buggy when already the self-propelled vehicle is in existence and has been demonstrated.

. . . CBS, however, does not and cannot deny that its system has been designed for and is confined by the limitations of a mechanical disk. Therefore it does not and never can have the performance capabilities of a true electronic system.

It is my purpose here today to urge you, as public officers, not to turn back the television clock but to look ahead and take a long-range view. The adoption of the CBS system, whose obsolescence is already foreshadowed in this fast-developing electronic art, would earn the scorn of the world. At the very moment I am appearing before you, the United States delegates are at a meeting of the Interna-

tional Radio Consultative Committee in London to advocate world
television standards on a basis equivalent to present American
black-and-white standards. For this Commission to degrade the
standards of American television by adopting the inferior CBS system only would be to show the world that we do not have any faith
in the standards which our own State Department is recommending
to the world.

Adoption of the CBS system exclusively would also earn the
dissatisfaction of American families. They would be induced to buy
CBS-type sets by a decision of this Commission made at a time
when it was evident that CBS itself would shelve its mechanical
system in favor of an all-electronic system.

Today, in America, we have a highly successful black-and-white
television service. Its quality is attested by the present great demand for home receivers.

The public's appraisal of this newest of the arts is indeed a critical one. If the CBS color system, with all its known defects, is now
imposed upon the public, great harm will be done to the growth of
television and its public acceptance.

. . . In my judgment, no achievement of RCA or anyone else
in the history of the television art surpasses in importance the development of the RCA all-electronic color-television system, including the RCA direct-view tricolor tubes.

**The Importance of
RCA's Achievement**

I have watched the developments of radio and electronics for
more than forty years and never before have I seen compressed into
a single effort so much ingenuity, so much brain power, and such
phenomenal results as are represented in these new developments.

The question might be asked as to why RCA has spent so much
money and the energies of so many people on the development of
its all-electronic color-television system and its tricolor tubes. The
answer is clear. We in RCA have been and are 100 percent for color
television.

. . . From a purely practical standpoint, we have as much to
gain from the development of color television as anybody. We are in
the television-broadcasting business. We are in the business of man-

ufacturing and selling receiving sets, transmitters, and tubes. It is, and has been, to our interest to advance the day when color television is translated into a practical service for the home.

**Color Work
Undiminished**

. . . Since the end of the war, RCA's color work has continued undiminished. In the hearings before this Commission, in 1946–1947, we stated:

> We propose to carry on with our research and development work in monochrome and color with all the resources at our command, regardless of the . . . adoption or nonadoption of standards. We will not cease our efforts to improve service to the public.

This program has been fully carried out. We have continuously increased the amount of manpower and money we have devoted to the development of color television. There has been no gap in our intensive work on color television. We will continue to use our brain power and our resources and our facilities for the advance of color television.

. . . At the beginning of these hearings, when RCA announced its new all-electronic, compatible, high-definition color-television system, we stated that we had developed a system in which we had complete confidence and which offered unlimited scope for future development. We did not claim that the receivers we originally demonstrated to the Commission were the finished product. We were interested in demonstrating the potentialities of our system, and we frankly said that our receivers and tubes were in the development stage and would be improved. Since that time we have steadily worked to improve our performance.

. . . Our faith in the RCA all-electronic color-television system already has been fully justified.

Response to Questions

. . . During these hearings, questions have been asked as to what the policy of RCA would be in the event of certain hypothetical decisions of the Commission. I shall now address myself to these questions.

138

David Sarnoff at age 16 when he was office boy for the Marconi Wireless Telegraph Company of America.

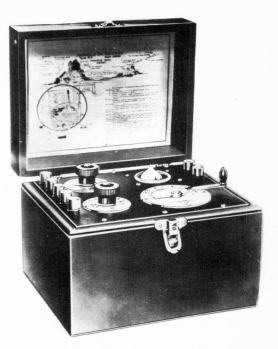

In 1915, Sarnoff sent a memorandum to the Marconi Company's general manager proposing a "Radio Music Box" which would bring music, entertainment, and news into the home.

Guglielmo Marconi at his wireless receiving set at St. John's, Newfoundland, in 1901. Here, in December of that year, he picked up the letter "S" transmitted in code across the Atlantic.

Sarnoff as wireless operator at the John Wanamaker Station, 1912. On the night of April 14, he picked up the messages about the *Titanic* sinking.

The first RCA laboratory, set up in 1919 in a tent at Riverhead, Long Island, to develop transoceanic wireless communications.

The first radio photographs were flashed across the Atlantic in 1924 from New York to London and retransmitted back to New York.

The chief officer of the famed U.S. liner *Leviathan* displays his ship's 1926 wireless equipment which made possible radio contact with both shores during transoceanic crossings.

A 1933 view of the RCA international wireless message center in New York City.

Thompson H. Mitchell (standing), President of RCA Communications, Inc., in 1964, and engineer R. K. Andres demonstrate the world's first computerized international public telegraph system.

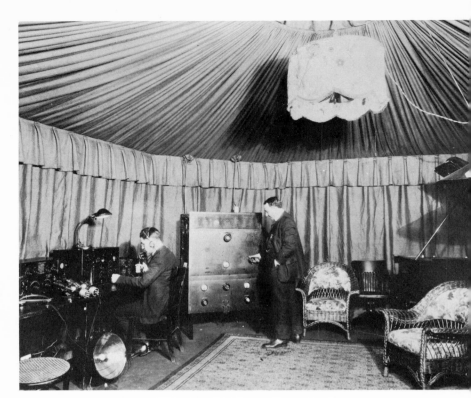

RCA's first broadcasting studio, WDY, established in Roselle Park, N.J., in 1921. By 1924, RCA operated nine stations. In 1926, the National Broadcasting Company was born.

A Victor Talking Machine recording studio in the 1920s. Sarnoff wedded the phonograph to the radio in one instrument.

Radio on the farm—1938. An Illinois farmer gives NBC "Farm and Home Hour" listeners a report on local crop conditions. His tractor is radio-equipped for listening.

Jack Dempsey listens to a "Radio Music Box" tuned by Major J. Andrew White just before the Dempsey-Carpentier championship title fight in 1921.

The "Radiola Super VIII," an RCA Super-Heterodyne receiver of 1925. This high-receptivity receiver revolutionized radio.

Maestro Arturo Toscanini being greeted by David Sarnoff in 1938, the first year of the conductor's seventeen-year association with the NBC Symphony Orchestra.

Dr. Walter Damrosch, musical conductor of NBC Radio's famed "Music Appreciation Hour," is shown in 1942 at the age of 80. He continued to conduct his program until his 84th year.

Will Rogers, one of radio's top performers, brought his wit to a nation of listeners. Radio made new entertainment stars literally overnight.

Radio networks carried President Franklin D. Roosevelt's famed "Fireside Chats" to the nation in the 1930s. (*Culver Pictures.*)

A 1939 RCA Victor television receiver. The 9-inch kinescope reproduced images 5½ by 7½ inches for direct viewing from the front of the cabinet.

RCA engineers testing a 1939 black-and-white kinescope picture tube of the television receiver.

Dr. Vladimir K. Zworykin, inventor of the iconoscope, all-electronic "eye" of the television camera.

Early television star: Felix the Cat rotates on a phonograph table in a 1930 NBC experimental television broadcast.

Television covers the World Series. Audiences of millions are grandstand spectators at major athletic events.

The first telecast of a political convention. Americans were able to watch the nomination of Wendell Willkie at the Republican Convention in 1940. (*Wide World Photos.*)

David Sarnoff inaugurates America's first television service, April 20, 1939, at the New York World's Fair.

The first RCA commercial color-television receivers come off the production line in March, 1954, three months after the FCC approved all-electronic compatible color.

An RCA research engineer checks component parts in an experimental 1946 electronic color-television receiver.

Scientists from the David Sarnoff Research Center in Princeton, N.J., examine five different types of 1951 color-television picture tubes. Dr. Elmer W. Engstrom (second from left) later became RCA's president.

ELECTIONS '66

NBC newscasters Chet Huntley and David Brinkley at work before the electronic election display board, one of several devices used to speed election returns to television viewers.

Opera on television. The miracle scene from Menotti's opera, "Amahl and the Night Visitors," shown in color on NBC Television Network during the Christmas season.

General Sarnoff, addressing the National Press Club in 1961, displays a pocket-size color-television receiver of the future.

Saturn I blasts off from Cape Kennedy, August 25, 1966. The launching was part of the program to land Americans on the moon. (*NASA.*)

Tiros weather satellite in polar orbit rotates so that cameras on alternate sides send back pictures of the earth.

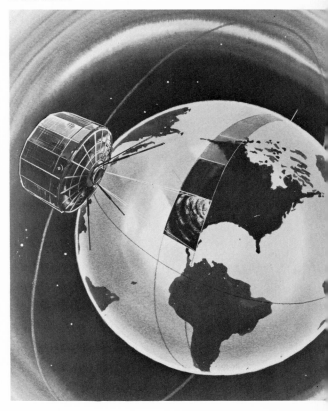

What the world's weather looks like from outer space is shown in this photograph taken from a Tiros IX weather satellite. (*NASA and ESSA.*)

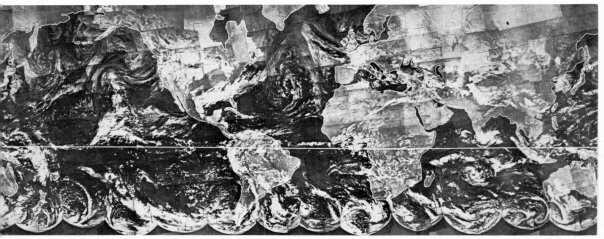

An electronic system makes possible simultaneous translation in five languages at United Nations meetings. Sarnoff proposed the UN be given its own satellite communications television channel. (*United Nations.*)

Surgery via satellite. Dr. Michael E. DeBakey, world-famous surgeon, shown performing a heart operation on a transoceanic television broadcast via Early Bird satellite in 1965.

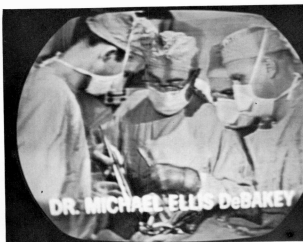

The first international television broadcast from space, July, 1962, relayed from Cape Canaveral via the Telstar communications satellite. (*Wide World Photos.*)

This suitcase-size Electronic Study Center, first demonstrated in **August, 1967**, brings students prerecorded television lessons. It also features a slide projector and audio tape recorder.

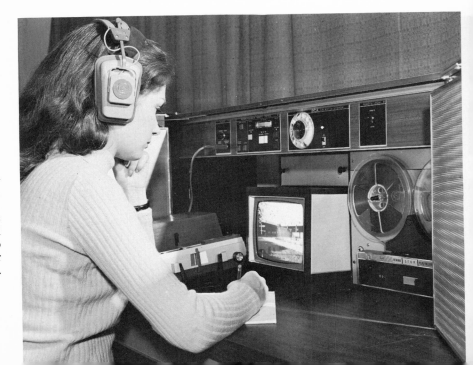

An RCA computer scientist inspects an experimental memory device which can store a quarter-million bits of information when immersed in liquid helium.

An RCA scientist discusses the Tiros weather satellite at a 1962 David Sarnoff Industry-Science Teaching Program session in a high school physics class.

This historic first photograph of earth from deep space (232,000 miles away) was taken August 23, 1966, by Lunar Orbiter I. (NASA.)

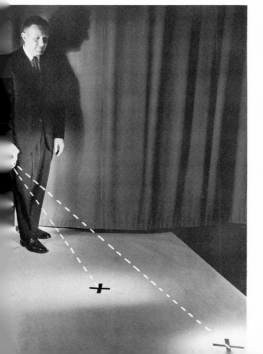

An experimental laser cane for the blind detects irregularities in the surface just ahead.

An electron microscope, used with a television set that displays the specimen under observation, is a key research tool at New York's Lenox Hill Hospital.

The 1956 electronic light amplifier which General Sarnoff requested as one of three 50th anniversary gifts.

This Relay satellite, shown here suspended upside down, was the second to be launched by NASA in its series of experiments in space communications.

"Hitchhiking" on television, this RCA Experimental Home Facsimile System can deliver printed material in the home or office while a program is being viewed.

An argon gas laser built for the National Aeronautics and Space Administration to track space vehicles is tested at the David Sarnoff Research Center.

A nun operates a computer which handles patients' billing for Detroit's Mount Carmel Mercy Hospital Medicare patients.

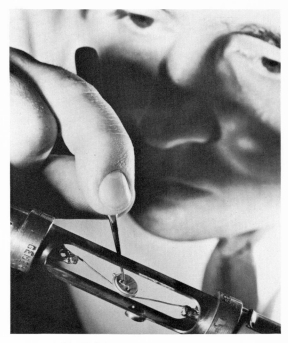

An RCA scientist points to an almost invisible speck of gallium arsenide hooked up to electric terminals. It functions as an FM radio transmitter.

By linking computer and television techniques, an electronic type composition system can set text at 900 lines a minute.

General Sarnoff and the then Vice President, Lyndon B. Johnson, with (left to right) Senators Aiken, Magnuson, Javits, Pastore, and Keating at the 1961 Senate luncheon honoring Sarnoff's 55th anniversary in communications.

A model of the Apollo Lunar Module, designed for a manned landing on the moon's surface, stands on terrain approximating that which spacemen will encounter.

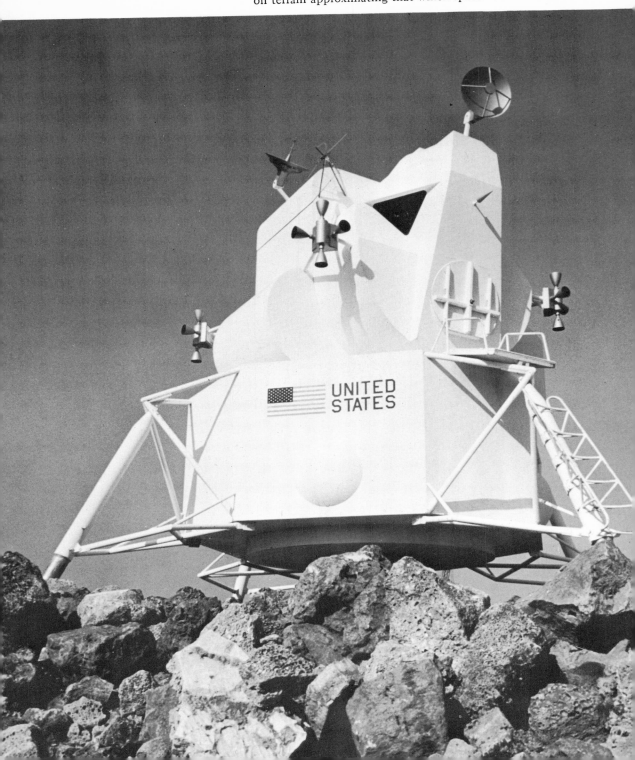

. . . If the Commission were to adopt the CBS proposal only,
we would be confronted with a field-sequential color system which
gives a degraded picture and is incompatible. We would then find
ourselves saddled with a system which we firmly believe is inadequate and inferior and which we seriously doubt would prove acceptable to the public.

We do not believe that the public will want adaptation to a degraded CBS picture at this or at any other price. Nor do we believe
that the public should be forced to pay this tax of $100 million a
year in order to receive the degraded CBS picture.

If we are wrong, the public will prove us wrong. In all these
plans, we would necessarily be guided by public reactions and competitive conditions. We would have to modify or adjust our plans in
accordance with such reactions and conditions. And we will have to
make receivers with adapters if future experience proves that this is
what the public wants.

RCA stands on its record of energetically developing those
things in which we have confidence and which we believe the public will want. We have done this, even though on occasion we have
stood alone. I think our record in the development of radio and television will fully confirm this statement. On the other hand, I do not
assume that we would be expected to be in the vanguard of promoting any system in which we have no confidence and which we
believe is inferior and unsound—a system whose length of life commercially is open to serious question.

. . . Presumably, the Commission would not decide to adopt **"The Best Will**
the Columbia proposal on any theory other than the theory that it is **Sell Itself"**
"the best" system. If the Commission has adopted the best system,
then no one in our competitive and free-enterprise economy of today is going to be able to keep the public from getting it—if it really
is the best. . . . For it goes without saying that no commitment or
compulsion will be needed to sell the public "the best." The best
will sell itself on its own merits. Competition will see to that.

. . . Asking RCA this question now [what RCA would do if
the FCC should rule in favor of the CBS standards] is like asking a

prizefighter who, after 9-1/2 rounds, is way ahead on points and has
been steadily gaining throughout the fight, what he will do after the
fight is over if he is felled by an unexpected blow in the last half of
the last round and has to be carried from the ring. The only answer
he can have is that, while he may be felled, he will retain a fighting
heart and will do the best he can under the circumstances.

If the Commission approves the RCA system . . . our confidence in the new RCA tricolor tubes, which have been demonstrated before this Commission and the industry, is so strong that
we are already proceeding with plans for acquiring a new factory
and the machinery necessary to produce these color tubes in quantity.

These steps involve heavy financial commitments on the part of
RCA.

**RCA's Production
Plans**

By June of next year, we expect to commence the manufacture
of color tubes on a mass-production basis. . . . By that time, our
pilot plant will have produced a sufficient number of color tubes not
only to meet our own needs for testing and design purposes but also
to supply those tubes to competitors in the set and tube industries
for the same purposes.

. . . Within sixty to ninety days from now, we expect to have
about ten developmental-model color receivers, using the tricolor
kinescopes available in the Washington area for field-test purposes.

. . . If final standards are adopted and commercial operation in
color is authorized soon, RCA could and would be in factory production of color-television receivers by June of next year. This
would amount to a weekly production rate of 200 color receivers.
By the end of that year, our color-receiver rate of production will
have reached over a thousand per week. Thereafter, we expect production quantities to rise substantially.

We assume, of course, that competing manufacturers would likewise gear their facilities for production of color tubes and receiving
sets once the Commission determines the standards.

140

. . . We firmly believe that, with the development of its all-

electronic, high-definition, compatible color-television system and its
tricolor tubes, RCA has shown the way for the adoption of color
standards now. We recommend that the Commission set color-television standards based on the RCA color system.

(Book: *Radio and David Sarnoff*, by E. E. Bucher, part
10, p. 2248; part 14, pp. 571–572; part 18, pp. 1558–
1573.)

Objections to Incompatible Color

Statement to the press
New York City, October 10, 1950

RCA disagrees with today's action by the Federal Communications
Commission and with the reasons it has given for the adoption of an
incompatible, degraded color-television system.

We regard this decision as scientifically unsound and against the
public interest. No incompatible system is good enough for the
American public. The hundreds of millions of dollars that present
set owners would have to spend and that future set owners would
have to pay to obtain a degraded picture with an incompatible system reduces today's order to an absurdity.

RCA continues to maintain its position that the public interest can be served only by the adoption of standards that provide
for a color-television system which is fully compatible with existing sets, that is, a system which requires no changes whatever in
existing sets and involves no expense to the present owners of
television sets.

Regardless of what anyone else may feel called upon to do,
RCA will continue its efforts to advance the bedrock principles on
which the sound future of color television can be built and will be
built. . . .

(Book: *Radio and David Sarnoff*, by E. E. Bucher, part
20, pp. 2439–2441. Photostat of press release: "Sarnoff
Calls FCC Decision on Color Television Scientifically
Unsound and against the Public Interest"; David Sarnoff
Library, Princeton, N.J.)   **141**

Assessing Color Television

Introduction to RCA brochure, "Color Television"
Published December, 1953

To create television in color "as red as any rose" was a gigantic task. When we first began to think of television in the early twenties, we would have been content if only the rose could have been televised in black and white. That miracle had no sooner been achieved than the eye, sensitive to color, observed that the rose in monochrome lacked its true beauty, and the cry went up for color. Never had scientists been put under such pressure and demand.

Once American vision, ingenuity, and industry were applied to the task, tints began to appear on television screens in the laboratories. To televise an apple and have it appear as an apple was problem enough. But to televise a pretty girl—the true color of her hair, eyes, lips, and facial features—added to the complexity of the task. And then to capture in motion a toss of the head, a wink, a smile, and add the sound of the voice . . . seemed like asking for the impossible.

But the word "impossible" is not to be found in the vocabulary of the scientist. Color television is a reality and will be recorded in the history of the twentieth century as one of the greatest, if not the greatest, of man's triumphs in linking science with the arts in the full glory of Nature. Flowers and flags, birds and beauties now are televised in color. Sunrises and sunsets, the rainbow, and even the sky, which Ruskin described as "not blue color merely, but blue fire that could not be painted," now are televised in color.

The Miracle of Color

Color follows light, to which radio and television are akin. The electronic camera scans a simple garden scene, an array of flowers or an oak in its copper-hued autumn garb. In the twinkling of an eye, the television transmitter transforms the picture into invisible waves that are broadcast to all points of the compass. Antennas atop millions of homes pluck the pictorial waves from space and guide them in the form of electricity to the television receiving set. At the flick of a switch or the turn of a dial, the scene reappears on

142

the screen exactly as the camera "eye" saw it many miles away. To perform this split-second magic with true fidelity to colors and to make it realistic by every sound in the original scene—even the rustle of the wind or the buzz of a bee—is the miracle of color television. . . .

Color television has marshaled a great corps of experts from practically all fields of science. Many of them already have achieved fame and worldwide recognition in developing the RCA black-and-white television system. As I watch the results of their genius on the color screen, I often wonder if they, too, sit back and view with amazement and pride their successful emulation of Nature.

(Printed booklet: "Color Television," Introduction by
David Sarnoff, pp. 2–3.)

FCC Approval of Compatible Color Television

Statement to the press
New York City, December 17, 1953

Color television opens a new era in electronic communications and adds a new dimension to the entertainment arts. It supplies a new power to advertising and greatly increases its merchandising possibilities. It adds realism to journalism, intensifies television as a social and educational force, and opens the way for a significant advance in service to the public.

The day on which the FCC approved standards for the commercial broadcasting of compatible color television will be remembered in the annals of communications along with the historic date of April 30, 1939, when RCA and the National Broadcasting Company introduced all-electronic black-and-white television as a new broadcast service to the public at the opening of the World's Fair in New York.

At that time we added sight to sound. Now we add color to sight.

(Photostat of press release: "Sarnoff Says FCC Approval of
Compatible Color Television Will Benefit the Public and
Television Industry"; David Sarnoff Library, Princeton,
N.J.)

Faith in Color Television Vindicated

Statement before 35th annual meeting of RCA shareholders
New York City, May 4, 1954

RCA pioneered and developed compatible color television, just as it pioneered and developed radiotelegraph communications, radio broadcasting, and black-and-white television. Our steadfast faith and confidence in the ultimate triumph of the compatible color system, which we advocated, were completely vindicated when the Federal Communications Commission in December, 1953, approved compatible-signal standards for commercial operation of color television.

We have intensified our efforts to bring the benefits of this great advance to the American people as rapidly as possible, and we have helped and encouraged others in the industry to do likewise.

Progress continues in development of the RCA tricolor tube, the only one to date which has reached the stature of commercial production. We expect to improve its performance, increase the picture size, and reduce the cost, just as we did with black-and-white television.

We believe that color television will speed the day when the volume of RCA business will reach and exceed a billion dollars a year.

The youngest child in the electronics industry—color television —offers the greatest stimulus for progress and the surest promise for prosperity. In our new, rapidly developing, and fast-changing art and industry, it is only natural to find growing pains and constant need for appraisal and adjustment. However, these symptoms of youth respond to intelligent treatment with much greater promise for a healthy future than do the ailments of old age.

We look forward to the future of this promising industry and the maintenance of RCA's recognized position of leadership with complete confidence.

(Printed booklet: "Statement by David Sarnoff at 35th Annual Meeting of Shareholders." Mimeographed text issued with news release: David Sarnoff Library, Princeton, N.J.)

Color in the Sixties

Year-end statement
New York City, December 30, 1959

During the decade of the sixties, Americans will have increasing leisure for home entertainment, and every type of entertainment will be readily accessible—on television and radio, on record and tape. Color television will continue to grow, and eventually most programs will be telecast in full color. . . .

A large number of advertisers are already sponsoring color programs on NBC and are presenting their commercials in color. It is expected that, as sales of color sets increase, substantial advertising support will be available for additional color programs and color commercials because of the tremendously greater impact of color over black and white, both in programming and in commercials. This will bring about the classic upward spiral of increased advertising support leading to increased color programming and, in turn, to color circulation, until color television becomes established as a basic program and advertising medium. . . .

History will repeat, in color TV, the story of black-and-white television, radios, phonographs, and other household devices. Every decade has seen one particular product lead the surge, and we at RCA are confident that color TV will fill this role in the sixties.

We are firm in our belief that the future of television is in color and that our pioneering efforts and investments in this new field will repay our shareholders and also benefit the television industry as a whole. . . .

(Printed booklet: "RCA 1959 Year-end Statement.")

Space Added to Color

Remarks at dedication and preview of the RCA Exhibit
New York World's Fair, April 2, 1964

In a broad sense, the 1939 World's Fair marked the beginning of television's development on a national basis. From the primitive transmitting and small-screen receiving instruments of 1939, we have advanced to this complex array of tape machines, remote pick-up units, and large-screen color. But what we are dedicating today is not merely television at its current level of technical excellence—it is the progress of television over a generation as a unique service of entertainment, instruction, and information. Eighty-two nations now operate their own television systems, with audiences measured in multiples of millions.

Appropriately, the 1964 World's Fair coincides with a most important development in the life of television. Through communication satellites, such as Telstar and Relay, international television signals are moving at the speed of light through outer space. The technical means now exist to give television a new programming dimension that is distinctively global in character.

Only last week we saw the Prime Minister of Japan speak to Americans across 6,500 miles of the Pacific, his features as clearly defined as the regular image on our home screens. In earlier months, this country and the nations of Western Europe engaged in transatlantic television dialogues via satellite. As more communication satellites are placed in orbit, regular live-programming exchanges between nations and continents will become feasible, and audiences for single programs will number in the hundreds of millions.

Within the Fair itself, the RCA Exhibit will serve to further the medium's bright new promise for moving the world closer to civilized harmony. Our programs in color will be fed on a regular basis into the exhibits and pavilions of many foreign nations. These nations, in turn, will furnish people and programs to the RCA studio to be integrated with the domestic offerings on our closed-circuit broadcast service.

146   In this World's Fair of today, we therefore have the foreshadowings of the television service of tomorrow. It will be a service to which all nations can contribute and from which all nations can benefit. It can give new meaning to the theme of this great international exposition: *peace through understanding.*

We have added sight to sound, color to sight, and now space to color. There is neither end nor limit to the capacities of this service, which began a quarter century ago here in Flushing Meadows.

(Mimeographed text issued with news release: David Sarnoff
Library, Princeton, N.J.)

First Coast-to-coast Color-TV Link for Shareholders

Statement before 45th annual meeting of RCA shareholders
NBC Studios, Burbank, Calif., and New York City, May 5, 1964

Today, we are participating together in an innovation in shareholder relations and in electronic communications. The proceedings here in California, including the remarks I am making right now, are being carried by color television to the NBC Peacock Studio at the RCA Building in New York. Shareholders in the New York area have gathered there and can see and hear us on color receivers placed around the studio. The system is so arranged that, when we switch to New York, shareholders there can also be seen and heard on our color receivers in California. This means that persons at both locations will have the opportunity to be heard, just as though we were all in one place. This is the first annual meeting of any company ever carried across the country by two-way closed-circuit color television so that shareholders a continent's width away can see and take part in the proceedings. We have come to California because RCA's shareholders here have not yet had the opportunity to take direct part in an annual meeting that concerns them as fully as it does their fellow shareholders in New York.

(Printed booklet: "1964 Annual Meeting of RCA Shareholders," pp. 3–4.)

The Year of Fulfillment

Statement before 46th annual meeting of RCA shareholders
Chicago, Ill., May 4, 1965

This is the year of fulfillment for RCA's long struggle to establish color TV as a service to the public. After many years of virtually solitary effort by RCA and NBC, color finally has come into full status as the new broadcasting medium.

Those who only a few years ago advanced the specious argument that an engineer is needed for each color receiver are now manufacturing and selling these receivers themselves. Any child can tune a color set and, in fact, this has been the case for years. The three broadcasting networks are committed to color as a programming service. All of the major television manufacturers have thrown their resources into the production and marketing of receivers. In the coming years, color will continue to expand until everybody interested in television will own a color set.

Today, the question is not whether color has taken hold but how soon supply can catch up with demand. Consumer interest is at the stage that characterized the boom years of black and white, and the output of color picture tubes and sets simply cannot keep pace. A new industry is now firmly rooted as the fastest-growing business in the consumer sector of the economy, and before the next five years are ended, it will triple its present billion-dollar status.

Now color is moving forward toward full international status. It is indicative of the strength of the system developed by RCA that, despite the efforts of electronics laboratories throughout the world to achieve new breakthroughs in color systems, our basic concepts of colorcasting are about to become standard in many parts of the world. Recently, when delegates from European and other countries met in Vienna to decide on what color standards to adopt, a clear-cut preference emerged among most of the major nations for the system based on RCA pioneering, or a German variant. This happened despite an intensive political drive by the French, with Russian support, to promote their own system—a system which, incidentally, was demonstrated at Vienna using an RCA color picture tube. The

148

picture tube, as you know, is the heart of any color receiver. Thus,
RCA's opportunities from its color investment are continuing to
broaden. . . .

Today, color is rapidly becoming the dominant factor in the television industry, and the beneficiaries are not this company and its shareholders alone but the entire television industry and, of course, the American public. . . .

(Printed booklet: "1965 Annual Meeting of RCA Shareholders.")

CHAPTER 5

The Communications Revolution

In 1948, Claude E. Shannon of the Bell Telephone Laboratories developed a logical framework for describing the process of communication in a way that would be usable to scientists. The concept that underlies his classic paper, "A Mathematical Theory of Communication," is that information is "whatever resolves uncertainty." It seems odd, in view of this definition, that the period in which we live, characterized as it is by more uncertainties than mankind has probably ever had to face before, should often be referred to as the Age of Information. But, in fact, the name is a good one. We are today in the midst of a knowledge explosion comparable to (and in some ways related to) the population explosion.

The axle tree around which our vastly complicated, expansive technology revolves is communications, and much of today's research effort is being directed toward increasing the speed and effectiveness and scope of systems for exchanging and disseminating information among the nations of the world.

After World War II, in a world that was steadily becoming smaller and smaller, global communications became an urgent necessity, and outer space seemed to offer a logical possibility for new development. This was recognized very early by Sarnoff. Writing in the American Magazine of April, 1948—almost ten years before Sputnik—he discussed the possibility of using heavenly bodies to "bounce" electronic signals from one part of the earth to another. "The moon, less than two seconds away, might serve as a sounding board to relay broadcasts or as a mirror to reflect television pictures. We may even find future broadcasters staking claims to Jupiter or Saturn!" It was an easy matter to adjust this theory, so essentially correct, to incorporate the man-made moons that became a reality a decade later. In 1959, he suggested to President Eisenhower that a satellite be equipped "with suitable communication gear . . . to serve as a relay station which would enable television to span the Atlantic Ocean. . . ." The first experimental communications satellite, "serving as a high tower in space," was launched in 1962, and that same year, the Communications Satellite Corporation (Comsat) was established by Act of Congress. Within three **153** years, Comsat's Early Bird, the first commercial communications satellite, was in orbit above the earth.

The early, experimental communications satellites, Telstar and Relay, were not continuously useful. As they orbited the earth at relatively low altitudes, their positions in relation to the earth were constantly changing, moving them in and out of range of the microwave antennas used to track them. They could therefore function as relay stations only during limited periods of each day, and a great many of them would have been required to provide uninterrupted service. Sarnoff advocated a better solution. Speaking in 1962, immediately after the first experimental launching, he said, "In its advanced form, I believe our space-communications system will consist of three synchronous satellites, each positioned about 22,300 miles above the equator." Early Bird, built for Comsat, was launched into a synchronous orbit some 22,300 miles above the equator in April, 1965. Its period of rotation is 24 hours, exactly that of earth, so that it appears to stay fixed in space above a point in the South Atlantic. From this position, Early Bird can relay radio and television signals uninterruptedly between the United States and Europe. At this writing (1967), Early Bird is still in successful operation.

In October, 1966, Comsat launched Pacific 1, another synchronous satellite, larger and more powerful than Early Bird and providing a minimum of 240 two-way voice channels. Pacific 2 went into orbit over the central Pacific in September, 1967. Together, the two satellites beam telephone, teletype, data, and television broadcasts across the Pacific. A third satellite, scheduled for synchronous orbit over the Atlantic, will greatly expand transatlantic capability and link South America and Africa into the global system.

"The future," Sarnoff said in 1962, "is orbiting in the skies above us." By 1967, that future had begun to take shape. For example, during 1967:

—The FCC considered proposals for a domestic communication service by satellite. The pilot program would include two synchronous satellites serving thirty-four domestic ground stations, with each satellite providing 12 color-TV channels, 21,600

154

trunk message channels, and 9,600 multipoint message channels.

—NATO sources stated that it was considering proposals for a satellite-communication system involving two synchronous satellites positioned over the Atlantic Ocean to serve ground stations in the United States and Western Europe. With scrambled or otherwise encoded voice or teletype messages directed toward either satellite and relayed toward any of the ground terminals in the network, the system would permit fast, interference-free, and relatively jam-proof communications.

—The Soviet Union, with five communications satellites in orbit, began constructing a network of more than twenty earth stations to link its eastern provinces with Moscow—over distances up to almost 6,000 miles.

—France and West Germany announced plans to launch a joint communications satellite in late 1970.

—The U.S. Navy's navigational satellite system, based on three orbiting "lighthouses" which enable a ship to determine its position at sea with great accuracy, was made available to commercial ships and ocean researchers. The Navy further announced that it was asking for bids on backpacks that could fix a soldier's position on land by signals from these same navigational satellites.

The communications revolution was indeed under way!

Airborne Transoceanic Radio Relay

Letter to James V. Forrestal, Secretary of Defense
October 22, 1948

I write to recommend the establishment by the armed forces of an airborne transoceanic radio relay system. Radio Corporation of America has engaged in airborne radio-relay research over a period of many years; others have done work in the same field. Westinghouse Electric Corporation has recently proposed the application of airborne radio relay to a television service within the United States. As I have indicated, my proposal is for a transoceanic service and is of much broader application than to television alone.

155

In my opinion, such a project would enable the armed forces to obtain valuable information in connection with modern developments involving national security. It would at the same time provide facilities for carrying on advanced experiments in the fields of international telephone, teleprinter, television, and broadcasting program transmission.

There is enclosed with this letter a general outline of the system I propose. I realize, of course, that the project is one of real magnitude and that its full development will take some time. And I make no claim that we know all the answers today to some of the problems it presents. I do feel, however, that it holds such promise of valuable results for our national security as well as for commerce and other public services that I should recommend it for your consideration.

For purposes of illustration, communication circuits from the United States to the United Kingdom will be used in this outline.

Elements of the Proposed System

Aircraft would act as the radio relay stations. They would be dispatched from the United States at regular intervals and along the same route so as to space the craft about 250 to 300 miles apart throughout their eastbound flights. Each would fly at 10,000 to 15,000 feet, or higher, and thus remain within line of sight of both its predecessor and its successor. Ground contact at the ends would be shifted at regular intervals to each succeeding plane.

Each plane would be equipped with two transmitters and two receivers. A two-way circuit would thus be established through a single-file series of eastbound flights. A duplicate and entirely separate two-way channel would be obtained by use of the westbound flights. The system would thus provide 2 two-way radio relay circuits. One of these would serve as the spare for the other. Twelve to fourteen airborne radio relay stations would be required in each circuit.

Traffic-handling Capabilities

Each two-way circuit of 5-mc bandwidth could accommodate one of the following services:

1. Several hundred two-way telephone channels
2. An ultrafax system at 540,000 words a minute in each direction
3. A television relay in each direction

156

4. Several thousand teleprinter channels, each working at 60 words a minute in each direction

5. Up to 100 high-quality broadcasting program channels each way.

Some of the voice channels provided by (1) could be assigned for telegraph operation (4), while the remainder were used for telephone service; or other combinations could readily be set up.

Aircraft Operations

If the desired spacing between aircraft is 250 miles, an eastbound flight should be dispatched every fifty minutes for an average ground speed of 300 miles per hour. If standard cruising speed is maintained, tail winds require more frequent schedules.

Thus there should be approximately thirty flights in each direction daily, and the schedules should be uniformly distributed to provide a continuous circuit. We have been informed that during the wartime peak, the Air Transport Command flew sixty flights in each direction daily across the North Atlantic.

Load Factor

The weight of the complete radio relay installation would be only a minor part of the carrying capacity of a large aircraft. With such a load factor, the aircraft which would serve as the relay stations would obviously not be confined to that function alone but could perform transport or other duties.

Aircraft Operating Problems

There are obviously problems of substantial magnitude relating to the operation of aircraft which would be involved in the project. These include weather, mechanical reliability of aircraft in flight, traffic congestion, and operation and maintenance delays. They are problems which do not fall within our ordinary fields of engineering work and are not therefore dealt with here, except to recognize that they are, of course, relevant in balancing the promise which the project holds against obstacles such as these.

Military Significance

It is beyond our province to assess the military significance of the system, and this outline makes no attempt to do so. It may be helpful, however, to mention a few of the factors which would appear to be involved in such an assessment.

The mobility of the system is obviously such that it could be set

157

up overnight. It could be torn down and moved with equal facility.

The frequency channels presently available for long-distance international communication are decidedly limited in number, and in general, it is not possible to operate more than one transmitter on any one of those frequencies anywhere in the world without probability of interference. The system proposed would operate in the microwaves, where there is no such frequency limitation and where the frequencies used could be duplicated on many transmitters at relatively close spacing.

The frequencies presently used for transoceanic service have the further disadvantage of severe limitations in the classes of service for which they may be used. They are wholly unsuitable for television. Multipath effects limit the modulation-frequency band so much that even telephony would be considered impractical in those frequencies if anything better were available. The system proposed would, of course, make available distinctly better frequencies for telephony, as well as providing channels for transoceanic television which are unattainable by any other means we have today.

The much smaller distance traveled by the microwaves as compared with the radio frequencies presently in use and the special secrecy devices and features which can be incorporated into this system would provide an important factor of military security.

(Mimeographed text and outline of proposal in bound volume: *Correspondence between President Harry S. Truman and David Sarnoff, 1945–1958*; David Sarnoff Library, Princeton, N.J.)

Satellite Television

Letter to Gen. A. J. Goodpaster, Staff Secretary
The White House, January 12, 1959

The experimental projects which I suggested to you in Washington on January 7, 1959, as being of possible interest to the President include the following:

. . . Equip a satellite with television and related gear so that it would, while in flight, televise from space to earth pictures of what its television camera could observe of the terrain and objects below.

Equip another satellite with suitable communication gear for radio, telegraph, telephone, and television transmission and reception. This satellite to serve as a relay station which would enable television to span the Atlantic Ocean—east and west.

The objectives would be to enable the President of the United States to carry on a casual conversation with the heads of governments in England, France, and Germany—both parties to the conversation to be seen and heard by the public in these countries on their standard television sets in their homes. . . .

If undertaken, these experimental projects should be executed one at a time, suitably spaced so that their effects would be dramatic, continuing, and cumulative over a reasonable period of time. . . .

The importance of the "time element" need not, I am sure, be stressed by me, for it is obvious that to achieve our psychological objective we must accomplish these results before the Russians achieve any of them. Under ordinary circumstances, these experimental projects might take a long time to develop and execute. However, if the President finds these suggestions of interest and decides to have them executed, I believe it reasonable to expect that under such circumstances the projects would be executed within a period of approximately six months. . . .

> (Copy of letter in bound volume: *Correspondence between President Dwight D. Eisenhower and David Sarnoff, 1947–1961*; David Sarnoff Library, Princeton, N.J.)

A United Nations TV Channel

Address at University of Detroit
Detroit, Mich., April 5, 1961

Regardless of whom it serves, television has become . . . a vital part of the worldwide struggle for the possession of men's minds.

. . . Ten years hence—if vigorous foreign growth continues—there will be TV stations in virtually every nation on earth telecasting to some 200 million receivers. An audience of a billion people **159** might then be watching the same program at the same time, with simultaneous translation techniques making it understandable to all. In a world where nearly half of the population is illiterate or semi-literate, no other means of mass communication could equal television's reach and impact upon the human mind. . . .

Over the years, I have suggested on several occasions to the United Nations that its membership, by resolution, establish the principle of "Freedom to Listen and Freedom to Look" and that it provide itself with facilities to broadcast its public proceedings and its pronouncements, with the aim of reaching people everywhere, regardless of race, creed, color, or political philosophy.

America will soon be in a position to offer dramatic new support for that principle by enlisting global television in the service of the world community. Specifically, we can do so by agreeing that, when America's satellite-communication system is functioning, a television channel will be made available for use by the United Nations.

Such an offer should have no strings attached. The UN should provide its own studio facilities and staff and should be master of its own programming content, just as privately owned networks and stations are in America. However, I suggest that its most useful programs would be its own deliberations: the Security Council at moments of urgent discussion, the Assembly in deliberation on such fateful questions as now face it in Laos, the Congo, and Berlin.

It would not always be a placid picture that humanity viewed, for world political discussions are seldom constrained. But, contentious or pleasing, it would be life as it is mirrored in the only existing world forum where ideas are publicly exchanged and debated. . . .

Frequently, suggestions are made that the United Nations be supported in its quest for world peace by a permanent UN military force, trained and equipped for a high degree of mobility and maintained on an alert basis for use anywhere in the world. Without questioning the merits of these proposals, I believe we can agree that it would be far more complex and expensive to organize and maintain such a force than to develop a UN global television service, which would also serve the aim of advancing world peace.

Personally, I favor the adoption of both concepts, for they are
more complementary than contradictory. In the early stages of a cri-

sis, global television might create an understanding of the issues involved and thus minimize or even obviate the need for armed
intervention. If it did not, the military sinews would still be available
to uphold the UN's decisions.

A UNITED
NATIONS TV
CHANNEL

(Printed booklet: "Television: A Channel for Freedom,"
an address by David Sarnoff.)

Developments in Personal Communications

Address before the National Press Club
Washington, D.C., June 28, 1961

Our principal job in the next stage of the communications blueprint
will be to . . . permit direct man-to-man sight-and-sound communications over the ultimate in distances.

The speed with which we accomplish this will depend, in part,
upon the speed with which we can shrink electronic gear. This is another great challenge facing electronics today: Make it smaller!

Through formidable advances in micromodules, we are achieving
new diminutives daily. We can now foresee a computer so compact
that it will have a density equivalent to 100 million active elements
per cubic foot—a density approaching the compactness of the human
brain itself. And this computer, indeed, will perform many functions
of the brain.

I have with me today the type of communications unit that will
probably be the reporter's best friend in the seventies. It is a pocket-
size color-TV set, with combination AM-FM radio. This mock-up
was put together at our Advanced Design Center, and the date of its
availability depends upon the time required to learn how to reduce
further the size of certain components. . . . I am bold enough to
predict that the actual unit will be several times smaller than this,
and it will consist of both a receiver and a transmitter, radio, television, AM, FM, black and white, and color.

This prototype model is a symbol of our reach for the diminutive.
I believe you will someday see transmitter-receiver units a half or a
third the size of this. Each receiver will have a decoding unit, respon-

**Ultimate in News
Coverage**
161

sive to only one of a million or more arrangements of pulses sent out from a transmitter, which means that you can be called while you have this in your pocket. You can decide whether that is an advantage or not. With complete privacy, a foreign editor in his office will one day be able to see and talk with a foreign correspondent in an airplane over Tokyo, in a boat on the Red Sea, or in a tractor at the moon camp. . . .

The price for achieving the communications advances I have outlined will come high—in dollars, in planning, and in work.

We will have the scientific manpower and know-how to meet and to surpass any challenge in this area. But something else must accompany it: a firm national resolve to do whatever must be done to assure our ultimate success.

. . . It is my conviction that America can be the first to achieve practical worldwide satellite communications and that we can complete the cycle by which man will communicate with man directly, wherever he may be. I also believe that . . . it will be possible to achieve automatic translation of languages so that when we speak to each other, we will *understand* each other . . . that, after all, is the goal not only of our science of communications but of humanity itself.

(Printed booklet: "Communications: A Look Ahead," an address by David Sarnoff.)

A Satellite-communications Policy

Address before American Bar Association
San Francisco, Calif., August 7, 1962

Until last month, it was not possible to transmit television over long distances through the air except by the use of numerous microwave towers, and this made television across the oceans impracticable. Now we have the satellite serving as the high tower in space, extending sight and sound not over a few miles but over at least 6,000 miles —or more than the air distance from San Francisco to Paris.

162   Communications satellites are forerunners of a system that within the coming decade will provide virtually instantaneous telegraph, telephone, data, television, and other forms of communications to practically any point on earth. They open a dramatic vista of unlimited range for linking the world in a common dialogue, with incalculable effects on the thinking, the understanding, the culture of all mankind. . . .

In its advanced form, I believe our space-communication system will consist of three synchronous satellites, each positioned about 22,300 miles above the equator. Moving at a speed matching that of the earth's rotation, they will, in effect, hover over a fixed point on its surface. Three such satellites, one each over the Atlantic, Pacific, and Indian oceans, would cover the entire global land area except the polar regions. One of these satellites above the Atlantic could interconnect with services that presently include over 90 percent of all the telephones in use in the world. It could also transmit to television stations over an area extending from the eastern half of the United States across Western Europe and including all of Africa and South America. . . .

From these facts, we can begin to postulate the communicating world of tomorrow. Global conferences, whether of statesmen, businessmen, or lawyers, will take place with each participant sitting in his own office or home, in full view and hearing of the others, exchanging thoughts, documents, and data through desk instruments and a color-TV screen on the wall.

Storage of information, its retrieval and transmission, will be directed from centralized computer facilities and widely distributed memory systems. It is possible to foresee practically instantaneous up-to-the-minute status reports on any major national or international problem—legal, medical, economic, political, or other—flashing from continent to continent.

The great libraries of the world, including legal libraries, will be codified for electronic search and retrieval, very probably with simultaneous translation into many languages. With the growth of international commerce, facilitated by satellite communications, the lawyer in New York, San Francisco, or Tokyo will have instant access to the pertinent laws, regulations, and procedures of any country with which he is dealing. . . .

163

New Policies Needed   Our communications policies, as they now stand, offer striking examples of the difficulties in designing the future based on blueprints of the past.

These random policies governing today's operations have evolved principally from the separate historic developments of the landline telegraph, ocean cables, wireless telegraphy, radiotelephone, and national and international broadcasting. Some of these policies began in the middle of the last century. All of them are regulated by laws based more on tradition than on the needs of an expanding society in a changing world of science and technology.

. . . It seems to me this is the time, the golden opportunity, to set about establishing a basic national policy which will bring coherence and viability to our entire communications service—that which exists today and that which will come tomorrow. We should, before we are swept into the turbulence of coming events, make a concerted effort to determine our interest and needs and adjust our national posture accordingly. . . .

Single U.S. Company   . . . Based on long experience in this field, my own belief is that
Proposed   the most practical solution would prove to be the creation of a single, privately owned American company, uniting the facilities and operations of the present competing U.S. carriers, *in the international communications field*. This company should be completely independent in its policies and operations, subject only to appropriate government regulations.

Such a unified company would be able to render a complete service to the public, with all the advantages made possible by modern science and technology. And surely there is every logical reason for such a company to give further cohesion to our entire communications structure by interconnecting the flow of its international traffic with established domestic facilities.

Through these steps, our international communications services would become more flexible, more convenient, and more economical to the public—at home and abroad. And our unified American company would be able, for the first time, to deal on equal terms with foreign government monopolies.

164   Above all, this plan for unity would eliminate the present weaknesses in our communications structure and secure for America a position of strength commensurate with our nation's contributions to worldwide communications.

We cannot today claim ignorance of what is to come. The future is orbiting in the skies above us. On the threshold of the Age of Space the supreme challenge to the law is to bring new concepts of order in harmony with new concepts of change.

(Printed booklet: "Communications and the Law," an address by David Sarnoff.)

Global Communications—Three Phases

Article in *Saturday Review*
Issue of Jan. 12, 1963

The technology of electronics is reaching today for summits of national, global, and space communications beyond anything conceived since the invention of movable type.

. . . The way is opened technically for the establishment over the next few decades of a communications system by which governments, organizations, or individuals may establish contact with anyone, anywhere, at any time, by voice, sight, or document, separately or in combination. In its most advanced form, such a system would be based upon communication via satellite without intermediate routing or wired connection.

. . . I see the development of satellite communications occurring in three phases, whose timing will be determined as much by economics and social demand as by technology.

Phase 1, between 1965 and 1970, should see a global system of low-power synchronous satellites. . . . Positioned approximately 22,300 miles above the equator and completing an orbit in the same twenty-four-hour period required for full rotation of the earth, they will, in effect, hover constantly over a single point on the earth's surface. At its high altitude, each of the satellites will be within direct line-of-sight range of about one-third of the globe.

Communications to and from these satellites will be handled **165** through high-power earth terminals whose antennas will be fixed permanently on one or more of the space relays. These stations, varying from simple installations to complex trunk types, will be linked with landline and microwave networks crisscrossing the continents. Most nations are likely to maintain their own terminal facilities, in keeping with the present pattern of national systems.

With these facilities, communications could develop to the point of direct telephone dialing between users anywhere in the world. The system would accommodate television broadcasting and closed-circuit television, although the latter would probably be limited by economics to governmental use.

**Nuclear-powered
Satellites**

Phase 2, between 1970 and 1980, may mark the beginning of international satellite communications between cities rather than through centralized national terminal facilities.

Nuclear-powered synchronous satellites, weighing 3 tons or more, would generate approximately 60 kilowatts of power. . . . The far greater output power of the satellite would permit substantial reductions in the cost and complexity of the earth terminals, placing them within reasonable economic range for small nations and users and permitting the design of mobile or stationary units that could be simply assembled.

With such stations, the larger population centers could readily undertake their own direct communications via satellite relay. For example, a direct link could be maintained between New York and New Delhi, employing simple base stations at or near each city and a relay stage of microwave or even laser beams between the synchronous satellites serving the respective regions.

The introduction of city-to-city communications can bring immensely significant change to both commercial and private services. For nongovernmental organizations and business enterprises, closed-circuit television on an international scale would become available at reasonable cost. For broadcasters, new prospects would be opened by the ability of the high-powered satellites to transmit directly to television receivers in the home.

Person-to-person voice communications could be provided

166 through fixed or mobile telephone and even pocket-radio links between individuals and the earth terminals of the satellite system. When this happens, an individual moving within a city or its environs could have wireless contact with any similarly positioned and equipped individual on any continent.

Phase 3, beyond 1980, envisages an all-embracing satellite-communication system: direct personal transmission of voice and sight through satellites without intermediate routing.

**Direct Personal
Communications**

Manned satellites, assembled in space, would range up to 100 feet in diameter and weigh some 100 to 150 tons. Nuclear energy in the space station would provide up to 1 million watts of power, equal to the output of twenty high-power present-day broadcasting stations.

Each such satellite in a system of perhaps five to ten would provide up to 500,000 voice and 500 television channels. Directional antennas would link the satellite with individual cities through narrow microwave "shafts" containing thousands of voice and hundreds of television channels. Equipped with a high-speed computing system, the satellite would serve as a switchboard in space to route calls from city to city, country to country, and continent to continent.

With this system would come the facility for direct two-way contact through television receiver-transmitters installed in private homes and offices. Beyond this, a new dimension in individual communications might be accomplished through parallel advances in miniaturization of electronic devices, circuits, and power sources, together with continued progress in the development of communications theory. This would lead to the incorporation of television as well as sound in a two-way pocket-size device. . . .

Even in the early stages of this process, the impact of satellite communications upon human society will be profound. There will, for example, be an enormous hastening of economic development in the vast regions which have yet to derive substantial benefit from twentieth century science and technology. As the accessibility, accuracy, and swiftness of intelligence are increased through the coming global systems, commercial activities will be extended through areas hitherto too remote for consideration. It will be a two-pronged

**The Social Impact
of Satellite
Communications**

167

stimulus—from people demanding more goods and services as they see and hear about them and from enterprises moving with surer knowledge to meet the rising demand.

More and more, the full range of human, commercial, educational, and cultural activities will become international in scope, encouraged by the ability to communicate across a span of continents with even greater facility than we communicate today within a single country. . . . Despite the pace of technological growth, it is likely that the rate of progress toward the future global and interplanetary communications systems will be determined as much by political, social, and economic factors as by technical accomplishment.

I feel, however, that the very existence of satellite communications will in large measure determine the solutions to the nontechnical problems that stand between the promise and its full realization. For example, the day of the closed or remote society is coming to an end. No barriers of time or distance or ideology can long withstand the mounting flow of information and the vastly improved access to information across the oceans and the continents. The awareness of knowledge is the first step to its acquisition, and the acquisition of knowledge is, in turn, fundamental to human advance in every sphere. . . .

(Photocopy of full text: "A Wireless World," article by
David Sarnoff.)

INFORMATION-PROCESSING MACHINES

At the heart of the contemporary revolution in communications is   *Editor's Note*
the high-speed computer. In the scant twenty years of its existence,
the computer has fundamentally changed business methods, in-
dustrial techniques, the physical sciences, and in many ways, our
very lives. Yet its potential impact is only just beginning to be felt.
According to a report by the American Federation of Information
Processing Societies, there were only ten or fifteen computers at work
in the United States in 1950. Today (1967) there are 35,200, and it
is estimated that by 1975 there will be more than 85,000.

Computers, Communications, and Defense

Address before Army data-processing seminar
Fort Monmouth, N.J., March 5, 1964

Enormous changes have taken place not only in the arts of war but
in the means of communications.

In this era of telescoped space and time, our power is deployed
across the face of the globe. . . . We must measure reaction time in
minutes, be prepared to rush strike forces to any point on earth
within hours, and take only a little longer to move units of division
and army size across oceans. In the field, our forces are further dis-
persed by the threat of atomic strikes and by the terrain and methods
of guerrilla warfare.

Our worldwide commitments of men and machines and the need
for instant reflex require the timely accumulation of masses of intelligence from many parts of the globe, quickly evaluated for command
decision.

This, in turn, requires a communications capability that can fuse
every element of this vast organization—from command headquarters to the most distant outpost—into a single swiftly responsive
unit.

To accomplish this broad purpose—the acquisition, transmis-   **169** sion, and interpretation of intelligence and the communication of commands—we must have an integrated system, completely automated in its routine processing but always requiring human intervention where seasoned judgment is called into play.

This broad concept already is taking form and substance in our defense establishment. Today, with equipment and techniques in being or just over the horizon, we can visualize a new generation of computers and communication systems transforming our military planning and operations.

As I envisage it—and I know that many of you are thinking along similar lines—a computer complex will be at the heart of a total system in which it is possible to achieve—from the Pentagon, the White House, or a remote secret site—effective real-time command over any situation or combination of situations anywhere in the world.

Anticipating Events　　When fully implemented, this system should make it possible to anticipate many developments before they actually happen and so gain vital time to take precautionary or preventive measures. It will convert the army of tomorrow into a highly mobile, ultraswift fighting force, unencumbered by the long supply tail that used to wag the military body. . . .

The computers of the future system will assume important intelligence and counterintelligence roles. For example, they will assess the enemy's intentions—taking into account all possible assumptions about his politico-military objectives, both strategic and tactical, his capabilities and limitations, what circumstances will stimulate what level of response, and so on. By playing and replaying any number of conceivable enemy combinations, the computer will ultimately reduce the possible to the plausible.

As incredible as all this might have seemed a decade ago, it is, today, only the prelude to still other communications advances. We can, for example, foresee two-way global sight, data, and sound communications with any person in the field, down to the individual GI, if need be. The linkup will be accomplished by a small portable transceiver connecting by radio through a ground terminal to a communications satellite. It will be possible to communicate directly simply by dialing the appropriate code number. In a similar way, computers will be able to contact other computers or surveillance devices anywhere in the world. . . .

In addition to the satellite network, future communication systems will include high-capacity transistorized cables, laser beams operating in space and through cables on the ground, and communications through rock strata under the surface of the earth. . . .

Masses of data—assembled, sorted, evaluated, digested, and integrated—ultimately will feed out of a battery of computers in tomorrow's war room onto a huge cycloramic television screen showing a constantly updated sweep of events around the world.

A Television Cyclorama

The television cyclorama will be in color for clarity, differentiation, and emphasis. It will be divided into segments, each section handling a different facet of the total display. For example, one such section might be a status map of the entire world, showing the global situation at a glance. Another would show one area in detail, perhaps in three-dimensional relief. A third would present a live TV coverage of an event in process of happening. On another segment of the screen, the computer will report, in written English, what and where the problems are. Another section will delineate the alternatives, still another suggest appropriate actions, and a fourth assess the probable and actual results. The visual information, incidentally, will be transmitted via satellite from TV cameras on the spot, operating from remote-controlled planes or inspection satellites.

Certain conclusions may be drawn from these developments, and I will mention only three briefly.

The Human Element Supreme

First, for all its versatility and usefulness, I do not believe that any computer or combination of computers will replace personal judgment, intuition, or inspiration or will ever conceive the heights to which the human spirit can soar. What, for example, would a computer have told Churchill in June, 1940, after his army was shattered at Dunkirk and the *Luftwaffe* was droning over England? Certainly, the computer cannot be given final authority for the fate of a nation. Man's future, for better or for worse, can never be surrendered to a machine.

171

Second, with computers in extensive use, there is bound to be a trend toward greater participation by headquarters in tactical operations. Although field decisions certainly will rest with the field commander, knowledge of how his actions will affect other theaters will offer opportunities for greater global coordination.

Finally, although human judgment will remain supreme, the military leaders of tomorrow must possess a broad working knowledge of computers, their uses, and potentialities. Such indoctrination will be basic to every officer's training and will be an integral part of the study courses in our service academies and elsewhere. . . .

(Printed booklet: "Computers, Communications and Defense," by David Sarnoff; David Sarnoff Library, Princeton, N.J.)

Computers and Social Change

Address before American Bankers Association meeting
New York World's Fair, July 16, 1964

Just as television has extended human sight across the barriers of time and distance, so the computer multiplies to a remarkable degree the capacity of the mind to deal with information in endless variation and almost limitless quantity.

The use of the computer provides a vast opportunity for finding answers to many of our most complex social problems—in education, conservation of natural resources, air and water pollution, urban planning and renewal, the retraining of persons displaced by automation, the reduction of poverty. Over the next twenty years, I am convinced, computers will touch off an explosion in the social sciences comparable to that which we witnessed during the past half century in the physical sciences.

. . . I see society making profound adjustments in many directions. The five main areas affected are likely to be work, leisure, education, health, and politics. Let me sketch briefly some foreseeable developments in each of these categories:

Work. Many executives today spend as much as a quarter or a

third of their time traveling and preparing to travel to and from their
homes and to distant meetings.

. . . I believe that the computer and its allied communications will alter this pattern to a significant extent. With instruments of information and command within easy reach, it will be possible to conduct many managerial operations without physically going to an office every day and devoting additional hours or weeks to more distant travel.

Eventually, by making physical presence less essential to the discharge of business, the computer and communications complex will eliminate much of the rush and stress of modern living. Thus, ironically, the utmost in speed will cancel out the worst consequences of the modern vice of speed.

Leisure. The reduction of work will apply not only to executives but in varying degrees to all echelons of our economic structure. Science and technology and the progressive refinement of automation will, in the next twenty years, justify the reduction of the workday to four or five hours.

This will pose, ever more forcefully, the problem—and the opportunities—of expanded leisure. It will demand new approaches to the planning and use of our time, new psychological attitudes toward so-called "free time." We will be forced to revise the traditional view of leisure as a species of idleness and, therefore, a form of sin.

. . . Man's accumulated knowledge and cultural treasures will be made available to nearly everybody through computer centers, somewhat in the way that they are now available in the largest cities through libraries and museums. It will simply be a matter of pushing the correct buttons on computerized telephones, radios, and televisions. Any document—from an automatically translated literary work to the latest technical publication—will be made quickly available. . . .

Education. In the school of tomorrow, the computer will multiply the capabilities of the teacher. It will help speed and improve the learning processes from grade school through university. Elementary school children will be introduced earlier to many high school studies, and work in high school frequently will be at the college level.

173

In the classroom, the computerized teaching machine will handle the routine or informational aspects, drilling the student in his subjects and helping him correct his answers. It will proceed at the pace set by the learning capacity of the student. We may see, at last, youngsters progressing not necessarily by formal, standardized grades but by individual intelligence and ability. . . .

But the educational contribution of computers will not end with the classroom. Learning will become a continuing process. Scientists and engineers, for instance, will spend a substantial part of their time reeducating themselves to changes in their particular fields, as will doctors, lawyers, accountants, and teachers themselves. Technology is moving forward so swiftly that many youngsters starting today will have to relearn every facet of their vocations at least three times during their careers.

In short, electronic devices, computerized techniques and systems will open to millions of people the roads to a lifetime of self-instruction. . . .

Health. The health of its population is a nation's greatest asset. The computer will emerge as a major tool of the medical fraternity as it strives to eradicate disease and extend the span of life. . . . No less important, the years thus added will be active years of living, not merely existing.

In the electronic future, it will be possible to maintain a complete medical profile of every person in the community and in the nation. The record, begun at birth, will be constantly updated in a central community or regional computer for instant access to the physician or hospital as required. Because so many factors will have been tabulated in advance, examination and diagnosis will be easier, more comprehensive, and more revealing than by traditional methods.

Taken together, these individual reports will form the basis of a continuing, up-to-the-minute health profile of the entire country. Any trends that may affect the public health will be noted without delay, and their meaning swiftly interpreted. This could include the recurrence of certain symptoms which are the warning prelude to an epidemic.

On a longer range basis, the correlation of vast quantities of data would facilitate definitive research not only on specific diseases but on possible relations between air pollution and cancer or the relationship of nutrition to health and longevity or an analysis of drug effects. Medical progress anywhere will become easily available everywhere. . . .

Politics. The computer will make it possible to restore a direct dialogue between the people and their political leaders, in the tradition of an Athenian assembly or a New England town meeting.

. . . In the future, it will be technically feasible for voting to be done in the home, with maximum personal convenience. The balloting would be done through television, the computerized telephone, standard and high-speed phone circuits of regional and national computers. For the dwindling minority of citizens who might still lack these units in the home, special telephone polling places would be provided.

. . . Within minutes after closing time, the regional computers would forward the data to national computers serving as central tabulators, and results would be announced less than an hour after the closing of the home polls. At the same time, the computer would provide detailed analyses of the election for use on the airwaves and in the press. By these means, it could be possible to achieve an almost total expression of the popular will by those qualified to vote. . . .

There are those today who wish to see the computer disconnected through fear that it will dehumanize our society. The fact is that we cannot pull the plug on the computer, or on the communications with which it will be integrated, any more than we can return to the covered wagon or the sailing ship.

. . . Since the computer is here to stay, we will be seriously remiss in our responsibilities to ourselves and our posterity if we fail to use it to help define and resolve great social questions, just as we already employ it to advance the physical sciences. In economics, sociology, political science, and various aspects of applied psychology, the computer can be an instrument of incalculable importance.

. . . In the final analysis, what comes out of the computer is determined by what goes into it. If we have the wisdom to introduce

The Computer Is Here to Stay

175

into this versatile instrument a program for social progress, the answers it provides can be of profound importance to the welfare of
future generations.

(Printed pamphlet: "The Social Impact of Computers,"
an address by David Sarnoff.)

Standards in Electronics

Address before the Fall Joint Computer Conference
San Francisco, Calif., October 27, 1964

During my fifty-eight years in electronics, I have seen several dynamic industries emerge from conceptual beginnings in the laboratory. The most memorable were radio communications, radio
broadcasting, sound movies, black-and-white television, and color
television. While their origins differed in detail, all shared a common
experience that has a distinct parallel today in the rise of computers
as another major member of the electronics family.

All were intensely competitive from the beginning and have remained so. But they began fulfilling their potential only after agreement had been achieved for technical standards prescribing the kind
and quality of service to the public. A pattern for progress was thus
fashioned without sacrificing the vital stimulus of competition in developing newer, better, and more economical equipment and in furnishing more efficient service to the user.

I am convinced that this same process must occur in the computer industry. . . .

From the two-score or so machines in existence barely a dozen
years ago, there are now some 17,000 general-purpose computers in
the United States alone, and the number is increasing at a rate of
more than 500 a month. Within the coming decade, the computer
population can increase enormously.

Whether it realizes its full growth potential depends in very large
degree, however, on the measures we undertake now to establish the
basis for orderly development. The interests of the industry and the
176 needs of the user demand a far greater measure of compatibility and

standardization among the competing makes of computers and in the means by which they receive and transmit information.

Neither the operators nor the machines we have built for the processing and transmission of information can yet speak to each other in a commonly understood and accepted language. The means of preparing data, of forwarding and entering data in the machine, and of instructing the machine in its use differ sufficiently from one make of equipment to the next so that none can readily accept the product of another.

We function today in a technological Tower of Babel. There are, by conservative count, more than 1,000 programming languages. And there are languages within languages—in one instance, twenty-six dialects and in another, thirty-five dialects. There are eight computer wordlengths in use. There are hundreds of character codes in being, at a ratio of 1 code for every 2 machines marketed. Four magnetic-tape sizes are employed, with at least fifty different tape tracks and codes.

Standards have not been accepted even for commonly used symbols, instruction vocabulary, or program-development procedures. Words which have currency throughout the industry assume different meanings, depending on whether a man has trained in Pasadena, Poughkeepsie, or Camden. We have yet to produce a universally accepted computer glossary.

No means have yet been perfected for a program in one basic language to be run efficiently into computers of different makes. The result has been needless duplication, delay, and waste—both to the manufacturer and to the user—in cost, in equipment, in operating efficiency, and in manpower skills.

Incompatibility has compelled the manufacturer to build optional choices into peripheral equipment for the input and output of data. It has required him to maintain various types of the same equipment or to build to a customer's specifications on each order. It has diverted needed engineering and programming talent from the vital work of new-product and systems development.

The burden of incompatibility has been even more onerous to the user. It has meant the extra cost of providing hardware and programs to handle the differences between incompatible systems, the **177** cost of extra machine time to process data set for another computer, the cost of training people to do things differently, the cost of not being able to do the job immediately.

Last year, an estimated $2 billion was spent by American business and government for privately developed computer programs, representing thousands of man-years of effort. Yet, when a change to new equipment is made, portions of this effort must be thrown away because they have no validity to another make of machine or are retrievable only at further cost.

I have heard it said that even a degree of standardization and compatibility might inhibit the progress of the art. In my judgment, this argument is without substance. The nature of a computer is such that its operation is governed far less by its internal construction than by the program that is given to it.

The effort to bring order to the flow of computer intelligence need not affect competition either in creating programs or in seeking new generations of increasingly efficient machines. On the contrary, the result could be a greater concentration of effort toward this primary goal. . . .

All of us in computer manufacturing, in communications, and among the user groups—at the technical as well as the managerial level—share a common interest in the free interchange of information and in the media and equipment through which it flows.

This demands that we give compatibility the urgent consideration which it merits but which it has not yet received. It requires the wholehearted support by all of us of the standardization work that is now going forward and implementation of the results with all deliberate speed. It will require that we submerge our differences, through fair and equitable compromise, to achieve greater ends.

I do not suggest that existing systems be discarded. That would be unrealistic as well as costly. Even today's computer has reached maturity in one basic respect: Its average time between failures, measured in minutes only a decade ago, is now measured in months. This is a level of operating reliability far beyond that of either the automobile or the airplane.

But new generations of systems are coming, and the time to bring order into progress is now, before they have fully arrived. Standards can be established which, if planned with thought and foresight, can guide us in the future, linking our separate efforts and facilitating the common evolution of our industry. Such standards are indispensable to continued progress.

As the shape of tomorrow's technology takes form, the volume and accessibility of data stored in the computer will play a decisive role. All information as to what to do, how to do it, and what data to do it with resides in the memory of the machine. With larger and faster memories, there are few limits to the tasks that can be solved or to the speed with which they can be completed.

The Computer's Impact on the Future

The time is soon coming when these memories will be capable of storing up to 100 million bits of information, retrievable in fractional millionths of a second. For external memories, the goal is a trillion bits, possibly advancing later to capacities that are many times greater. By these means, we can hope to store all of the information that is presently contained in all the world's libraries.

Tomorrow's standard computers and their peripheral equipment will instantly recognize a handwritten note, a design, or a drawing, which they will store and instantly retrieve in original form.

The computer of the future will respond to commands from human voices in different languages and with different vocal inflections.

Its vocabulary will extend to thousands of basic words in the language of its country of residence, and machines will automatically translate the speech of one country into the spoken words of another.

The computer itself will become the hub of a vast network of remote data stations and information banks feeding into the machine at transmission rates of a billion or more bits of information a second. . . .

The computer already is opening areas of knowledge long denied us by the sheer magnitude of the mathematics involved. The implications are no less fundamental for the social and life sciences than for the physical disciplines.

By correlating vast quantities of data and uncovering new relationships, we can for the first time obtain significant information on social and human behavior—from the destructive tendencies of some to the learning power of all.

179

The Ultimate Challenge of the Computer

The ultimate implication of the computer is that it provides a means of releasing the productive powers of the human brain to an almost limitless degree. Yet the computer imposes as a precondition the sternest discipline to which the mind has yet been subjected.

Even to use the machine, we must apply clear and precise logic to situations which heretofore were assumed to be beyond analysis. We must state precisely what we know or do not know and what we wish to know.

If we are to develop the computer to its full potential as a reference storehouse of human knowledge, we face the immense intellectual challenge of researching every major field of human activity, of assembling, analyzing, and identifying its documents, and of reducing the information to acceptable machine form.

Before the end of the century, I believe that these codification efforts will coalesce into what unquestionably will become the greatest adventure of the human mind. We shall achieve a far more comprehensive understanding than we have today of man and his environment. We shall do so through the orderly compilation of accumulated knowledge and wisdom, beginning with the days of clay tablets and papyrus scrolls. The human horizon will then encompass all that man has ever known and all that his science will enable him to know. . . .

(Printed booklet: "The Promise and Challenge of the Computer," an address by David Sarnoff.)

NEW ASPECTS OF
COMMUNICATIONS SERVICES

At present, since signals from communications satellites must be   Editor's Note
picked up and rebroadcast from ground stations, any country can
prevent radio and television signals that it regards as undesirable from
being received in the homes of its people. In 1965, Sarnoff stated:
"Within a decade, I believe it will be technically feasible to broad-
cast directly into the home from synchronous satellites." This de-
velopment will pose some very serious legal and political problems.
Satellite-communication systems are becoming steadily less prohibi-
tive in cost and technical requirements, and soon many nations may
have their own orbiting relay stations to beam their messages, wel-
come or unwelcome, directly into homes all over the world. The
need for establishing the necessary legal machinery, both domestic
and international, to control space communications for the benefit
of all nations and all people has characteristically been a matter of
great concern to Sarnoff.

Direct Broadcasting by Satellite

Address before the Armed Forces Communications
and Electronics Association
Washington, D.C., May 26, 1965

We must look for entirely new procedures, attuned to the realities of
the Space Age, if our communications services are to function in harmony with the new technology and if America is to maintain its
leadership in this vital field.

. . . Three years ago, I called attention to the anachronisms of a
communications policy which continued to enforce separation of
voice and record transmissions and the channels over which they
traveled. Since then, many other voices in industry and government
have been raised against such clearly outmoded regulations, which   **181**

impede our progress and hamper our leadership in world communications.

. . . Beyond these jurisdictional problems, there is now a different operational environment for satellite communications than had been anticipated when legislation on the subject was enacted.

When Congressional hearings were conducted in 1961 and 1962, the estimated costs of a complete system—including the development program, the satellites, and ground stations—were extremely high. The technology was complex. The reliability of booster rockets was uncertain, with a possible ratio of two or three failures for every successful orbital launching.

As far as anyone could foresee, it appeared certain that one global system would probably do the job for a long time into the future and that satellite communication was neither technically nor economically feasible for any but the richest and most technically advanced nation to undertake. . . . Today, the costs and the technical requirements for a satellite-communication system have diminished until they are well within the capability of many nations that possess relatively moderate industrial and technical resources, not to mention nations whose capabilities approach our own.

**Russia's
Communications
Satellite**

A month ago, the Soviet Union launched its first communications satellite and began to broadcast television programs across the 4,000 miles between Moscow and Vladivostok. The satellite's capability also extends to two-way multichannel telephone, radiophoto, and telegraph communications.

Satellites serve a political and psychological as well as communications function, and no nation is more keenly alert to the broader implications of space than the Russians. They will use their new capabilities, ultimately, to pose a new challenge to America, to demonstrate their technological power, and to attempt to make valid in the eyes of other nations their claims of space superiority. . . .

**Direct Satellite
Broadcasting**

182

Within a decade, and possibly less, I believe it will be technically feasible to broadcast directly into the home from synchronous satellites. All of the basic components and technology already exist for radio and television broadcast transmitters to operate in space.

These would be high-power satellites, weighing about 5,000 pounds and powered by nuclear reactors of the same general type as the smaller, experimental SNAP 10A, which is now in space operation. These reactors may well generate up to 30 kilowatts of power, sufficient to transmit three separate radio and television signals directly to home receivers on earth. They would also permit a tremendous expansion of every other type of communications service.

. . . Placed in synchronous orbit over the equator, each satellite could broadcast to an area of 1 million square miles, covering such nations and regions as Brazil, India, Western Europe, or the United States. These satellites would operate in the UHF TV band. To receive them would require only minor modification in the home receiver and redirection of its antenna. A 6-foot antenna would be sufficient to receive a clear television signal in the home. The total cost of adapting home receivers and antennas would be minimal.

Apart from developmental costs for the system, the actual cost of the launching, the booster, and the direct-broadcast satellite would be in the area of $10 million. Cost of the ground station to transmit programs to the satellite would approximate $5 million.

With three such satellites—together costing about $30 million, exclusive of ground stations—three TV channels would be available through each satellite to beam programs to the entire United States and north into Canada. To purchase a single leading VHF television station now operating in a major American market would cost approximately as much as this entire three-satellite system.

. . . For countries such as India or Brazil, where there is urgent need of a national television network to educate a growing population, a satellite broadcast system offers a most promising solution. Its cost would be, perhaps, half of the minimum needed for the present type of ground-based broadcast service.

Whether used for education, entertainment, or political indoctrination, direct-broadcast satellite systems will ultimately be within the technical and economic reach of many nations, and they will penetrate many barriers, with unpredictable social, political, and economic results.

183

A Policy for Leadership . . . What forms of jurisdiction must be established to prevent the television spaceways from degenerating into a confusion of sounds and images? Again, how do we preserve American interests and assure continued American leadership in the new era of space communications?

In 1962, I suggested that the way to achieve these goals was through the establishment of a unified national communications policy suitable to our current and future needs. Such a policy should recognize the fact that competition in international communications is no longer *within* nations—it is *among* nations.

. . . Today, when the means for transmitting and receiving intelligence extend to every corner of the globe, the maintenance of our communications position in space and elsewhere must command the highest priority. It is a fact of twentieth century life that the nation which leads in communications is also equipped for leadership in many other crucial areas of national and international endeavor. . . .

(Printed booklet: "The Communications Explosion," an address by David Sarnoff, pp. 9–28.)

World Agreement and Satellite Broadcasting

Address at World Peace through Law Conference
Washington, D.C., September 17, 1965

The rate of change in the art of communications is so great that, if we delay even five years in coming to grips with its problems, they may pass beyond our control. Our hopes for progress might then degenerate into further confusion and deepening of world disorder. . . .

By the end of the decade, there will be not only one communications satellite but many, not a single global satellite system but possibly several in competition with one another, not a sole operating agency dealing with many nations but many nations with their own operating agencies pursuing different satellite-communication plans and objectives.

As the number of satellites multiplies in space, a corresponding number of problems will multiply on earth. We are faced not only with a new technology but with a new means of reaching the minds and influencing the actions of every society and individual on the surface of the globe. . . .

This is not a remote, hypothetical possibility. Progress in the area of satellite-communication technology is far more rapid than was first anticipated.

**Progress More Rapid
Than Anticipated**

. . . Technology, in fact, is moving so rapidly that the establishment of a satellite service has now come within the economic capability of many nations. . . . Within five to ten years, I believe that we will develop high-power broadcasting satellites capable of transmitting television and radio directly into the home.

. . . Direct-broadcast satellites will alter the entire pattern of relationships in international communications, and their operation will obviously involve far more than simply positioning the satellites in orbit. When many nations possess the capability for transmission through space to any place on earth, they must agree to a new pattern of global regulation. Otherwise, the prospect of social and economic gains will be thwarted by the ensuing chaos in the world's airwaves.

. . . When, for example, a Russian satellite can broadcast directly to a Kansas farm or an American satellite can broadcast directly to a Hungarian collective, what will be the reaction of both countries? When we can reach the homes of the world with instantaneous sight and sound, what rules of conduct are to apply, and who is to establish them? This question evades the jurisdiction of any established body, yet it will affect the welfare of all nations and all people.

. . . If direct satellite broadcasting is to fulfill its destiny, I am convinced that some type of modus vivendi must be established among the many rival national and ideological interests. It would be a travesty on the hopes of humanity if this immense force for enlightenment, understanding, and social advancement were to be subverted to narrow national ends or to become discredited by the failure of nations to agree upon its beneficial uses.

We live in a world in which open and closed societies exist side

185

by side in varying degrees of mistrust. They differ, among other things, on what is to be accessible to the eyes, ears, and minds of their people.

**Five Areas for
Understanding**

To counter this deeply rooted division, it seems to me that we should concern ourselves initially with an examination of the broad fields of subject matter that might be acceptable to all nations and peoples. I visualize five broad areas in which we might achieve some form of understanding prior to the orbiting of the first direct-broadcast satellite.

The first is in the field of culture. In the midst of national rivalries, an interchange of art forms continues to grow—in painting, music, drama, ballet, and the folk arts. All of these are readily transferable to the medium of global television, and all strike a chord of response in civilized man, regardless of his nationality or ideological allegiance.

The second area could extend to the presentation of certain types of major news events. Whatever our personal loyalties, there are events and occasions that move us all to wonder and pride. For example, the first astronaut to set foot on the moon will place man on the threshold of a world far vaster than anything discovered in the age of Columbus and Magellan. Happenings such as this transcend all national boundaries, and here, too, it should be possible to reach a broad consensus on what could be broadcast to all people everywhere.

A third area of exploration might be the use of global satellite broadcasting as a direct channel of communications between nations. Agreement on this basic concept might ultimately lead to summit conferences in which the principals would confer face to face without leaving their capitals. If closed sessions were desired, the transmissions could be scrambled and decoded by special equipment at each terminal, comparable to today's "hot line" between Washington and Moscow. If no need for secrecy existed, the conferences could be available for all people to see and hear.

The fourth area of examination lies in a realm of political activity where all nations share a common interest. Perhaps an agreement could be achieved whereby one channel in each space system would be allocated for the deliberations of the United Nations. It would mirror society through the only world forum where all ideas are publicly exchanged and debated. Global television by the UN would at least help to create an understanding of the issues involved and thus further the cause of peace.

The fifth area in the search for a common accord is instructional. The greatest promise of direct satellite television rests on its ability to educate millions simultaneously, to bring people everywhere into instant contact with technological and social progress. The prospects for educational programming by satellites are virtually limitless, and they offer, perhaps, the greatest hope for advancing the world to a higher plateau of understanding and peace.

If we can achieve broad agreement in these five areas, it should not be beyond our ingenuity to devise arrangements for utilizing all satellite-broadcasting facilities on suitable occasions as a world network serving the interests of all nations. Inevitably, as the world continues to grow smaller in distance and time, I believe we will find more things to unite rather than to separate the community of man.

. . . The adjustment of law to technology, and of technology to law, may well be the enduring task of this generation. It is a challenge to our combined wisdom and leadership. We can meet it by joining all mankind in a brotherhood of sight and sound through global communications.

(Printed pamphlet: "Law, Worldwide Communications, and World Peace," an address by David Sarnoff.)

The Communications Revolution

Address at the Advertising Council annual dinner
New York City, December 13, 1965

The ultimate effect of the coming revolution in communications will be the transformation and unification of all techniques for the exchange of ideas and information, of culture and learning. It not only will generate new knowledge but will supply the means for its worldwide dissemination and absorption.

. . . We are now able to transmit across vast distances all types of information—print and picture, the spoken word, telegraphic messages, televised images, and even the esoteric language of computers.

Today, a synchronous satellite positioned 22,300 miles over the equator enables millions of persons on both sides of the Atlantic to view the same television broadcasts at the same time. And high-capacity cables are being equipped to handle not only telegraphy and telephony but also all other forms of electronic communications.

These are only the early harbingers of tomorrow's technology. On planning boards, in research laboratories and engineering centers, further advances in electronic communications are now in development. They should reach practical form in the 1970s. Together, they will weave a pattern of total communications, joining homes, communities, and nations.

New Communications Tools

Here are some of the tools that will be employed:

1. *Laser "pipes" providing superhighways for communication among major population centers.* These narrow light beams will have a total capacity millions of times greater than the most advanced systems today. Through lasers, any individual will be able to have his private "line" for sound-and-sight communication across any distance, just as he now has his private telephone line.

2. *Microwave channels carrying television, telephone, facsimile newspaper, telegraph message, and computer data into the home or office.* They will give the individual new access to the entire world through sight, sound, and signal communications.

3. *Continental and global networks of computer centers.* These will serve scholars, scientists, professional men, and businessmen as instant sources of all known and recorded data on any conceivable subject, from ancient history to market trends, from social statistics to medical knowledge. Already, computers have been linked experimentally across the Atlantic. In due time, they will communicate freely with one another, as well as with people, regardless of the distance involved.

4. *Transmitting satellites of vastly greater power and versatility.* In synchronous orbit, they will broadcast directly to individual tele-

vision sets and FM radio receivers in the home, anywhere on earth. They will beam their programs simultaneously over vast areas, and where necessary, they will provide the picture signals with a number of sound channels from which the viewer can select one in his own language.

The development of these tools is already beyond the theoretical stage. They are, in fact, fast approaching reality. Ultimately, a master communication system utilizing all of them will emerge.

Individual broadcast satellites, for instance, would normally broadcast programs to a limited portion of the earth. But on occasions of universal significance, all of them could be linked for simultaneous transmission of a single program. A summit meeting of world leaders, a critical session of the United Nations, a telecast from men on the moon could be seen and heard at the same moment by people everywhere.

Information Sharing

To the advanced nations, satellite broadcasting will open broad new avenues for direct sharing of information, ideas, and cultures. To the developing nations, it will provide instruments of tremendous power for education, knowledge, and self-expression.

It should be relatively easy to design and produce low-cost, single-channel television receivers for use in primitive or underdeveloped areas of the globe. These sets could be built by assembly-line techniques, housed in simple metal or plastic cases, and equipped with transistorized circuits consuming very little energy. They could be made to run on batteries rechargeable by wind, hydraulic, or even animal power.

Such sets could be distributed throughout the developing regions in quantities suitable to local conditions. If they were programmed from regional stations transmitting through a few broadcasting satellites, the tragic effects of illiteracy could be virtually abolished in ten years.

This application of broadcast satellites will represent a major achievement of the communications revolution. However, other developments now under way will lead to a basic transformation of the entire communications structure.

189

... With the introduction of microwave channels and the appearance of communications satellites and high-capacity cables, there is no longer any distinction among the various forms of communications. All of them—voice or picture, telegraph or data—pass simultaneously through the same relays in the form of identical electronic pulses. Henceforth—in marked contrast with the past—developments that extend the reach of one will extend the reach of all.

An Integrated System

This same process of unification will inevitably occur, I believe, in all media of communications. Not only television and telephone but books, magazines, and newspapers will be converted into identical bits of energy for transmission over any distance. At the receiving end, these electronic signals will be converted into any form we choose—in visual display or recorded sounds or printed pages.

Today's console and table-model furniture may be displaced by an all-purpose television screen, mounted on the wall. It would be coupled to a sound system and a high-speed electronic printer for recording any information the viewer wished to retain.

A single integrated system means that the major channel of news, information, and entertainment in the home will combine all of the separate electronic instruments and printed means of communication used today—television set, radio, newspaper, magazine, and book.

The home will thus be joined to a new, all-embracing informational medium with a global reach. This medium will serve a vast public of differing nationalities, languages, and customs, and its impact will be profound.

A Universal Language

One result, I think, will be the emergence of a universal language, spoken and understood by all men in addition to their native tongues. It is almost certain that this new language will derive very largely from English. . . .

With a single language accessible to all men, new opportunities will be opened to commerce, the sciences, and the spoken and written word. A traveler in any part of the world will understand, and be understood by, the people around him.

We can expect also to see some form of universal culture take its place alongside the world's national and regional cultures.

. . . Certainly, all of us on this earth have much to give and to receive from one another, and no one need lose his soul or his shirt in the bargain.

We can expect a quickening of worldwide business and economic activities as a by-product of the communications revolution. As illiteracy is reduced and exposure to new ideas through global media becomes standard, dramatic rises will follow in consumer demand for all goods and services. Common markets will become commonplace. One may even anticipate the day when a single market encompassing the entire free world may become possible.

A Challenge to Communicators

Already, technology has carried us from local to regional, regional to national, and national to international scope in both individual and mass communications. Now we are advancing toward true universality, embracing global audiences, global enterprises, global markets. . . .

There is challenge enough here for all who generate and disseminate ideas—businessmen, scientists, communicators, statesmen, and sociologists alike. But none, perhaps, are more sharply challenged than those who deal in mass communications, for one of tomorrow's great tasks will be to develop maximum clarity and simplicity of expression when speaking simultaneously to the full spectrum of humanity.

. . . In preparing for this task, however, we must learn from the past. Thus far, the history of international mass communications has been a succession of missed or neglected opportunities for achieving greater harmony among men and nations. National rivalries have outweighed technological promises. In place of the free interchange of information and ideas, we have had a discord of conflicting voices and, in certain instances, deliberate distortion and political subversion practiced over the airwaves as well as in print and pictures.

The impending communications revolution provides humanity with a fresh opportunity to remedy the mistakes of the past. Prompt action is imperative if the new technology is to be harnessed in the cause of greater understanding and well-being among people everywhere. . . .

(Printed pamphlet: "New Dimensions in Mass Communications," an address by David Sarnoff.)

CHAPTER 6

Science, Technology, and Human Affairs

"A bold expert on the future"—these words were used by William S. Paley, Board Chairman of CBS, to describe David Sarnoff. That such generous praise from a competitor is well deserved is a point which no one with any knowledge of the radio-television industry would dispute. As we have seen in this rather specialized history of twentieth century communications, Sarnoff has again and again demonstrated an amazing ability to be right about things to come. The young man who modestly proposed a Radio Music Box (surely one of the more revolutionary ideas of this century) became the "televisionary" and, later, the embattled champion of electronic color TV. He anticipated the use of space for communications years before the first communications satellite was launched. Time and again, he has scouted the territory far in advance, and time and again, the industry has (sometimes reluctantly) followed him.

The future has always been Sarnoff's particular preoccupation—a very useful one in an age of rapid and fundamental change—but it would be unfair to his special kind of genius to concentrate too much on its prophetic aspects. The future must, after all, be based in the present, and Sarnoff's so-called "visions" have invariably been the result of a logical, hard-headed analysis of carefully assembled facts. As he has grown older and become, to use his own phrase about himself, "encumbered with a little knowledge and many facts," his analyses have tended toward greater detail and the facts assembled have been more technical, but the enthusiasm, the optimism, and the clear insight have remained.

These qualities are very apparent in this final chapter, which includes papers and speeches covering a remarkable range of subjects over a period of more than forty years. The unifying theme is the expanding role of science and technology in shaping the present and future of mankind. As the years pass and the pace of technological advance accelerates, Sarnoff's concern with the social as well as technical responsibilities of science and industry gradually increases. The "golden future" that technology offers man is marred by terrifying possibilities. In 1960, Sarnoff writes, "Never before have we been challenged so directly and so **195** urgently by the need for learning how to live with what we have created."

Man's "technological prowess" has brought him to the point where he is now capable of almost totally annihilating himself. This is a constant and dreadful menace in a divided world. Equally threatening is the prospect of widespread famine. In the underdeveloped nations of Asia, Africa, and Latin America live 2 billion people, about two-thirds of the world's population. In most parts of the world, the population is increasing so rapidly that it is expected to double within the next twenty-five or thirty years. Many experts feel that these rapidly rising populations are on a collision course with starvation and that no technology can be spread with sufficient speed to avert the catastrophe.

Yet, as Sarnoff writes in the same memorandum (1960), ". . . science and technology offer the possibility of raising all of mankind to far higher standards of life." We are offered a longer life, better health, greater opportunities for leisure, and above all, freedom from want. Our problem, apparently, is to learn how to survive long enough to enjoy these benefits. It is a problem which, in spite of his essentially optimistic nature, Sarnoff does not for a moment overlook.

Military Applications of Science

Address at Army Industrial College
Washington, D.C., February 20, 1926

Is it not reasonable to visualize the possibility that future great wars may well be fought and won on the basis of brains and scientific devices rather than numerical preponderance?

Startling as this statement may seem, it is not inconceivable that a future great war may last five minutes rather than five years and yet be infinitely more destructive and decisive than the last world war.

Consider, for example, a few of the possibilities which exist in offensive warfare along scientific lines. It is now conceivable that

heavy charges of high explosives may be secreted under important government buildings, docks, factories, and other strategically important points, these charges being connected to radio receiving equipment capable of detonating the explosives when a certain secret code signal is sent on a particular wavelength. If a potential enemy were to prepare in this way for anticipated hostilities, on the outbreak of war, he could readily send out the signal of destruction and to a considerable extent paralyze his opponent.

We know enough today about the radio control of remote mechanisms (the field of radioteledynamics) to expect that, as development proceeds, unmanned airplanes, surface vessels, submarines, and land tanks carrying dangerously destructive explosives . . . could be aimed at the population centers of the enemy and sent to their destination in shoals.

The various forms of destructive radiation have not yet been worked out thoroughly, although we know that the x-rays and heat rays are extremely injurious in sufficient concentration. An investigation of these and perhaps as yet unknown rays, as well as other incendiary or disintegrating agencies, may well lead to the development of extremely powerful methods of warfare.

. . . In consideration of the possible development of the ultra-dangerous scientific methods of wholesale destruction, consideration of the appropriate countermeasures should be taken by any prudent and patriotic people. If victory is to be largely influenced by scientific knowledge as well as military and industrial organization, it certainly follows that now is the time to study intensively scientific agencies of destruction and, perhaps even more vigorously, the countermeasures for combating them on a wholesale defensive scale. This work cannot be completely developed by civilian industrial companies. In the first place, it is a highly specialized field and requires a detailed and confidential knowledge of military problems and methods. In the second place, it is considerably removed in its early stages from any commercial application, and the expenditures of time, energy, and money which are involved in such work would not be normally undertaken by industrial concerns without some direction by government agencies.

Development of Countermeasures

On the other hand, the personnel necessary to carry forward **197** scientific military research must be drawn from the universities and the great industrial concerns of the United States. It may well be that scientists and engineers should be borrowed by the Military Department from time to time. Also, it is not unlikely that their military research would have some by-product results capable of commercial application. The reverse may also be desirable; that is, military experts might well be assigned at regular periods for some training and experience at commercial laboratories and plants.

Some of the fields of research which require attention by such a military scientific group are the remote control of mechanisms; the production and rapid transmission by wire, radio, or otherwise of photographs; radio direction finding on all wavelengths; the further development of secret methods of communication; the study of all forms of offensive radiation, chemicals, and other substances; and the development of protective measures against each of these offensive devices. To carry forward such work would require the coordination of existing facilities or the establishment of new optical, electrical, chemical, and biological research laboratories and the placement of recognized experts in their respective fields on the staffs of such laboratories.

Radio-broadcasting Resources

A special offshoot of the main problem of scientific preparedness is the question of the effective utilization of our existing radio resources during a war. The status of broadcasting, in particular, is peculiar. Millions of receiving sets have been placed in American homes, and they are not licensed by the government. Their nature and location are therefore practically unknown, and they are, in fact, very readily concealed. They have become as much a part of the life of the community as the newspaper or other agencies of instruction and entertainment.

During the Great War, radio reception by the public was prohibited. This would be a mistake under the conditions which may obtain during any future hostilities. It is far better to utilize the capabilities of radio broadcasting than to discard them. Of course, radio-broadcast transmission would have to be strictly controlled by the government under wartime conditions, but reception should be permitted. It would be possible for the government to issue expeditiously and simultaneously reports and stimulating announcements to many millions of listeners and possibly the entire nation. In cases of airplane raids or other impending attacks, warnings could be issued which would reach the entire population practically instantly. Announcements dealing with mobilization and other military matters could be broadcast, and by the appointment of a definite hour at which such announcements would be broadcast, there could be in effect a daily military-bulletin service of high efficiency and universal scope. . . .

It is certain that the existence of millions of receiving sets in the homes of the citizens of this country, together with the availability of great interconnected networks of broadcasting stations, will place at the disposal of the government during any possible later war a most powerful weapon for organization and for the maintenance of national morale. And this very fact, also, makes it necessary to perfect plans whereby the enemy's . . . propaganda may be under control.

Briefly, then, the United States needs manpower and it needs industrial organization, but to my mind, as important as these and possibly even more so, are scientific research and preparedness to meet the military problems of the future, which are sure to be infinitely more complex and destructive than those of the past.

(Mimeographed text: "Radio in Relation to the Problems of National Defense," an address by David Sarnoff.)

Communications and National Security

Address at Army War College
Washington, D.C., January 31, 1927

The vast facilities of communications opened up by radio have many important political and military implications. The modern agencies of communications are spreading a network over the world, so that we can foresee the time when no center of human activity is not in instant communication with the rest of the world, when no ship at sea will be out of touch with the shore or some other ship afloat, **199** when no home able to afford a simple radio receiving set will be isolated from the thought and activity of the world.

On the one hand, radio broadcasting is bound to intensify greatly the white light of publicity which now attends the formation of national policies and the expression of national aspirations. The political implication is obvious. With the whole world eventually listening in, it is reasonable to suppose that in the future, national policies will have to be determined with more regard to whether such policies can be justified to the world at large. The modern interests of nations are so intertwined that conflict between single nations is becoming almost as remote as the single combats of the Middle Ages. World opinion, therefore, is becoming an increasingly important factor in national security.

On the other hand, in immeasurably shortening the distance between continents and bringing the nations of the earth within speaking distance of each other, the agencies of modern communications have created new political factors which remoteness did not entail. It is certain that many problems of national defense would not exist were it not for the fact that, measured by the unit of time; we are now living in a fifth-of-a-second world, insofar as communications are concerned.

The very fact that the United States is within less than a week's steaming distance from a possible enemy across the Atlantic and is probably less than a day's distance from air attack is what demands a scale of preparedness hardly foreseen twenty-five years ago. . . .

In the emergency of war, modern communications are an essential feature not only of political education and industrial operations at the home front but of tactical operations in the field. In this respect, the great advantage of radio communication is its extreme flexibility. It does not require a fixed metallic circuit to connect its terminals. It is not subject to destruction by human agencies, as is the case with landlines and cables.

The whole structure of modern naval operation, we are told, rests upon a foundation of efficient communications. Given two fleets of equal strength, the one having the support of better communication resources, it is obvious, would have the advantage. Radio is now the principal source of modern naval communications.

To those charged with the defense of the nation's interests in wartime, therefore, radio poses a series of problems which demand solution. These might be summarized as follows:

Mobilizing and coordinating communications. In addition to a vast network of telegraph and telephone wires that would cover every city, town, and hamlet in the United States, in addition to a system of submarine cables that would connect this continent with Europe and Asia, in addition to a system of transoceanic stations that would place us in direct touch with nearly every civilized country in the world, and in addition to a series of coastal stations that would provide communication with ships at sea, we can readily foresee that, if another national emergency arises, there will be 20 million or more radio receiving sets in the United States commanding a listening audience of approximately 60 million people in this country and served by hundreds of broadcasting stations. . . .

How this colossal system of external and internal communications is to be mobilized, coordinated, and made to serve the highest public interest in the event of war is a problem that deserves the deepest consideration. Radio within a few years will have woven itself firmly into the warp and woof of modern communications. This problem, it is submitted, warrants study and consideration in time of peace.

Maintenance of national morale. The experience of the last war amply proved that temporary defeat of an army at the battlefront may be of less serious consequence than the destruction of the nation's morale behind the lines. Those who will lead us in the next national emergency, therefore, must be prepared to take urgent measures to maintain the highest morale at the home front as well as at the battlefront.

The next war will thus involve a great problem of mass education, in which radio must play a predominant role. Through the institution of broadcasting, radio is the first universal system of one-way mass communication developed by man. No other agency can speak with a single voice at the same instant to millions of people. By no other means can the same thought or the same appeal be conveyed by one living voice speaking to vast multitudes simultaneously.

Next in importance to the maintenance of our own national morale in time of war is the creation and preservation of a favorable attitude toward our cause in neutral countries. The primacy of our broadcasting system, in power, range, and scope, would place us in an exceptional position in this respect. Even now some of our broadcasting stations are frequently heard in Europe and Latin America and are regularly heard by our neighbors across the borderlines. It is to be expected that within the next five years, by the use of suitable wavelengths and adequate power, we shall be able to make ourselves heard in any part of the civilized world.

Nevertheless, the greatest problem of mass communication that is likely to face us in the next national emergency is the problem of counteracting the deluge of enemy propaganda that might pour in upon us through the air. It is neither desirable that we should nor hardly conceivable that we could collect or seal the 20 million radio receiving sets which probably will be in use in the United States within the next few years. We may expect each set to be a target for enemy propaganda. Through either high-power or shortwave transmission, it is probable that the enemy will attempt to flood American homes with false reports of disaster at the front, with victories never won by the enemy on the battlefield, and with garbled or manufactured accounts of our diplomatic and political positions abroad.

On the other hand, if we maintain our present progress, we will be better equipped, perhaps, than the rest of the world to sow consternation in the rear while our military forces are attacking the enemy at the front. It is unlikely that we could entirely prevent the broadcasting of enemy propaganda to the United States by any form of electrical interference, in view of the probable use of mobile broadcasting stations, high-power transmission, and constant changes of wavelength by the enemy. Indeed, it may not even be desirable to interrupt our own internal broadcasting system in order to destroy the enemy's efforts.

The wiser policy might be to seek to counteract rather than to destroy broadcast propaganda. Otherwise, the cure might be worse than the disease. To attempt to interfere, for instance, with enemy broadcasting might create rumors of disaster and panic much more injurious to our national morale than the garbled report transmitted to us. But these circumstances will naturally create new problems of censorship. While this problem is now raised, no concrete method for its solution is here suggested.

Application of latest radio developments to military operations. Since time is an important factor in the success of any military operation, the development of facsimile transmission by radio opens new and great possibilities in military communication. If high-speed facsimile transmission is to solve the problem of secrecy for military dispatches, it will do away very largely with the need for coding and decoding, the present bane of military communication by whatever method used. Military information sent in facsimile will carry its own proof of authenticity.

Sufficient progress has been made in our industrial laboratories to warrant the prediction that it will not be long before mechanisms will be available whereby scouting airplanes soaring over the enemy's lines will be able to send back to headquarters maps and photographs of enemy positions within a few minutes of the time that the photographs were made.

We may foresee the day when a fleet of aircraft with no human occupants and loaded with bombs may be sent against the enemy's lines, with all controlling operations performed by radio.

We can imagine a fleet of scout planes, each with a photoradio transmitter, its lens directed to the ground, automatically sending photoradio maps of the territory which it traverses. The fact that the aircraft would move forward during the five or ten seconds of photographic exposure should not destroy the sharpness of the map. It would simply mean that the extreme right of the picture was made ten seconds later than the extreme left. The map nevertheless would be of great military value.

It may also become possible for the staff at a military base to follow the progress of an air raid more or less accurately by comparing the photoradio maps transmitted with photographs previously taken of the same ground. Thus the progress of the fleet could be plotted and the aircraft steered by radio so that bombs might be dropped when the desired position was reached. After their work had been performed, the craft might be steered to return. But even

203

if driven to their destruction, they might accomplish their purpose by exploding their charges after they had been brought to the ground.

As the principles of remote control by radio already have been determined, it is not impossible to conceive the radio-controlled tank of the future, without human pilotage, being driven toward the enemy's lines.

Perhaps it would be too fantastic to consider the part that might be played by direct television in the war of the future, but it is not too early to consider the direction which laboratory development should take in its application to military uses. It is conceivable that a radio-television transmitter installed in an airplane might be useful in transmitting a direct image of the enemy's terrain, thus enabling greater accuracy in gunfire.

While the radio art in its present phases has no more definite limits than the bounds of imagination, it is an admirable principle that commands men to keep their feet on the ground in discussing a subject of practical importance. Yet it is the anomaly of the age we live in that while men may desire to keep their feet firmly planted on Mother Earth, scientific progress may whirl the very ground from under them.

(Book: *Radio and David Sarnoff*, by E. E. Bucher, part 4, pp. 1115–1125; part 7, pp. 1631–1641; part 11, pp. 2–4; part 12, pp. 33–35; part 23, p. 2952; part 25, pp. 3489–3490.)

Supplantive Competition

Address before the University Club
Boston, Mass., January 28, 1928

We are still largely in the throes of ancient conceptions of the forces that make for or against industrial and commercial growth. Competition is still worshipped as the life of trade, denounced as an uneconomic force, embraced as a balance between buying and selling interests—nursed upon one hand and hated upon the other. Mass production is still offered as a cure-all for failing markets and ailing sales. More lately, high-pressure salesmanship, which would solve all distribution problems with one fell swoop, has been currying favor with many industrial elements.

More recently, too, there has been raised before us the specter of gigantic competition between industry and industry, wherein wheat and meat are to struggle for primacy, where coal and oil are to engage in a combat, where coffee and milk are to race for the public cup, where cotton and silk are to fight for favor.

Now, no one can properly decry the study of these forces by business executives and the proper adjustment of them in industry, but the attempt to pigeonhole each in its own permanent compartment, in a world of constantly shifting elements, is an uncertain procedure.

Without desiring to commit an economic heresy, the question might be raised whether competition, in the popular sense, *is* the modern spur to industrial progress. It bears no permanently constructive or destructive relation to industry. Instances could be cited to fit either circumstance. . . .

The great menace to the life of any industry is not in the competition for a share of the public dollar but in the supplantive competition which modern science may breed in the laboratory. The ghost of industrial obsolescence stalks after any industry that is so thoroughly stabilized that it can only grow around the waist. The competition which may make as well as mar, depending upon the breadth of view in modern industry, is the competition between the old and the new, between those who have made the better mousetraps which caused the world to mark a path to their door and those who have invented a product, developed a method, or found a means that would make mousetraps unnecessary.

There is dawning, it would seem, a new attitude on the part of industry toward supplantive competition, whose first faint beginnings rise out of the laboratory. . . .

It betokens the day of a much closer relationship and sympathy between industrial development and advanced scientific research.

The new day of swiftly moving scientific progress and rapid technical achievement calls for industrial flexibility rather than rigid stabilization—flexibility that makes for open-minded executives in **205** control of great industrial enterprises, for greater creativeness in production and sales plans based upon the changing conditions of industry, for the constant improvement of commodity, equipment, or service in order to meet rising public standards.

The new day of progress demands the adoption by industry of larger plans for research—research that will give a proper balance of industrial insurance. For no industry involving the sciences can be called permanently sound whose technical achievements are entirely at an end.

The new day demands the emancipation of industrial research —away from too rigidly directed lines and toward broader fields of investigation. For again it must be said that the specter of supplantive competition first takes shape in the laboratory. Fortunate the industry broad-gauged enough to recognize in each new scientific and technical development a beneficent wraith rather than a demon of obsolescence whose breath means decay and whose touch means extinction.

(Printed press release: "The Rising Tide of a New Art";
David Sarnoff Library, Princeton, N.J.)

Science and Business

Address at Harvard Business School
Boston, Mass., April 16, 1928

In an industrial era in which discovery and science play such important parts, I need not remind you of the changing order of things in the world of business. We have gone far since the day when barter and sale were the main principles of business. Motives other than mere economic gain are beginning to influence industrial leadership. Men are contending not so directly for a share of the public dollar as in the endeavor to develop and perfect those unlimited possibilities of achievement which science is breeding in the laboratory and executive genius exploiting in the promotion offices of modern industrial organizations. Stability must be tempered with flexibility in modern industrial development. Business no longer operates in fixed grooves and along restricted lines; it has become a highly specialized art, alive as never before to its varied possibilities and demanding nothing so insistently as . . . room to grow and expand, opportunity for larger and deeper service to humanity.

The needs of the times will bring forth, perhaps, a new type of executive, trained in a manner not always associated with the requirements of business management. He will have to reckon with the constant changes in industry that scientific research is bringing. He will have to be able to approximate the value of technical development, to understand the significance of scientific research. He will be equipped with . . . knowledge of the relationship between his business and similar businesses in the same field, between his industry and other industries which it may affect or be affected by, between business and government, and even between business and politics, for no great industrial enterprise is safe from political attack. "Mind your own business" is ceasing to be an all-embracing business axiom. It may be the other fellow's business that will determine the success or failure of your own.

. . . The protean part which a single art may play in modern **Radio and Modern** industry has no better illustration than the position of the radio art **Industry** and the radio industry and its growth and development since 1920. For radio encompasses telegraphic communication, as exemplified in our transoceanic wireless system; sound communication, as accomplished in telephony; mass communication, as inherent in broadcasting; sight communication, as promised by television. It is an art that embraces and goes beyond the arts of electrical, mechanical, telegraph, and telephone engineering and that touches upon the photographic and dramatic arts and is infusing new ideas into both; it is an art that has definite relations to chemistry, to metallurgy, to physics, to astronomy, to meteorology, to acoustics, and to dynamics.

. . . At the present time, an entirely new era of radio communication—radio television—is opening before us. We are not now manufacturing radio-television apparatus for the home, because, frankly, we do not yet know how to make a simplified and low-priced television receiver practicable for home use. Nevertheless, I **207** firmly believe that within the next few years such equipment and service will be developed and made available to the home. A virgin territory, an unlimited field, and a reward greater than present imagination can conceive await those who will bring sight as well as sound to the home. What a magnificent opportunity for inventive genius and industrial enterprise to express themselves! . . .

We are not now engaged in the many other applications of radio which are hopes and aspirations today but which will challenge accomplishment tomorrow. Why? Because we have not yet been able to find satisfactory technical solutions for the problems involved. But when solutions are found, they will appear to be simple. Most great things are.

. . . Fundamentally, the problems of radio still call for study and experimentation. We do not yet know to how many uses a given radio device may be put. We know little of the laws that govern radio transmission. We have only an inkling of what the next day may bring forth from the laboratory.

No future Alexander of the business world need cry, therefore, for the lack of worlds to conquer in this new art of communication, which is still unfolding. No industry offers a greater laboratory for business and industrial effort. None has so many virgin problems to solve. None bears so intimate a relation to other established industries, and none shows a greater promise of still further industrial expansion. It is upon you, the future leaders of the business world, that the greater burden and the greater glory of radio development must rest.

(Printed booklet: "The Development of the Radio Art and Radio Industry since 1920," an address by David Sarnoff. Book: *Radio and David Sarnoff*, by E. E. Bucher, part 26, pp. 3585–3589.)

THE YEARS OF THE DEPRESSION

The Depression created in American business in the 1930s a gener-   Editor's Note
ally defeatist attitude regarding the future. Most businessmen be-
lieved that their economic survival depended on cutting from the
budget any expenses that did not relate directly to the immediate
conduct of business. New industries, new markets, new products
were too laden with risk and future profits too uncertain to attract
the little free money still available. It was therefore very disturbing
to many of his colleagues and to RCA shareholders that Sarnoff
continued in the thirties to speak and write of "the forces of scien-
tific progress." Worse still, he not only maintained RCA research
expenditures when almost every major American industry had
dropped this "luxury" item, he actually expanded them! Sarnoff's
invincible faith in the future was not to be shaken—not even by a
Great Depression.

Increasing the World's Purchasing Power

Memorandum relating to the World Economic Conference in London
June 10, 1933

Two different schools of thought seem recently to have developed,
each urging its own philosophy as best suited to solving the complex
problems of world economics. The first proposes solutions along international lines, and the second along national lines. Each school
has its quota of earnest and well-intentioned advocates, but the ultimate objective sought is the same, i.e., national security, peace,
and prosperity.

The political, financial, and economic problems which now beset the world will be sharpened and defined at the Disarmament
Conference in Geneva and the World Economic Conference in London, to which the principal nations of the world have sent their
representatives.

Whether these world problems will be squarely faced and dealt   **209** with at the London Conference will depend not so much upon the validity of the theories advanced by either school as upon the immediate question of whether or not anyone can submit a practical program for dealing with them along international lines. If no such program can be advanced, the World Economic Conference could not succeed along world lines. The inevitable result would be the adoption by each of the principal nations of a policy of economic nationalism.

Should the Economic Conference fail, it is difficult to see how the Disarmament Conference could succeed. A policy of economic nationalism is not a promising background for advancing a program of international harmony. . . .

What is now most desired by the nations of the world is an increase in world trade and a rise in price levels. The accomplishment of these aims would result in disposition of troublesome surpluses and an increase in employment. This would make for greater stability along social, political, financial, and economic lines everywhere. Improvement in these directions would form the proper background for world peace. In such an atmosphere, substantial reduction in armaments could be reasonably achieved. . . .

Of the total of 2 billion persons inhabiting the earth, only 500 million reside in the so-called "industrialized nations" (the United States, Great Britain, France, Germany, Italy, Japan, etc.). The remaining 1,500 million live in the industrially undeveloped parts of the world (Russia, China, India, Africa, etc.).

The maximum international competition is now largely concentrated within the half-billion area. In this region, the competitive struggle becomes fiercer with each advance of the laboratory and each improvement of the machine. Artificial tariff barriers merely serve to emphasize the world's disequilibrium so long as the world is measured in terms of the half-billion area.

What is most needed then is a program which will open up the undeveloped 1,500 million area to the commodities, products, and services produced by the half-billion area. We need to convert the potential consumer of the larger area into an actual consumer for the goods and services of the smaller area. But since the inhabitants of **210** the larger area do not, in the main, now produce goods which they can exchange for that which we wish to furnish them and since they have not the money with which to make such purchases, it is clear that we must erect a credit bridge between the present producer and the potential consumer.

With the foregoing in mind, the following program is suggested:

1. Let the Bank for International Settlements (BIS) express the larger function intended for it by its sponsors. . . . That function was to serve not merely as a transfer agent but also as *an instrument for the opening of new world markets through the cooperative action of the central banks.* . . .

2. Let the BIS issue its own currency up to a maximum amount of $10 billion. This currency may constitute the basis for the issuance of legal tender in the nations of the world subscribing to the plan. It may be used by central banks as part of the reserves behind their own national currencies, along with gold, silver, eligible commercial paper, etc.

3. Back of the BIS currency there shall be placed the following: A gold cover equal to 20 percent of the total currency issued. With the consent of the Board of Governors of the BIS, this cover may be replaced to a reasonable extent, at any time, by silver or eligible commercial paper (analogous to our Federal Reserve methods).

   The guarantee of the industrial nations subscribing to the plan. Each nation subscribing to the plan is to limit its individual guarantee to a specified percentage of the total currency to be issued by the BIS, the percentages to be agreed upon among the subscribing nations.

   Bonds to be issued by the nations borrowing such BIS currency in an amount equal to the credit extended them for the purpose of making purchases from the industrial nations. . . .

4. Each nation's respective share of the gold cover is to be held in its central bank under "earmark" for the purpose indicated.

5. Suitable machinery shall be devised by the experts of the central banks, and an account shall be kept at BIS and settled periodically whereby transfers will be made from the gold account of one nation to another, dependent upon the flow of BIS currency

211

from debtor to creditor countries, so that as the BIS currency holdings of a country increase, the gold coverage behind it will correspondingly increase. This will operate as a natural restraint against overaccumulation of BIS currency in any one country.

6. The Board of Governors of the BIS, which shall be representative of the nations guaranteeing the BIS currency, shall determine the extent and amount of credit to be issued to a borrowing nation as well as the terms and conditions upon which such loans will be made. . . .

7. Machinery shall be set up in the BIS whereby the purchases to be made by borrowing nations will be divided among the industrial nations on a quota basis, such quotas to bear a reasonable relationship to the amount of BIS currency guaranteed by the nation making the sale.

8. Suitable machinery, or an acceptable formula, shall be adopted whereby the prices to be charged by selling nations for goods supplied to borrowing nations will bear a proper relationship to prices charged for similar goods or services supplied to others. . . .

9. . . . It is assumed that the United States is moving in the direction of increased trade relations with Russia. If this assumption is correct, it would seem reasonable to expect Russia to become a party to the proposed plan. Since Russia, more than any other country, requires for the development of her internal economy the commodities, products, and services of the producing nations of the world, it is assumed not only that Russia would be ready to accept credits from the BIS and to issue its bonds therefor but also that Russia would furnish an immediate and substantial market for the goods of the industrial nations. . . .

**Increase in
Consumptive Power
and Volume of
Services Needed by
Undeveloped
Countries**

In seeking new markets for the products of industrial countries, the prosperity of which depends to a large extent upon their exports, it is well to remember that such exports must not be limited to mere "consumption goods." The development of transportation, communications, and electrification in the so-called "undeveloped" countries would provide a large market for "production goods"— heavy machinery, engineering services, and organization experts.

The history of the United States has shown, over a period of
150 years, that a nation can develop on a debtor basis through the upbuilding of its resources and through the rendering of services to the inhabitants of other countries, enabling a constant balance of settlements to be made. Thus the undeveloped areas of the world, by reason of the fact that improved standards of living will be introduced and credit or purchasing power will be made available, can create markets for domestic interchange. It is a well-known fact that the turnover of goods and services within a country brings a momentum and velocity which, in time, enables that country to discharge its external indebtedness. Sometimes these items constitute an invisible exchange, as for instance the development of tourist traffic and other services which are now at a minimum in these great undeveloped areas of the world. . . .

In addition to the benefits of increasing trade by supplying goods and services to the vast undeveloped markets of the world, it is also to be remembered that one aim of our civilization is continually to raise the standard of living among all human beings. . . . The improvement in employment and real wages that would result from extending trade to undeveloped markets would, by increasing home purchasing power, also raise the living standards at home and thus broaden the domestic markets of the industrial nations. At the same time, the flow of goods would be increased between the industrial nations. In this respect, it may be assumed that there is no saturation point to man's desire for the better things of life.

If a program along the lines discussed in this memorandum, or some similar program having the same objectives, could be adopted by the London Conference, it would seem wise to defer the final deliberations of the Disarmament Conference until the conclusion of the World Economic Conference. If the principal nations of the world subscribed to an economic program in which they had confidence, the probabilities of success at a disarmament conference would be enhanced.

An economic partnership of the principal nations of the world would strengthen the bonds of friendship between them and vitalize the objectives sought by the Disarmament Conference. An increase in the world's purchasing power would inevitably help to bring the stability so anxiously sought today by every nation in the world.

(Mimeographed text: David Sarnoff Library, Princeton, N.J.)

Opportunities in Space

Address before Ohio Society of New York
New York City, January 8, 1934

Continued progress is certain to bring new problems. Any attempt to freeze society and industry at a given time or point will be as ineffectual as undertaking to hold back the onward rush of time. Whatever the measures taken for the present, they will not be adequate to suit the future. The very plans developed to remedy conditions today may unloose forces that will create the problems of tomorrow. A great gain will have been attained in our national thinking if we can disillusion ourselves from the idea that sound remedies must be effective throughout the ages. Measures, like governments, should be flexible. They should not bear the rigidity of finality.

Of increasing importance is the charting of future paths through the fostering of research, invention, enterprise, and initiative. Those who have challenged the social benefits resulting from individualism have contended that individual opportunity is a closed story in human progress. It may be true that no youthful telegrapher of the future can travel Edison's exact path and that no young physicist can duplicate the precise work of Marconi. Yet the total of the world's inventive enterprise and scientific resourcefulness has not eliminated one frontier of our knowledge. It has merely pressed those frontiers forward a little more into the mists of the unknown, a territory still larger than the limited area of our knowledge. . . .

We might point to the great frontier that lies daily and nightly above us and ask if there is not enough wealth and mystery in the air and sky to test the ingenuity of several future generations.

. . . The gifts of the soil are perhaps gifts from heaven. If, as astronomers believe, the earth was torn from the sun, miners and reapers through the ages have but harvested what was the ancient gift of the sun. Sustenance and wealth have literally come to us from the skies. And yet, curiously enough, we have looked down and not up to find them. Man has been content, in the main, to scratch the globe on which he dwelt, to take his toll, and to search no farther. True, man has penetrated nearly every corner of the world and has burrowed into it to amazing depths for its natural, buried treasure. He has learned how to build himself shelter against unfriendly climates and to manufacture all manner of comforts in abundance. But until a comparatively short time ago, he was still essentially a two-dimensional being, moving about his affairs over the earth's surface, . . . in awe of the mysteries that lay above and beyond his power of conquest.

Already, in our own generation, we have seen men turn from the more obvious means of wresting wealth from the earth to rise above it, finding new triumphs of industry and amazing sources of wealth. In our time, we have seen the airplane become an everyday vehicle of swift transportation and communications. We read of intrepid scientists bumping along in curiously outfitted balloons in quest of a region above the layer of atmosphere in which we have so long been prisoners. The planes or rocket ships of tomorrow may be largely free from even the small retarding influence of the air, traveling at speeds so incredible that the whole world will be one neighborhood.

Fortunes above the Earth

The rise of radio communications and radio broadcasting during the past decade has made space the main path of communication, and the laboratory promises still further radio services. Entertainment and education, the spoken and printed words, and still or motion pictures already can be carried on the wings of the ether wave. Individual communication and mass communication alike are within the scope of the radio channel, which knows no obstacle of sea or mountain or other barrier to earthbound communications.

Material things of great value are to be found in the gaseous ocean of the air. We have seen a startling example in the fixation of

215

atmospheric nitrogen by electrical methods. Practically inexhaustible supplies of cheap fertilizer have thus become available. It is
suggested by some bold prognosticators that the air is also a potential source of energy. Perhaps sunlight can be trapped, and cosmic
radiations, known and unknown, may be put to work for mankind.
The power of winds and the temperature gradients of atmosphere
afford other interesting possibilities. The air throbs with great stores
of energy which may ultimately be harnessed to the uses of man.

. . . We have broken our earthly bonds and have started to
hammer at a new frontier, vaster beyond all imagination than any
within human experience.

(Printed pamphlet: "Looking Up," an address by David
Sarnoff.)

Science and World Progress

Address before third annual Woman's Congress
Sponsored by the *Chicago Tribune*
Chicago, Ill., February 14, 1936

Our destiny will be more profoundly revolutionized by the forces of
scientific progress than by the panaceas of theoretical sociologists.
And that progress will be more beneficent to the masses under an
orderly system of free government than under restrictions imposed
by any dictatorship.

Science repeatedly has shown its ability to transcend the limitations of the human intellect. It has crashed through physical barriers too vast for our minds to encompass. It has harnessed natural
forces that we can hardly define, let alone understand.

More than that, science often has outstripped the human imagination. We know now that Leonardo da Vinci's daring dream of
a man flying through space stopped short of the everyday realities of
our own generation. The scientific fantasies of a Jules Verne seem
tame against the modern submarine and the stratosphere balloons of
our day. Even Shakespeare's immortal fancy lagged far behind the
fact of today when he made Puck boast: "I'll put a girdle 'round the

earth in forty minutes." Today, radio girdles the earth in one-seventh of a second.

We have watched the unfolding of these scientific miracles in our own lifetime. The spectacle has been so continuous that sometimes it seems that our sense of wonder has been deadened. We have lost much of the thrill felt by our fathers and grandfathers, as the marvels of the steam engine have receded before the greater marvels of the electric dynamo, as motion pictures have been followed by radio broadcasting. But however we may lose the thrill, we do not lose the hope. We accept the latest triumphs of science a little humbly, conscious of the immense mystery still beyond.

Until our own generation, the wealth of the world came from below the surface of our globe—from the mines and waters and fertile soils. It is only in the last thirty-odd years that humanity has begun to reach upward for new wealth—upward into the air, into the stratosphere. Already, we have made an impressive beginning with transportation and communication through the air, through aviation and radio. It is only a small beginning, but one could speculate at length on the potential resources that still lie untouched in ultra-short waves, in sun energy, and in the stratospheric lanes. Americans once faced the frontiers of geography. Today, we face new frontiers of science.

Only about one-half of the human race is, at present, within the orbit of industrialized civilization. Untapped resources of science may soon bring the other half into this sphere, may create immense new producing and consuming areas, and may provide greater scope for growth and general worldwide enrichment than we now dare imagine. I believe that the solution of the world's economic problems will yet be found through the progress of science.

(Book: *Radio and David Sarnoff*, by E. E. Bucher (address titled "Communications and Democracy"), part 3, pp. 858–868.)

Proposals for Economic Recovery

Letter to President Franklin D. Roosevelt
June 12, 1936

During my recent visit to your office in Washington, I took the liberty of making several suggestions to you orally and you were good enough to ask me to set them forth to you in a letter. I am sending this communication to you so that it may reach you about the time you return from your present trip.

The suggestions I respectfully submit for your consideration are as follows:

Facts on Unemployment There appears to be a great deal of controversy as to the actual number of people in our country now unemployed. Various estimates of the number have been made by different agencies, and some of them differ substantially from others. None of these estimates contains definite information as to the exact number of unemployed in the different states and cities, the nature of the work in which those now out of employment were previously engaged, their age, sex, and citizenship, and whether or not they are employable at this time. Already one hears talk in various parts of the country of the shortage of skilled labor and, indeed, of unskilled labor.

Since the subject of unemployment is doubtless one of the major problems, if not *the* major problem, of the country facing all of us and since a great part of legislation, both enacted and likely to be enacted, must necessarily take this problem of unemployment into account, I firmly believe it would be helpful to those in and out of government to have before them the precise facts of the situation.

With the foregoing in mind, it occurs to me to suggest that there be designated an existing governmental agency in each local community—for example, the local post office or the machinery of the draft—to which all those now on relief or unemployed be requested to come and fill out a questionnaire which would give the answers to the questions above indicated and such other information as might

be desired by the government. The Department of Labor could
doubtless prepare a simple form of questionnaire calling for all the
information on the subject which might be desired.

In order to facilitate such a program of inquiry, the broadcasting stations of the country, and in particular the networks, might be
asked to make a suitable announcement over the air each day or
evening for a consecutive period of thirty days, encouraging those
concerned to cooperate with the government by promptly filling out
the questionnaire at the place designated in their respective locality.
The President of the United States might launch this appeal offi-
cially, and this would doubtless stimulate early response. . . .

The completed questionnaires should be mailed by the local
agencies to a central office in Washington designated for this purpose. At such place, the questionnaires could be tabulated and the
essential information summarized for ready reference. If the proposed idea proved workable, the central office in Washington
could devise plans for keeping this information up to date, in order
that a revised statement of the facts and figures could be made
available monthly. In this way, there would be before you and the
country current facts on this vital subject of unemployment.

My second suggestion is that either in the tax bill now under
consideration or in a separate bill there be included a provision giving employers of labor abatement of income taxes in direct ratio
to their increased employment of labor for a stated period—perhaps
two years. The effects of this provision might apply to such increases in employment as are made from the date of the passage of
the bill. The object of this suggestion is to encourage industry to increase employment speedily. The Treasury Department experts
could doubtless devise a suitable formula dealing more specifically
than I am in this letter with the ratio of tax abatement to increased
employment.

**Tax Abatement to
Employers of Labor
Based on Increased
Employment**

To the extent that this idea would prove effective in operation,
the government would be relieved from payments now made to
those on relief who might be absorbed by industry. Increased employment means increased consumption, which, in turn, means in-

219

creased business and profits and therefore increased tax returns to the government. Thus what the government might yield on the one hand it should more than regain on the other. Again, should the idea not result in increased employment by industry, then of course there would be no abatement in taxes and thus no decrease in tax revenue to the government.

**Attracting Idle Capital
to New Industries**

The creation and development of new industries were never more vitally necessary than now. These mean added work, increased employment, new national wealth, and wider opportunities for those in our country. New enterprises necessarily involve greater risks for capital than established businesses do. Those who have capital to invest are often more reluctant to risk that capital in times of depression than they are in periods of prosperity. This reluctance and this doubt on the part of owners of idle capital are cumulative in their adverse effects. When to these effects there is added the obligation to pay a high income tax on profits which might be derived from venturing into the unknown, the tendency is to avoid risking the definite principal for indefinite profits. This vicious circle results in idle money, and its unemployment is also devastating in its effects upon society.

In view of the above, my third suggestion for your consideration is that in order to put idle money to work, especially in new enterprises, the tax bill now under discussion, or a new tax bill, incorporate a provision relieving corporations or individuals who invest their funds in the creation and development of new enterprises from a large measure of taxes on profits earned on their investments in such enterprises during a reasonable period of time, at least such time as may be necessary to enable the investor to determine the stability of the enterprise or to obtain a reasonable portion of his principal. Such a provision would encourage idle capital to seek investment in new enterprises and would also serve the purpose of retaining in such new enterprises the capital needed for their rapid development.

I recognize the need of defining "new enterprises" specifically if this suggestion should prove of interest. I have not attempted to do

so in this letter because such definition can best be devised by the experts in the various government departments who are in contact with the many industries of this country.

(Original letter in bound volume: *Correspondence between President Franklin D. Roosevelt and David Sarnoff, 1933–1947*; David Sarnoff Library, Princeton, N.J.)

Science, Society, and Industry

Address before American Physical Society
Washington, D.C., April 30, 1937

The scientist and the sociologist have viewpoints which are perhaps too widely separated. The scientist is engaged in the pursuit of truth, the knowledge of which is the most valuable of our acquired assets. The sociologist is concerned with the ultimate effects of truth upon human behavior. To the scientist, the discovery of truth is an end in itself. To the sociologist, it is only a means to an end. . . .

Today, the sociologist rightly may claim that many of the gifts of science and industry are in the nature of a two-edged sword. It is a sword which, like the *Nothung* of Siegfried, can be used to slay the dragons of ignorance, intolerance, and greed; but there is always a chance that it will turn out to be a weapon with which civilization may destroy itself.

One does not have to go far to find illustrations of the blessings and dangers that go side by side in the discoveries of science. The chemical that safeguards the work of the surgeon can poison the city's water supply. The airplane that speeds transportation and commerce can drop bombs from the air to blow women and children to atoms.

There are other dangers, less obvious and more subtle. Radio, for example, can be used for propaganda and regimentation as well as for education and entertainment. Science laid the same gift of radio at the feet of society in Europe as it did in America. It is true that in the United States there is room for improvement in some of the programs broadcast on the air and that we still have to learn how to derive the greatest social benefit from radio. But no one raised in the tradition of liberty and democracy can doubt that our use of it is in

221

the direction of social betterment, while in certain parts of Europe, where radio has been commandeered by the forces of regimentation, its misuse points toward social degradation.

. . . The new art of television has similar potentialities to build up or tear down social values. Like sound broadcasting, it can make friendly neighbors of people who differ in race, creed, politics, and language, while at the same time it offers a powerful weapon to the warmaker and a medium of propaganda for the autocrat.

. . . It is too optimistic to assume that the mere translation of a scientific discovery into a usable commodity or instrument always advances civilization; that just because humanity can travel faster, communicate more freely, cook, wash, iron, and gather ice cubes with less effort than ever before, it has reached the all-time peak of civilization. Giving a man a hoe or a microscope does not make him a farmer or a scientist, and giving him a radio or an automobile does not make him civilized. It is the use that society makes of the products of science and industry that determines whether civilization is advanced or retarded.

Civilization depends for its advance upon our expanding knowledge of the social as well as the physical sciences, for society, no matter how benevolent its intentions, cannot solve its problems by intuition or rule of thumb. It must develop its own standards and technique. . . .

Science and Industry

Industry today is following the vanguard of science into new and infinite realms of knowledge. It would be a rash astronomer who said that he had calculated the outermost limits of space, beyond which there is nothing. It would be a rash physicist who claimed that he had dissected the atom into its ultimate, indivisible fragments. Science and knowledge have no boundaries.

So it would be a rash economist who predicted any limit to the tangible results of scientific thought in the form of new goods and services placed at the disposal of mankind. In fact, it is only by a constant development of new goods and services that we may expect to reengage the manpower released by technological improvements in established industries. The market for every new commodity

eventually reaches a saturation point and becomes primarily a replacement market, so that a more efficient technology reduces the number of workers needed in that field.

But science is simultaneously creating new employment, both by the modernization of established industries and by the creation of new ones. In our own generation, we have seen the automobile, the airplane, the motion picture, and the radio provide totally fresh fields of activity for millions of men and women. Many of our older industries have engaged scientists, with notable success, to develop new products and remodel old products to meet the needs of a modern era.

The industry which has not learned how to employ scientists to make it new, and keep it new, is doomed. Few industries are so stagnant as not to be aware of this; but there are some so conservative that the scientist is called upon to turn salesman and show them how modern science can rejuvenate them to meet present-day realities and survive.

(Book: *Radio and David Sarnoff*, by E. E. Bucher, part 3, pp. 876–886; part 4, pp. 970–971; part 12, pp. 113–114; part 23, pp. 29–59.)

THE WAR YEARS

Editor's Note *With all the vast resources of American industry mobilized for the war effort, the foundations were laid during the Second World War for the tremendous technological expansion that followed. In laboratories like those of RCA, scientists and technicians all over the country devoted themselves to basic and applied research. The immediate goals were military, but the by-products of this research were of enormous importance to theoretical science and to peacetime technology. The greatest single development of this period was, of course, the harnessing of atomic energy. It is a remarkable tribute to Sarnoff's breadth of vision that, in the midst of war, he was one of the first to perceive and publicly predict the great peaceful potential of the atom.*

Potential of the Atom

Address before American Life convention
Chicago, Ill., October 9, 1940

Looking at the facts immediately before our eyes, there is abundant reason to feel that 1940 may go down in history as one of its darkest pages. This is the year in which we have witnessed the fall of most of the democracies of Europe. It is the year in which we see Great Britain fighting heroically for her life. It is the year in which human freedom everywhere is in mortal danger. Yet, if this remaining fortress of democracy across the sea holds out and eventually conquers, what has passed may turn out to be only an evil, tragic dream, which will be dissipated in the dawn of a better day.

For it is not impossible that history may record the most momentous happening in 1940 as having taken place in the laboratory rather than on the battlefield. I am thinking that the truly epoch-making event of the year may be man's first successful attempt to release atomic energy, through the isolation of uranium 235.

224   The importance of this new discovery lies in the fact that a natural substance, existing in comparative abundance, has been found capable of releasing energy on an unbelievable scale. The isolation of that substance is an exceedingly difficult process, but—in laboratory quantities—it has now been accomplished. A single pound of uranium 235, it is said, will provide the energy equivalent of 3 million pounds of gasoline or 5 million pounds of coal. The utilization of that energy, once the substance is available in commercial quantities, becomes a practical matter.

Scientists are hopeful that a method of isolating uranium 235 in large quantities can be developed. I have learned from long experience to have more faith in the scientist than he has in himself. Experience and faith tell me that—given time, facilities, and freedom to follow where imagination leads—the scientist will do all he hopes to do, and more.

A New Society

What coming generations may be able to see with their own eyes and judge from their own experience is today almost beyond the scope of our imagination. With atomic power, people may be able to light, heat, ventilate, and refrigerate their homes with ease and at trifling expense.

Ships, railway trains, automobiles, and airplanes may be fueled for life at the time they are built. Men may carry in their pockets personal radiotelephones which will enable them to communicate throughout the world. A myriad of new products and services will become available to all. Many of the old hardships and deprivations —the sources of social and economic unrest—will disappear. A new society, dwelling in a new economy of abundance, will be born.

Is all this a dream? Yes, but it is the dreamstuff of science, and our dreamers are the scientists who are opening new vistas for civilization.

. . . In the shadow of the most terrible war in human history, conducted with every instrument of science, it may seem like blind confidence to speak of the benefits which more research and greater scientific development may bring to the future. It is true that science often has been perverted to the work of death and destruction. It is also true that art has often been made the servant of propaganda and that literature, when its expression is controlled by a dictator-

ship, may degrade rather than ennoble the human mind. But that
does not argue for loss of faith in science, art, or literature.

It is easy to assume that at a time when ruthlessness is systematically destroying the material work of men's minds and men's hands,
we are witnessing the destruction of civilization itself. It is natural
that when science is harnessed to the work of mass murder, men
should deplore the fertility of the human brain that has made it
possible.

But that is striking back at the shutter which the wind has
blown in your face. The time for black pessimism will be when men
cease to delve into the mysteries of nature, when they cease to invent the means and methods of conquering space and time, of
bringing more ease and security to life, of protecting humanity from
the inroads of disease, of giving man's nature a freer play in life, of
providing finer self-government for the political state. Dictators who
boast that what they are creating will last a thousand years ignore
the lessons of history. They will fail and must fail so long as there is
a single island where the human spirit survives and human intelligence is left free. . . .

(Printed pamphlet: "Science and Security," an address by
David Sarnoff.)

The Electronic Age

Address at RCA Laboratories dinner
Princeton, N.J., March 12, 1941

New inventions are geared to the times and to the generations in
which people live. There was the Steam Age, then came the Electrical Age, and later the Radio Age. Now, I think we are on the eve
of a new age—the Electronic Age. Just as electricity *electrified* industries and life in general, so these developments that you gentlemen
are producing with tubes and circuits will *electronize* industries and
create the Electronic Age.

By the establishment of the new RCA Laboratories, radio
quickens its pace alongside the older industries—electrical, steel, automobile, wire-communications, chemical, metallurgical, and others

—which, through research, have contributed to the industrial leader-ship and progress of this country. . . . No new industry in the history of this country has made greater strides in as short a time as radio or has contributed more extensive benefits to people in all walks of life.

The applications of electronics to the various uses of industries are more numerous than people outside of radio have any notion; they are more numerous than even those of us on the inside of radio can see today. Many problems in industrial mass production may be solved in large measure by the application of electronic devices.

None of us knows today what the problems, industrially and economically, will be when the present emergency is over. I, for one, have never shared the apprehensions of those who have pointed to the machine as the reason for unemployment or to technology as the cause of economic distress. I have always felt that if there be any solution to the problems of humanity, the solution will come princi-pally through greater science and more technology.

. . . I think that the establishment of the RCA Laboratories at Princeton offers a great measure of security to our organization. There is no security in standing still. Those who rest on the rock of stabilization sooner or later find that that rock becomes their tomb-stone. There is no security for the future in the mere knowledge of today. There is hope and opportunity in what we can learn tomor-row. That is the greatest asset on the balance sheet of humanity and on the balance sheet of any organization engaged in scientific pur-suits. And so I believe that this united front of scientific attack upon the problems of our particular art and its relationship to other in-dustries is the greatest forward step in the direction of security and in individual opportunity.

Whatever may be said about consolidations and mergers of physical assets and stocks and bonds, I have yet to hear the slightest word of criticism about the mobilization of brains. What we seek to consolidate in the new RCA Laboratories is the knowledge, the know-how, the experience, and the intelligence of those who repre-sent the vanguard of development. . . . To you, we look for the dis-covery of new needs, the creation of new products, new services, and new opportunities. . . .

227

I look upon you as our intellectual shock troops—whose purpose it is not only to do the job of today but to make life happier for mankind tomorrow and to lift the curtain of obscurity which for the moment befogs a struggling world.

I wish you every success. I pledge you every support. I am a firm advocate of research. . . . No step which the RCA organization has taken since I have been associated with it has given me more happiness, more confidence, more faith in the future and in you than the step we are commemorating tonight.

(Book: *Radio and David Sarnoff*, by E. E. Bucher, part 4, pp. 1133–1142; part 5, pp. 1278–1279.)

Research in Peace and War

Address at the dedication of the RCA Laboratories
Princeton, N.J., September 27, 1942

When the cornerstone of this building was laid in November of last year, I attended the ceremonies by radio on board a ship on the Pacific Ocean, somewhere between Honolulu and San Francisco. . . . At the very hour the cornerstone was put in place, the plans of the Japanese war staff to attack Pearl Harbor must have been completed. . . . Our days of peace were numbered, and their number was very few.

It is significant that the foundations of this building were laid in time of peace and that its superstructure has been raised in time of war. Similarly, the modern sciences of radio and electronics have their roots in peaceful soil—in the search by men of good will for ways and means to make the world a better place to live in. Yet these sciences, and all science, are now enlisted in total war.

Total war as it is fought today is more than a war of populations or a mere quantity of weapons or, alone, the human qualities of courage and endurance. More than ever before in history, this war is a contest between the brains and imagination and teamwork of the scientists, engineers, and production workers of one group of nations and those of another group. While it is true that the decision ultimately will be made on the battlefield, on the high seas, and in the air, the fighting men who have the greatest resources of science, engineering, and production back of them will be the victors.

Most people are aware that science is making a tremendous contribution to modern war in terms of guns, high explosives, airplanes, radio, and synthetic rubber. By developing and improving these vitally important products, a comparatively small number of scientists may be a far more powerful fighting force than an enemy army of millions of men.

But scarcely less important are scientific developments in many fields of chemistry, medicine, and agriculture. Plastics, synthetic textiles, dehydrated foods, high-octane gasoline, aluminum, magnesium, and scores of other materials and products important to the war effort are being produced on a vast scale, thanks in large measure to American industrial research.

Developments like these are the result of organized scientific effort in laboratories such as the one you dedicate here today. But organized research is a peacetime product, the result of the slow and careful assemblage of men and facilities long before the urgency of war makes its call for the utmost efforts of a nation.

The United States has been fortunate in the vision of its private enterprises and universities which, long prior to the war, assembled such staffs and built such facilities. True, they did not build them to serve as adjuncts to military forces, as did our enemies. America's purpose was not conquest of other nations but conquests over the forces of nature, over ignorance, over poverty, over disease.

. . . Only a portion of America's scientific manpower has been fully used thus far in the war effort. The results, however, are already apparent, both in new and improved equipment for our fighting forces and in the ingenuity displayed by industrial laboratories in developing ways of overcoming problems such as the shortages of critical materials. I have no doubt as to the ultimate result when all our available forces of science are organized and applied to the single purpose of achieving victory. . . .

(Mimeographed full text: "Scientific Research in War and Peace," an address by David Sarnoff; David Sarnoff Library, Princeton, N.J. Book: *Radio and David Sarnoff*, by E. E. Bucher, part 4, pp. 1150–1154; part 5, pp. 1280–1281.)

New Opportunities for Progress

Address before American Association for the Advancement of Science
Lancaster, Pa., November 11, 1943

When this war ends, we shall be on the threshold of a new era in radio—an era in which man will see, as well as hear, distant events. The first two decades of this century belonged to wireless telegraphy. The second two decades featured sound broadcasting; the third two decades promise television. It is not too bold to predict that the fourth two decades will introduce international television with pictures in color.

It is even possible that, in the two final decades, we may complete the century with power transmission by radio and its use in the operation of vehicles, automobiles, ships, railroads, and airplanes. When completed, the story of these first hundred years of radio will make fascinating reading. Even a Jules Verne could not tell us all that lies ahead in this magic realm of radio-electronics.

The science of radio is no longer confined to communications. Among its revolutionary accomplishments, in other lines, we have the electron microscope, one of the most important new scientific tools of the twentieth century.

. . . Wartime industrial research and engineering have rushed into use still another branch of radio—the art of utilizing high-frequency radio waves for heating. . . . The wide scope of its application ranges from case-hardening steel to dehydrating foods, from gluing prefabricated houses to seaming thermoplastic materials by means of a "radio sewing machine."

. . . Further afield from communications, research men are exploring supersonic vibrations, far above the range of the human ear. The use of these ultrasonics in chemistry may open a field in which high-intensity sound accelerates chemical reactions. Experiments also indicate important possibilities in many other fields, including underwater communication, emulsification of liquids, and precipitation of dust from the air.

We attribute all these lines of progress to the science of electronics. The heart of that science is the radio tube.

. . . Radio-electron tubes are as important in peace as in war.
They are the master keys to revolutionary advances in radio.

. . . The day may come when every person will have his own
little radio station tucked away in his pocket, to hear and to communicate with his home or his office as he walks or rides along the
street. We have much to learn about the microwaves, in which is
wrapped up this new world of individualized radio. Tiny electron
tubes may make it possible to design radio receivers and transmitters no larger than a fountain pen, a cigarette case, a billfold, or a
lady's powder box. Someday people may carry television screens on
their wrists as they now carry watches. As the useful spectrum of
radio approaches the frontiers of light, the apparatus will become
simpler and more compact.

Today, science is leading us out of a world in which radio has
been blind. Tomorrow, we shall have radio sight. By this I do not
mean that we shall look only at pictures in motion that travel
through the air. Radiovision will have many uses. It will serve
wherever sight is needed. For instance, it will be used to prevent
collisions on highways and railroads, on sea-lanes, and on the airways of the world. Radio will be the new eye of transportation and
commerce. Applications of radio optics are unlimited. With radio
ear and eye to guide them, the great stratoliners will be superhuman
in their instincts of hearing and seeing as they speed through space
with passengers and freight. Radio, which made the world a whispering gallery, will turn it into a world of mirrors.

. . . America's cultivation of science has proved the nation's
salvation in modern warfare. It must not be otherwise in peace.
Pioneering and research create wealth and employment.

In considering opportunities for employment after the war, we
must lift our sights to the skies. Man, long confined in his activities
to the surface of the earth and beneath the ground, now finds that
the air is a new dimension, offering new adventures and pioneering
by a new generation. The air is a universal chemical and physical
laboratory in which essential elements for life on earth are created.
Nature herself makes unlimited use of celestial space for transmission of light and heat from the sun. Only in recent years has man
learned to use the air. Only now is he beginning to discover its tre-

mendous potentialities. Literally out of thin air, chemists are creating new products, physicists are building new services, while man is talking on unseen waves and flying on invisible beams.

. . . Above the earth, aviation and radio, electronics and television can open the way for new opportunities in reemployment of war workers and the millions of men and women who will return from service.

It is estimated that 10 million jobs which did not exist in 1940 must be found to solve the postwar problem of employment. One great hope in helping to meet this unprecedented challenge will be found in the fertile and unexplored frontiers of space. Science, offering new incentives, is beckoning capital to venture into the open skies.

. . . Horace Greeley, if here today, might say, "Go up, young man, go up and grow up in space." There lies the unfathomed West of this century, with no last frontier; there lies a vast wilderness rich in resources, opportunities, and adventure. The forty-niners of the present decade will be prospectors in research. They will travel through the air to stake their claims to fame, fortune, and freedom. . . .

(Printed booklet: "Industrial Science Looks Ahead," an
address by David Sarnoff.)

Editor's Note   David Sarnoff's uncanny prescience entangled him inadvertently in World War II's most closely guarded secret.

On July 2, 1945, when he was a general on active service, he submitted an article to the War Department to be cleared for publication. In it, he predicted the infinite destructiveness of an atomic weapon dropped upon a city.

Sarnoff was startled when, a few days later, a colonel on General George Marshall's staff appeared in his office and without explanation informed him that the article could not be released.

"I was a one-star general, and General Marshall had five stars, and that was that," Sarnoff recalled.

232   A little more than a month later, on August 6, a B-29 loosed a

*deadly cargo on the Japanese city of Hiroshima and the era of the
atom bomb was born. That afternoon, Sarnoff's telephone buzzed.
General Marshall was on the other end.*

"Now you know why your article was not approved."

*Completely unknown to Sarnoff, American scientists were work-
ing at Los Alamos, New Mexico, in total secrecy to produce the very
type of weapon Sarnoff had predicted. Two weeks after he submitted the article below for clearance, on July 16, they succeeded.*

Science for Life or Death

Article in *The New York Times*, issue of Aug. 10, 1945
Copyright 1945 by The New York Times Company
Reprinted by permission

As final victory in this second world war approaches, mankind finds
itself at a fork in the road of time, where one route leads to peace
and the other to a third world war—to life or death! Which shall it
be? Man must make a choice.

Innovations in the domain of science have piled up so fast and
so dramatically under the impetus of the present war that the public, and even some leaders, have not yet fully grasped their implications for the future of our nation and of mankind.

Science, under the direction of evil aggressors on the one hand
and in the hands of freedom's defenders on the other, has developed
the twin forces of speed and explosive power to a point where a
short step will make it possible to demolish whole cities in a single
stroke. A third world war a generation hence would be so horrible in
its power of destruction as to constitute a threat to our national survival and to civilization itself!

. . . With the command of such terrifying velocity and such
overwhelming explosive force, war could be over almost before it
started. There would be no time for a nation to mobilize its armies
and navies, to draft men and to train them, and—in due course—to
marshal science and industry to defend itself against aggression.

So terrifying, in fact, are the prospects of these new weapons **233** that should some aggressively minded nation be the first to develop them, it might be tempted to use them immediately; to wait might mean its own eventual destruction. There might be no second chance!

. . . The first hope for civilization, I believe, lies in a world organization to achieve and maintain a lasting peace. But until such an organization has proved its effectiveness, we dare not relax in our efforts to provide the maximum degree of national security attainable. We must turn to science now for new weapons of offense and defense. We must have the means of detecting enemy-guided projectiles hundreds of miles from our coasts. And we must have similar projectiles or rays which we can instantly release to seek and to destroy these new forms of flying death before they reach their targets. . . .

Scientific preparedness must parallel military preparedness. It is not enough to train youth for warfare. Those with an aptitude for science should be trained for research and engineering. It may be more important that such a boy be trained in the sciences than that he be drilled as a foot soldier, a sailor, or a flyer. The daring and initiative of young men are as important in the laboratory as on the battlefield.

America has a great reservoir of scientific talent—therein lies one of the greatest hopes for the future of this country. For America to abandon military research and engineering development would be tantamount to national suicide. In peacetime as well as in war, research must be maintained on a wide basis in order to seek solutions of scientific problems from as many angles as possible. There cannot be too many laboratories; each presents opportunity for scientists to test and to develop new ideas. Competition among them is the spice of invention. . . .

It was through the perversion of science that Germany was able to wage two wars within a generation. This is a lesson free nations should never forget. Science must be kept free—there must always be freedom to experiment, to invent, and to produce. "The empires of the future," said Winston Churchill, "are the empires of the mind.". . .

234

There is no security in the argument that many decades may pass before science exhausts the ultimate possibilities of dealing death from the skies. Science moves quickly as years are measured. When Marconi first signaled across the English Channel, he was told by experts that radio waves never would be able to cross the oceans. Nevertheless, two years later, Marconi spanned the Atlantic with electromagnetic waves. Before he died, he heard his signals through space encircle the globe. No greater delay may be in prospect for guiding missiles through space!

Power politics and diplomacy, as tools to shape the destinies of nations and the lives of people, are dwarfed by the potential power of science. The peacemaker who overlooks science neglects future security. A nation may be stripped of its fleet, air force, and army, but if its laboratories are intact and its scientists unfettered, they will hold in their hands a power that may challenge any military and naval force. . . .

The end of the European war brought to light the evidence that development of new weapons of warfare is passing through several interesting stages:

1. Production of long-range high-speed missiles
2. Guidance of these missiles by either self-contained or outside means, such as radio
3. Intensive research into the possibilities of release and control of atomic energy

It is to be noted that the passage from each of these stages to the next has been greatly speeded by developments during World War II—the rapid development, for instance, of jet and rocket bombs, the flying speed of which lies between 300 and 3,000 miles per hour. In flight, they already have attained an altitude of 60 miles, and this height will be substantially increased. The explosive load, or warhead, of these 40- to 50-foot bombs contains about 2 tons of high explosive, the entire bomb weighing from 10 tons to several tens of tons. The difficulties of launching them are considerable, but these already have been fairly well overcome, and in the future, the remaining difficulties doubtless will be eliminated.

235

Within ten years or so, we may face a new form of long-range guided missile whose flying range will enable it to span the oceans. It is not too much to expect that speeds of 5,000 to 10,000 miles an hour will be attained and that these speeds will be suitably reduced for landing purposes and to prevent overheating the bomb by air friction, with consequent premature detonation. . . .

**Unlocking Atomic
Energy**
To supply the terrific driving force required by such a weapon, we find man struggling with Nature to learn the secret of atomic energy. Scientists know that locked within the atom is a reservoir of tremendous energy. Atomic power resides in the very center of the nucleus of the atom. It is a high-caliber energy tightly locked into place and requires extraordinary means for its release. This atomic energy must be distinguished from the energy obtained by burning ordinary fuels (such as gasoline or explosives). Fuels deliver energy only through chemical action—and the amount of energy they release in combustion is trifling in comparison with the atomic power available in the same amount of any material substance.

. . . Further research into the mysteries of atomic energy must be continued if its challenging possibilities are fully to be realized. That such research will achieve practical results is not only a possibility but an ever-increasing probability. Nations have learned in the present war that mass attacks on scientific problems yield results, just as do mass attacks on military or production problems.

In the field of military applications, atomic energy promises results that challenge the imagination. The range of a flying missile propelled by such energy could encircle the world. A nation could, without notice, launch a deadly cloud of these missiles accurately directed at an opposing nation. Such atomically propelled bombs could travel thousands of miles an hour at heights hundreds of miles above the earth. The warheads of such projectiles would need to contain only a few pounds of the material to be decomposed into energy by a mechanism capable of detonating the nuclei of the atoms.

When a bomb of this sort landed in a city within a moderate distance of a selected target, it might well convert a large region surrounding it into gas and debris. In view of its range of destruction, accuracy of aim no longer is a major factor. A scattered pattern of such bombs not only would destroy all life but would convert the city into a bed of rock, ashes, and dust.

It must not be overlooked, however, that never has science been outwitted in finding a weapon of defense for every new weapon of offense. The flying bomb is not likely to be an exception; it will not go unchallenged. It is not difficult to envisage accurately guided "bloodhound" missiles that will take off against the approaching bombs and, under scientific control, locate and destroy them before they have a chance to strike. But here we face new forces of destruction, prevention of which must be measured in minutes or in seconds instead of months or years, as in the past. This only emphasizes the great need for constant research to develop defensive as well as offensive weapons for instant use.

Man's Use of Science

A powerful nation today feels relatively secure as compared with one of the smaller nations. But that security may be sheer illusion in the future. No nation will be invulnerable to attack. No Goliath will be safe. Indeed, a small aggressor nation might have ample resources to destroy a great nation. Scientists of a small country may conceivably be the first to discover answers to unsolved scientific problems of the present. The possession of some secret weapon by a small nation might make it more powerful and more dangerous than its largest opponent if that opponent did not have such a weapon for instant use.

Man has entered the Rocket Era; the rocket, once a toy and now a missile of science, has brought him face to face with a new destiny. Peace or war—life or death? A radio-controlled rocket carrying mail, food, freight, or passengers through space at terrific speeds, or rockets loaded with the power of destruction—which is it to be?

What will man do with these astounding facilities that science is creating? Will he use them for beneficent purposes? Will he use them to make the world a better and happier place and to provide abundance everywhere so that those who now lack the basic requirements for comfortable living may secure them? Or will man prepare to use these agencies for aggression and destruction? No one knows. Yet no more important question faces the world.

Since man first roamed the earth, Nature has challenged him to

237

compete with her in supplying the basic necessities of life. Across the centuries, he has met the challenge to only a small degree. When, through science, man creates an ever-increasing abundance of food, clothing, and shelter, he will have gained new triumphs over famine, poverty, and disease. He will reduce the causes of war and diminish the areas of conflict. Prosperous nations, as General Eisenhower has observed, are not war-hungry, but a hungry nation will seek war in desperation.

As I see it, our great hope for world peace can best be advanced by achieving freedom from want through man's ingenuity in atomic energy, electronics, chemistry, physics, and the other sciences. All around us, Nature inspires and offers the perfect model for science to emulate and duplicate, whether it be an artificial potato or a kernel of wheat, oil, or cotton. Already, by ingeniously producing artificial fibers, man no longer is dependent upon the silkworm or the rubber tree; also, he has plastics for wood and vitamins condensed into tablets. He has produced and harnessed electricity, which as lightning defied him to put electrons to work. He has created artificial gas, and now the sun daily dares him to bottle its tremendous heat for use at will. With that revolutionary accomplishment, it would not be necessary to dig for Nature's black diamond, coal. I am sure that raw materials of endless varieties, from ores to paper, from clothing to food, will emerge from the test tube and from out of the air itself.

No reputable prophet would say today that there is nothing more to invent or to discover in science. War has destroyed all such theories and fantasy.

Peace now depends upon recognition by all nations of their individual responsibilities to prevent war. They must foster the *will to peace*. But while the world structure of peace is being built and developed, research and scientific preparedness by the United States must go forward through all the agencies of government and industry that have proved in the present war how to work together in the interests of our nation.

The vital role science can play in peace or war for the future calls for careful consideration of its potential influences upon the territorial, economic, social, and political problems which nations seek to solve. If there is to be world security, the voice of science should be heard in the halls where the architects of peace design our future. . . .

[Printed booklet: (Text of article in *The New York Times*)
"Science for Life or Death," by David Sarnoff.]

Science, the Future, and Peace

Address at 40th-anniversary dinner
New York City, September 30, 1946

Radio today appears no less filled with opportunity for growth than it was in the early days. . . . The pace of science has been swift, and the challenge to the new art has been great. That pace will be swifter and the challenge still greater as the future unfolds. . . .

In America, radio has grown rapidly as a great public servant—not only because of freedom to speak and freedom to listen but because of the freedom of science to advance. Science must be free. We can permit no restrictions to be placed upon the scientists' right to question, to experiment, and to think. Because America has held liberty above all else, distinguished men of science have come here to live, to work, and to seek new knowledge. The world has been the benefactor, and science has moved forward. In war, science dares the impossible; it must continue to dare the impossible in peace if a fuller life is to permeate society.

. . . Radio has become one of the world's great social forces; it educates, informs, and entertains. Distance has been annihilated. All people have been brought within the sound of a single voice. A nine-word message has encircled the earth in nine seconds! The face of the moon has felt the ping of a radar pulse and echoed it back in two seconds to revive predictions of interplanetary communications.

The evolution of radio is unending. It has produced television, radar, and a host of other electronic devices and services. We still can foresee so many changes that those who follow us may wonder how we of this generation were satisfied to talk around the world **239** and not to see at the same time. Our descendants will look back upon the radio services of this era and compare them as a candle to the electric light, the horse and buggy to the automobile, the ocean liner to the stratoliner.

**Challenge of the
Atom**

Already, the electron tube responds to our senses of touch, sound, and sight. We shall learn how to make it respond also to our senses of taste and smell. The tireless workers of radio science will produce a radio-mail system that will be inexpensive, secret, and faster than any mail-carrying plane can travel. Portable communication instruments will be developed that will enable an individual to communicate directly and promptly with anyone, anywhere in the world. . . . Science is continually at work to produce new discoveries and new engineering developments. But we must bear in mind that our destiny is linked not alone with advances of technology but also with the further development of society. Unfortunately, new forces are being released by science which threaten to bring an abrupt end to all progress unless they are properly controlled and usefully applied. In radio, we have met the challenge of the electron and have harnessed it. Now we must meet the challenge of the atom, which has split open a new era—the Atomic Age!

. . . Let us not be complacent in the thought that we in America are safe from destruction because we escaped invasion in the war just ended. The Atlantic and the Pacific are no more protection to our country today than is the English Channel to the British Isles. Pilotless planes and rockets flying 6,000 miles an hour in the stratosphere can carry explosives, poisons, or germs halfway around the globe to wipe out entire cities in a deluge of radioactivity, fire, mist, dust, debris, and disease.

. . . What defense can man devise against an unseen enemy waging war in this way? . . . There is only one real defense against war—and that is peace.

. . . Despite the fact that the handiworks of science are at stake, the scientist has little to say about how his discoveries and inventions are to be used. Inherently, he is a man of peace, but the products of his genius are often put to uses far afield from his original thoughts and motives.

If peace is the chosen course, scientists can turn their attention to the development of atomic power for industry and the conquest of disease. We would then hear less of biological warfare and more of new triumphs over diseases that have plagued man across the centuries, destroying him in greater numbers than war itself. The warlike idea that warm ocean currents could be shifted by science to turn fertile lands into deserts might be reversed in peacetime to modify or divert these currents to influence climate so that deserts would become gardens. With the aid of nuclear power plants, desert areas might be transformed into habitable and productive regions.

There is even the possibility that one of man's greatest enigmas —the weather—may someday be controlled. For example, man may learn how to deflect air movements, with consequent changes in weather, and he may discover how to neutralize a storm or detour it from its course.

Automatic radio weather stations in remote places in the polar regions, in deserts, in jungles, and on the seas can collect and broadcast weather data. Already, radar spots a hurricane, peers into its vortex, plots its movement, and photographs it from minute to minute. Radio-controlled and electronically equipped rockets will permit exploration of the upper atmosphere. Within minutes, new electronic computing devices can analyze such information on a global basis.

We may yet have rain or sunshine by pressing radio buttons! When that day comes, we shall need a World Weather Bureau in which global forecasting and control will have to be vested. Here is a poser for the isolationist and a poem for the internationalist!

What is the shape of things to come in the next forty years? The answer is difficult because the yardstick of the past is not always an accurate measure for the future. Most of the predictions of four decades ago fall short of present realities. . . . International broadcasting, undreamed of forty years ago, has taught us that in a science as universal as radio, reality surpasses prophecy. There will be many events and many discoveries to change radically anything that we foresee. An observation which today may seem trivial may be-

Man the Master of His Fate

come of utmost significance in the years ahead. Only a few years ago, the elusive radio echo seemed a scientific fantasy, yet from it came radar when wartime events called for it.

. . . The most difficult problems facing mankind are social and political rather than technical. . . . With courage and vision, we must see to it that there is unceasing exploration not only in the physical sciences but also in the political and social sciences. Only upon these forces can world unity be built and peace be maintained.

Man must learn to control himself as well as the new forces of science. . . . He must think not only of himself but also of his neighbors. He must recognize the fact that modern science has shrunk the world into one neighborhood. Now, more than ever, man must be the master of his fate. The frightening weapons within his grasp may yet prove the prime influence that will move him to concentrate on the problems of peace. But to achieve the blessings of peace, man must bring to these problems also his heart and his soul. . . .

(Printed booklet: "Forty Years in Radio," a compilation of addresses on the occasion of David Sarnoff's fortieth anniversary in the industry.)

Airborne Radio-relay Missile Intercept

Letter to President Harry S. Truman
November 30, 1948

On October 22, 1948, I proposed to the Secretary of Defense the establishment by the armed forces of an airborne transoceanic radio relay system. I stated that in my opinion such a project would enable the armed forces to obtain valuable information in connection with modern developments involving national security and that it holds such promise of important results in that field that I should recommend it for consideration by the government. The Secretary of Defense replied promptly and informed me that he had asked the Joint Chiefs of Staff to furnish him with their views in respect of my proposal. Copies of my letter to the Secretary of Defense and his reply are attached hereto.

Since my proposal of October 22 was made, I have conceived the idea that an airborne radio relay system could serve as a constant watchman to intercept guided missiles that might be traveling in our direction. There is enclosed a brief outline of my idea. The system I have in mind could detect and furnish information about enemy projectiles thousands of miles from our borders. As a result, countermeasures could be taken which would locate and destroy the missiles before they reached the United States.

A successful method of detecting missiles directed at the United States, at a great distance from our borders and with timely information as to their course and possible destination, may constitute one of the greatest aids to our national security in an atomic age.

The purpose of this letter is to bring my idea to your direct attention and to ask for your guidance as to the next step. . . .

Outline of Proposal
for the Use of Airborne Radio Relay Systems
for the Interception of Guided Missiles

The United States may be subject to attack by guided missiles traveling at high speed over long distances from hostile bases. Such missiles may be jet-propelled, may travel at great heights and at extremely high speeds, and may be provided with atomic warheads. If initially launched with sufficient accuracy and maintained on their course by precision devices, they may reach a planned destination with a small margin of error. Alternatively, if provided with signaling equipment by which their position at any time can be determined by the hostile base and if also provided with radio receiving and radio dynamic control equipment by which transmitters at the hostile base can systematically redirect or modify the course of the missile, the error in the landing point may be further minimized. . . .

Inasmuch as countermeasures against an atomic missile which is about to land and explode may be futile, it is clear that the desired solution is the interception and destruction of such missiles long before their arrival in the United States.

Such interception and destruction are obviously dependent in the first place upon the detection of the missiles, the determination of

Guided Missiles—The General Problem

243

their course, and also, preferably, a knowledge of the control signals used by the enemy. The subsequent interception and destruction of the missiles might be accomplished by countermissiles, e.g., of the homing or proximity-fuse type.

It should be recalled that the velocity of a stratospheric missile is of the order of a mile per second. It would accordingly seem essential that such missiles be detected at very considerable distances from the United States, and preferably at several thousand miles distance. In that case, if a system of instant communication of information as to the detection of the missiles can be provided, the better part of an hour would be available to plot their course, to launch countermissiles, and to destroy the enemy missiles at a substantial distance from the borders of the United States.

The essential factors are, therefore, the provision of a communications link and a method of interception. An airborne radio relay system could serve as the communications link. And the use of such a system for the interception of guided missiles could serve to detect the missiles in time.

An Airborne Radio Relay System—In Brief

An airborne radio relay system would provide a constant stream of regularly spaced aircraft, each of which would be a radio relay station. Such aircraft would fly serially in each direction between terminal points and would be spaced about 250 to 300 miles apart. Each plane would be equipped with two transmitters and two receivers. A two-way circuit would thus be established through a single-file series of one-way flights. The two-way communication so obtained would be on microwaves and of the broad-band variety.

Interception of Guided Missiles

In the use of the system for the interception of guided missiles, a radar set would be installed in each plane. Information so picked up could be relayed via the airborne radio relay system to a central control location, where the information would be evaluated. The line of flight of the planes in the system could be set up across the anticipated line of attack by the missiles so as to form an advance radar "fence."

244 In addition to the information collected by the relay planes themselves, signals could be picked up from strategically located long-distance radar intercept stations installed on land bases or picket ships. This information could be sent back by the airborne relay system to any desired central control location.

The relay planes and ground stations could also be equipped with panoramic receivers to pick up guidance signals to missiles, missile-response signals, and other information. This could also be relayed back to the control location for evaluation.

The principal advantage of an airborne radio relay system in the interception of guided missiles is that such a system would make it possible to launch countermeasures against guided missiles which could destroy them at great distances from the United States. It may be possible to accomplish this in the stratosphere, where the effects of an atomic explosion and its radioactive by-products may be minimized.

Destruction of Intercepted Missiles

Aircraft flying at a height of 5 or 6 miles might cover a detection volume roughly hemispherical in shape and of a radius in excess of 200 miles. The range in an upward direction, into the stratosphere, is less well known at this time. It may be that electric disturbances of cosmic origin will be found to limit the stratospheric range (upward) to 50 or 100 miles. It is also possible that the various ionized layers in the atmosphere may interfere with radar detection into the stratosphere, though appropriate selection of the radar-carrier frequency may avoid these difficulties. It is also conceivable, though unlikely, that false or erratic signals may, on occasion, be derived from large meteors. The number of these is, however, limited, and serious difficulty on this score seems unlikely.

Screen Coverage by Airborne Radio Relay Circuits

The wide communication band available in the relay system could be divided into many channels, either by time-division or by frequency-division multiplex, and these used for various purposes as required. For example, one "special channel" could be assigned to each plane in the relay chain, and it could send back all information it picks up, as well as information as to its own location, course, speed, altitude, etc., on this one channel.

Multichannel Use

Mobility. Because of the mobility of aircraft, an airborne radio relay system could be quickly moved to other locations. It is not necessary, of course, to have the control location at one end of the line. The line might be in the form of a T, with the advance "fence" across the top and the control location and base of operations at the bottom of the T. It could be set up in any other form at will—for example, as a triangle. The flexibility of the system is one of its advantages.

Serving commerce. Another important advantage of the system is the fact that the planes used could be . . . engaged in actual transport and other operations. The airborne radio relay system carried by these planes could be serving the uses of commerce in furnishing television, telephone, and telegraph channels for normal commercial operations and weather information to the Meteorological Service.

Secrecy. From the standpoint of secrecy and national security, such a system would have the further advantage that the enemy need not necessarily know of the incident, although very important, military significance of the aircraft, which would appear to be engaged only in transport or commercial operations. Thus the system could be worldwide in scope and serve important uses in addition to its military function.

(Copy of letter and outline of proposal in bound volume: *Correspondence between President Harry S. Truman and David Sarnoff, 1945–1958;* David Sarnoff Library, Princeton, N.J.)

Impressions of Postwar Europe

Statement on return from Europe
August 13, 1951

Mrs. Sarnoff and I were abroad two months and visited England, France, Italy, and Switzerland.

While there, I met and discussed current problems with Mr.
Winston Churchill, with General Eisenhower, and with leaders in

government, finance, and industry, as well as with wage earners, farmers, housewives, shopkeepers, and others.

In general, my impressions are that, with the help of the Marshall Plan, the free countries of Europe have made much progress with their problems of rehabilitation. But they have not yet achieved political, financial, economic, and social stability. . . .

While there is an awareness in Europe of the Russian menace, nevertheless there is an apparent lethargy about rearmament and a good deal of fatalistic thinking about the future.

In some countries, the domestic problems of higher costs of living, low wages, inadequate housing, and the poor living standards of the masses combine to distract the attention of the people from the greater danger of losing their freedom and their future through Communist aggression from the outside or its infiltration from the inside.

America can help, but it cannot solve the major domestic problems of the European countries. This is a long-term job they must do for themselves. But we must continue our substantial aid in men, money, and materials—at least during the next two critical years—while the rearmament program is under way. To attain our objective, this program must be made effective in Europe as well as at home.

If we leave the Western European countries to their own initiative and resources only, I believe that their defense and rearmament efforts would not be enough to deter Russia from attacking and overrunning them. And this would be fatal for Europe and disastrous for America.

On the other hand, I believe that with the progress being made at home on our program of armament production and military preparedness and with American aid supplied to our allies in the Atlantic Pact, such aggression and domination by Russia can be successfully prevented. Such tangible evidence of our determination to preserve peace will greatly increase the confidence of our European allies in their own ability to deter Communist aggression and to resist it effectively, if it comes.

In other words, I do not believe that a third world war is inevitable, if all of us do what we are able to do to prevent it. This must be our immediate objective.

Beyond this, there must be a long-term objective of a free, strong, and self-sustaining Europe. In my view, this objective will be achieved only through a federated Europe, a United States of Europe. Thus far, traditions, habits, fears, and prejudices have prevented realization of this ideal. But where logic and reason fail, events and realities often impose solutions. For example, today, the project for a European army to serve the common defense is nearing achievement. Only a few years ago, this would have seemed impossible.

I am aware of what adequate aid to our European friends—even during the next two years—involves in the way of sacrifices for all of us in America. But I see no practical alternative if we are determined, as I am certain we are determined, to preserve our own freedom, strengthen our own security, and protect our own way of life.

(Mimeographed text in bound volume: *Correspondence between President Dwight D. Eisenhower and David Sarnoff, 1947–1961*; David Sarnoff Library, Princeton, N.J.)

SCIENCE AND
TECHNOLOGY IN THE SPACE AGE

In the two decades following World War II, greater progress was made in science and technology than in all the thousands of years of man's history. RCA, with Sarnoff at its head, has played a leading role in this astonishing drama of exploration and intellectual adventure. It has contributed to almost every space project the United States has undertaken. Space vehicles designed and built by RCA are orbiting the earth. The television systems which provided the close-up photographs of the moon in the Ranger shots were RCA equipment. RCA microwave installations link space-communications satellites with the earth. RCA computers are integral parts of the complex control systems that make these projects possible. In other areas, solid-state lasers, a new tool in many fields of electronic development, are being marketed by RCA. A wide variety of new applications for television in the fields of biology, medicine, and education have been developed in the RCA Laboratories. Sarnoff's "visions" are thus no idle dreams; he speaks with probably as much information about the current state of progress in electronics as any man in America.

Editor's Note

A Request for Three Presents

Remarks at 45th-anniversary ceremony
naming the RCA Laboratories as the
David Sarnoff Research Center
Princeton, N.J., September 27, 1951

As you know, it is not regarded as improper, in the intimacy of one's own family, to make a suggestion occasionally or to throw out a friendly hint about the kind of a present you would like for your birthday or your anniversary.

. . . I would like to ask . . . the research men, the scientists,   **249** the physicists, and the engineers of RCA for three presents that I wish you would give me sometime between now and my fiftieth anniversary in radio. . . .

I should like to have you invent an electronic amplifier of light that will do for television what the amplifier of sound does for radio broadcasting. Such an amplifier of light would provide brighter pictures for television which could be projected in the home or the theater on a screen of any desired size. An amplifier of sound gave radio a loudspeaker, and an amplifier of light would give television a "big-looker."

A true photoamplifier that could produce bigger and brighter pictures in fine detail would greatly advance television in the home. It is also needed for theaters and for industrial purposes. The presently known optical systems cannot accomplish it. We can, of course, enlarge pictures optically, but in the process, light is lost and the pictures become dimmer instead of brighter. What is needed is a true amplifier of light itself. . . .

Another present I would ask from you also relates to television. I would like to have you invent a television-picture recorder that would record the video signals of television on an inexpensive tape, just as music and speech are now recorded on a phonograph disk or tape. Such recorded television pictures could be reproduced in the home or theater or elsewhere at any time. I would call it a "Videograph." . . .

In contrast with present kinescope recordings on film, the instantaneous recording of the actual television-picture signals on tape would be more economical, would save time in processing, and would simplify certain problems of distribution. Also, it would solve the national time-zone problems in telecasting. Any number of copies of such tapes could be made instantaneously, and copies could be preserved for historic reference or other use. The Videograph would be a new instrument that could reproduce television programs from tape at any time, in the home or elsewhere, in much the same way as the present phonograph reproduces the music you want when you want it. . . .

250 The third present I would like to have you invent is an electronic air conditioner for the home that would operate with tubes, or possibly through the action of electrons in solids, and without moving parts. It should be small, noiseless, and inexpensive, and it should fit into any size room. I would name this device "Electronair."

Perhaps you may feel that this item is a little out of your line, but I am sure you will agree that, if we can create a new product that will serve a useful purpose, it is not foreign to our activities. And a really good electronic air conditioner for the home would be a very useful product indeed.

I realize that such a device does not exist at the present time. However, generally speaking, anything that the human mind can conceive can ultimately be produced. . . .

The three presents I have immodestly asked you for are essential inventions for which there is a basic public need. They would expand existing industries and create new ones. . . .

Naturally, I look to the scientists and engineers of RCA to be first in solving these problems. But it is in the American spirit of competition under the private-enterprise system that I call attention, publicly, to the need for these inventions. Whether it be the lone inventor in the attic or the scientists in competing industrial laboratories who will produce these inventions, the results will spell new opportunities for service and progress for all. . . .

In RCA, we do not fear or resist change. The ghost of obsolescence that some folks see stalking around the corner of their industry does not frighten us. To those who believe, as we do, in research, invention, and pioneering, obsolescence often means progress rather than decay. Instead of a wicked ghost that threatens extinction, we see a beneficent wraith, whose proddings stimulate opportunity, advance prosperity, and raise the standards of living.

Only as we make yesterday's devices obsolete do we have the opportunity for replacing them with new and better devices tomorrow. In our organization, I have no fear of anything you can make obsolete. . . .

Let the Chairman and the President and the commercial vice-presidents of the Corporation worry about obsolescence. You keep on researching and inventing. Their job is to develop and fit the new

251

SCIENCE,
TECHNOLOGY,
AND HUMAN
AFFAIRS

products and the new services you create into the stream of public use.

Go on and research, discover, and invent to your heart's content. Pitch your mental tents in the field of imagination. . . .

(Printed booklet: "Commemorating David Sarnoff's 45 Years of Service in Radio. . . .")

Vladimir Zworykin, Television, and Science

Remarks at dinner honoring Dr. Vladimir K. Zworykin
David Sarnoff Research Center, Princeton, N.J., September 18, 1954

I should like to say a few words about my friend and colleague, Vladimir Zworykin, as a man and as a scientist.

As a man, I would characterize him, first, as a dreamer—but a dreamer who dreams of practical things. The more I have lived in the world of science and technology, the more I have become convinced that the really practical men in this field are the dreamers. They have to dream first, before reality can translate their dreams into practical results. Dr. Zworykin is that kind of a dreamer. After all, dreaming about television and the electron microscope and about instrumentalities of that nature calls for more than dreaming in a vacuum.

Salesman? . . . He's the greatest salesman I have ever known. . . .

Twenty-seven or twenty-eight years ago—when I first met this young man, Vladimir Zworykin—he told me about a cathode-ray tube that he envisaged, what it could do in television, and the great hope he had for it. About that time, technicians were having a "little difference" of view—a difference about a mechanical and an electronic method of doing the television job. Then, the argument was about black-and-white television. But, you will recall, the same little difference was repeated only recently, but more loudly, in color television. And the final decision, in both cases, was the same. The electronic method prevailed.

252

I confess that I understood little of Zworykin's first description of the tube, but I was greatly impressed with the man. So I asked him, "Assuming all you say is so, what would it cost the Radio Corporation of America to translate your ideas into practice? How much money would we have to spend before we could have a practical television system?" He took a good look at me, drew a deep breath, and answered confidently, "I think about $100,000 would do it."

Well, I felt a practical television system was certainly worth $100,000, so I fell for Zworykin's persuasiveness. How near right he was can best be understood when I tell you that before the Radio Corporation of America produced and sold the first commercial television receiver, we had spent $50 million! . . .

Vladimir Zworykin not only dreams, he also thinks. He is a thinker who thinks ahead of his time. . . . But we are living at a time when events are moving so rapidly that often they move faster than men think. . . .

Vladimir Zworykin is also a worker. And he is a worker of extraordinary character. I have seldom heard Zworykin discuss his work of yesterday or today. He always talks about tomorrow and the day after tomorrow. He is genuinely more interested in the job to be done than in the job that was done. I have never found him wasting much time in discussing achievements or accomplishments of the past. It is the dream, the imagination, of what is ahead that always occupies his mind, stimulates the expression of his thoughts, and inspires those around him. . . .

Perhaps it is not amiss to mention at this point the circumstances which best enable a scientist to work and to express the forces within him. For I am sure that Dr. Zworykin and his associates—especially those who worked with him in his earlier days across the seas—will agree that the opportunity to express the forces with which a man may be endowed depends much upon his environment. These very men, with all their genius, did not have the opportunity to express their talents in the environment of their native land.

But Zworykin found that opportunity in America. I think we may well reflect upon the important contribution which freedom makes to the scientist and the creative worker. Nowhere in the world is that freedom to be found in such measure as it exists in America.

When you add to the genius of Zworykin the freedom and the opportunities provided by America, you really nourish the divine spirit and ignite the divine spark of achievement.

Zworykin was also stimulated, as I am sure he will agree, by the scientific spirit which he found to pervade the men and women who constitute the RCA family. For we are an organization founded upon science. We make our living by the tiniest thing known in the world, the tiniest particle that scientists know about—the electron. And with that tiny electron, we are able to do big things and to serve the needs of mankind.

The electron has lifted RCA from a small company with a humble beginning and with very modest means to the role of leader in a great industry. . . . It was that scientific spirit and the enthusiasm and cooperation of the colleagues who have worked alongside Dr. Zworykin during the past quarter of a century that combined to produce the results of which we are so proud. . . .

A scientist like Vladimir Zworykin never retires. He does not even fade away. What he does is to acquire more time for thought, which leads to bigger ideas, greater discoveries, and more important inventions. For when the imagination and the creative instinct of the true scientist go, he generally goes with them—perhaps to a place of even greater knowledge.

A scientist operates upstairs. How high he reaches depends upon his imagination. But he never has hours, and he never has mileposts. He never has periods or semicolons or even commas in his poetry. He simply flows along like the waves of the ocean. . . .

Now, since we are in the midst of scientists and in this home of science, perhaps it may not be amiss to say a word or two about the relationship of scientists to the rest of us ordinary mortals.

I think there is something scientists, too, must know, and if they don't, they must learn it—and most of all, they must recognize it. One thing that they must recognize, it seems to me, is that the physical sciences alone are not enough to make this a better world in which to live. Important as they are, they are not enough. There are other aspects of life that must go hand in hand with their achievements in science.

254 The scientist must understand and appreciate the human problems of society and the impact of his discoveries and inventions upon slow-moving humanity. It is all very well for the scientist to sit back and say, "Well, I have forged this knife for you. Whether you use it with the skill of a surgeon and save a life or whether you use it with the abandon of an assassin and destroy a life is your problem, and there is nothing I can do about it." That is not enough.

I am not ready to place upon the scientist all the responsibility for human nature. But as a scientist must constantly seek the truth, I plead with him to recognize the truth about humanity as well. He must appreciate the distinctions between the particles of science and the organisms of human beings. After all, once you have learned how an electron, a neutron, a proton, or a meson behaves, you have learned that, in their own category, they all behave the same way. If you organize them in the same fashion, arrange them in the same manner, they will respond in the same way.

But there are no two human beings whose behavior is exactly the same. Atoms are alike—but Adams are different. And so the statesman, the politician, the businessman, or the executive, who has to deal with independent Adams all of the time, has not the control over his human associates that the scientist who deals with atoms has over his physical slaves. Therefore, each must learn to respect the capabilities and the limitations of the other. We now live in an Atomic and Electronic Age, which creates problems for society at a speed much faster than the ordinary human being is able to assimilate.

All of us are creatures of habit, and you know how difficult it is to change a habit. When we talk about controlling other people, how well do we do the job of controlling ourselves? Poorly, I think all of us will agree. But how much more difficult it is to control a hundred million or a billion people!

With the rapid march of science and its revolutionary impact upon society, the time has come for the scientist to appreciate the problem of the layman and for the layman to cooperate with the scientist. Only by working together, only by being sympathetic and cooperative with each other's problems, only by having a regard and respect for the other man's field can we possibly achieve the common goal.

255

If we deal in an understanding and helpful fashion with each other, we do not need mechanical instruments to measure our efforts. Our conscience is our guide. . . .

(Mimeographed text: David Sarnoff Library, Princeton, N.J.)

Science, Competition, and Art

Address before American Institute of Electrical Engineers
New York City, January 31, 1955

Competition can be as stimulating in research as in manufacturing and merchandising. As members of a profession deeply concerned with scientific research and pioneering development, you are well aware that the number of people willing to risk their money in research and pioneering is very small compared with those who are ready to risk their capital in established enterprises operating profitably.

In television and in other instances—where the information is not "classified" and does not involve our national security—RCA has continually made progress reports and released information that enabled others not only to catch up but at times even to move ahead of us. We welcome competition. It spurs our own activities and increases the possibilities of earlier achievement of desired results.

For instance, our faith and persistence in pioneering television—first, black and white, and then color—and our encouragement to others to get into the field led to its present state of development, which otherwise the American public might not have enjoyed for another ten years.

Whether we succeed in completing an invention before others whom we stimulate to work along similar lines may do so is not as important as bringing a new product or a new service into existence and use. In helping industry to grow and prosper, we believe that we contribute to the public benefit and, in the long run, to our own as well. If an organization is to progress, it must not stand in fear of obsolescence or competition.

256 Electronics, in the race to achieve new triumphs, is run on the

big track of Time, on which there is room for all who would compete. There is no finish line.

. . . The day is here when the engineer and the artist should
join forces and seek to understand the terminology and problems of
each other in order to advance together.

If you will form an intellectual camaraderie and arrive at a common language with your colleagues in the arts so that they can learn
how to make full use of science and technology, you will see the fruits
of your genius bloom in the vineyards of the cultural arts.

The liberal arts should not shrug off advances in science and
technology as too technical to understand. And engineers, at their
end, should not regard music and the arts as outside their natural
domain.

For more than a quarter of a century, the entertainment arts have
felt the magic touch of electronics. As a result, music, drama, motion
pictures, the phonograph, and even journalism have taken on new
dimensions. New interest has been created in them, and their audiences have multiplied from thousands to millions.

. . . For the good of America and the world in general, the arts
and sciences are challenged to work together and bring their respective talents and skills into focus. In effect, men of science and the
arts must play on the same team and understand each other's signals
so they can score together.

(Printed, illustrated booklet: "New Developments in Elec-
tronics," an address by David Sarnoff.)

SCIENTISTS AND SCIENCE TEACHING—
THREE STATEMENTS, 1956–1962

A National Educational Reserve

Address at Forrestal memorial dinner
National Security Industrial Association
Washington, D.C., January 26, 1956

In all fields affecting our national security, research and engineering are of surpassing importance. There is no substitute for brains or for practical training in a technical age. Our safety and our industrial strength rest upon our success in expanding the nation's reservoir of physicists and scientists, trained engineers and technicians. Our economy and national security alike will suffer seriously unless we solve this problem promptly and vigorously.

Science and technology are the very hallmarks of American civilization. It comes as a shock, therefore, to be told that Soviet Russia is turning out engineers at a higher rate than we are.

. . . One reason for this, of course, is that a police state can compel its youth to enter careers most useful to the state. It conscripts brains even as it conscripts bodies. . . .

A lack of qualified teachers has developed at grade levels for subjects like physics, chemistry, and mathematics. In some areas—New York City, for example—teacher recruitment in mathematics and the sciences is causing considerable concern. Certainly, the fact that teachers are underpaid, that the ablest of them can do better in private jobs, is an important factor in the present situation and one that needs to be remedied. But we cannot wait for long-term remedies. Unless the immediate lack is met quickly, it will show up a few years hence in an even more critical shortage of trained personnel.

In the presence of so many leaders of industry, I wish to offer a suggestion. It may not solve the problem completely, but it could go a long way toward a solution.

I propose the establishment of a "National Educational Reserve," comprising qualified teachers in mathematics, physics, chemistry, engineering, and related subjects, to be drawn from the technological ranks of industry. I have in mind the release—and with full pay for at least a year—of a reasonable number of men and women for teaching assignments in their local schools. This unique Reserve could also mobilize those who have reached the retirement age in the military services and in industry but whose knowledge and experience would make them inspiring teachers. In addition, it could include qualified people willing to volunteer their services to teach in night schools without giving up their industry jobs.

The number of teachers recruited from any single organization would be too small to entail hardship for any one—but the total number comprising the corps could be drawn from such an extensive list of organizations that it would be large enough to give new impetus to teaching of the sciences in our school system. This would be especially true at the high school level, which is our present major bottleneck.

This Educational Reserve would, of course, have to be strictly an interim program—let's say for five years—to help meet an immediate situation. Moreover, whether the initiative is taken by industry or government, the plan itself would naturally be drawn with the consent and cooperation of school authorities, who would prescribe the courses and regulate the instruction.

In some degree, such a plan would amount to the restitution by business of personnel it has siphoned off from the school system. Men and women who normally would have become teachers of the sciences have instead gone into industry, where the rewards are more enticing. I think it is fair to say, in fact, that in the current crisis, industry has an obligation to help develop this kind of Educational Reserve.

Obligation aside, industry would be well advised as a matter of self-interest to help replenish the reservoir of trained men and women by stimulating relevant studies at the lower educational levels. Industry will need more and more technically trained people for its own expanding operations.

Because of their practical experience, teachers in the Educational Reserve Corps would bring the breath of living reality into the classroom. They would help restore the sense of adventure to technical **259** careers and inspire many an able and imaginative student to follow the scientific and technological disciplines into the college years. Enthusiasm is contagious.

To make the project attractive, teachers in the Reserve Corps should be given recognition and status through membership in an organization somewhat similar to the various military Reserves. It should be set up on a national basis, perhaps created by an Act of Congress.

I have presented this concept in broad terms. There are many details to be discussed and formulated by educators, representatives of industry, and interested official agencies. But I trust that the basic idea has enough potential merit to justify closer examination.

(Printed booklet: "Our National Security," by David Sarnoff.)

A Crash Program to Beat the Teacher Shortage

Interview with David Sarnoff in *This Week*
Issue of Jan. 28, 1962

An urgent manhunt is going on today in the nation's schools. The search is for teachers trained in mathematics and in science, and your child's future and the future of this nation hang on its outcome.

U.S. welfare and security depend on our technical achievement. Our children today must be inspired to become the scientists of tomorrow. But we don't have enough teachers to go around . . . and the greatest shortage is in science and in math. . . .

The tragedy is that your child may have an important science potential that he never gets to realize because there is no science-trained teacher to awaken his spirit of inquiry.

We've got to do something, fast.

I would like to make a proposal. I suggest that scientists and engineers in industry and in government volunteer an hour or two a day to teaching in nearby schools and that their employers grant them time off to do the job with no loss in pay.

260 No organization would be asked to release more than one man from any research unit, and he would not be expected to serve more than one academic year.

If the program I suggest is adopted generally, the Radio Corporation of America would gladly participate in it. I know that RCA scientists and engineers around the country would eagerly volunteer. And I would do everything in my power to clear the way. Such a program would be the best investment any company or research organization could make to help insure for themselves and for America a future supply of scientific manpower.

There is one facet of the plan that I think offers an especially exciting prospect: the presence of a scientist in the classroom. Can you imagine anything more intriguing for an aspiring young biologist or chemist than to spend an hour a day with a working scientist? Such a person can make the textbook spring to life for young students.

Working scientists are already helping out in some classrooms. Many schools invite experts in for occasional lectures on specific subjects or ask them to meet after hours with scientific clubs.

It's ironic that many schools suffering from science-teacher shortages are located in areas swarming with skilled technicians. . . . Though there are sections of the country where my plan wouldn't work simply because the scientific manpower isn't available, I say that where it is available, the schools should try to tap it. . . .

This proposal for easing the shortage of science and math teachers requires no complicated organization, no coordinated national effort, no large sum of money. . . .

This plan is an emergency measure. But we're faced with an emergency. Of course, no responsible school official would relax his search for permanent, fully qualified instructors. But we must draw on every national resource to accomplish the scientific breakthroughs needed to preserve our way of life. Such technical advance begins with a spark of curiosity in a child's eye. Volunteer teachers from business and government research laboratories can generate this spark and fan it into great human achievements.

(Reprint of article in *This Week*; David Sarnoff Library, Princeton, N.J.)

New Landmarks in Education

Remarks at the announcement of the
David Sarnoff Industry-Science Teaching Program
New York City Board of Education, September 27, 1962

Today, we are embarking together on an exploration that is intended to establish new landmarks in the fields of science and education. With your own teachers as your guides and with the scientists of RCA to supplement their efforts, you have been selected to participate in a pioneering journey that can produce great rewards for our country, for our educational system, for private industry, and for you personally.

You are about to cross the frontier of science, which is the exciting frontier of twentieth century life. It possesses all the characteristics of romance and adventure, of conquest and triumph over the unknown, that were associated with the physical frontiers overcome by our forefathers. It offers for young men and women today the best possible visa to a useful and rewarding life. . . .

It does not require the rare mentality of a genius to produce a scientist. It requires only an alert and eager mind—a mind such as you youngsters possess—to absorb the technical knowledge that is the springboard to scientific innovation. If you are exposed to that knowledge when you are young, it can become your deposit on a lifetime of exciting and useful service to your country and the world.

That, very simply, is why I began in 1956 to propose a program such as the one we are launching on a test basis today.

The RCA scientists and engineers who will be assisting your science teachers this year already are leading explorations across new frontiers of knowledge. They come from the space development laboratory which produced the Tiros weather satellites and the television instruments for exploration of the moon. Others are at work converting the energy of the sun, the atom, and various forms of chemical fuel into almost limitless sources of power for the benefit of mankind.

You will learn of advanced developments in acoustics—where, for example, a typewriter taps out words that are spoken to it. Radar and microwave, computers, incredibly tiny solid-state devices, space communications—these are some of the subjects you will hear about from men and women actively working in these fields. I might add that much of what they have to say will not be found in textbooks because science has outdistanced the printing press.

In this voluntary work, the RCA scientists will be making a contribution to education and an investment in the future of American industry. For that future hinges on the ability of industry to recruit thousands of talented young men and women as scientists, engineers, and technicians for our laboratories and plants. The demand for them is never-ending, and it must be renewed on an increasing scale with each succeeding generation. The primary source of supply is the nation's school systems.

Our scientists, working with your teachers, will also be contributing to a broad national goal. It was defined by President Kennedy earlier this year when he said: "If this nation is to grow in wisdom and strength, then every able high school graduate should have the opportunity to develop his talents." The President properly emphasized opportunity at the high school level, for this is the critical time of career choice. The scientist of tomorrow is being formed in the high school of today. . . .

Even if you decide after our pilot program not to enter science or engineering, you will still be in a better position to fulfill your duties as citizens. Much of the basis for tomorrow's world is taking shape in the laboratory and on the drafting board. To be ignorant of science in our present environment is to be ignorant of the force which is molding our destinies. . . .

It is in the self-starting American tradition that a private industry and a public school system have come together on a voluntary basis to help seek the solution of a grave national problem. The plan, as I have presented it to your school officials, will require no extra appropriation of public funds at the local, state, or national level. The RCA scientists who will instruct you are volunteering their time and preparing their own demonstration equipment with funds provided by the company. I am sure that thousands of other equally devoted men and women of science would eagerly volunteer for similar work, supported by their industrial employers, if the opportunity were available to them. . . .

The sun, moon, and stars, the earth and everything that grows upon or lies within it, the atom and the electron—these have been with us since immemorial time. Yet we have known so very little about them. Now, one by one, we are crossing the frontiers, breaking through the barriers of mystery and ignorance. No generation of young people has ever faced more new worlds to conquer than yours. . . .

(Mimeographed text: David Sarnoff Library, Princeton, N.J.)

Science, Technology, and Society

Address at Golden-anniversary dinner
New York City, September 30, 1956

However impressive the events that have filled the last fifty years, or even the last century, I am convinced that they will be eclipsed by the events of the next twenty years. . . . Let us consider twenty major developments likely to affect all of us within the next twenty years. I need hardly warn, of course, that there are many imponderables— especially with regard to the social and political prospects—that may retard some of my expectations. On the other hand, they may advance them. To a large extent this will depend on the courage, character, and competence of our leadership. But those are the hazards of prophecy. . . .

1. *Nuclear energy.* We will have learned to extract atomic fuel from relatively inexpensive materials, thus making this power both plentiful and economical. Nuclear energy will be brought to a practical state of peacetime usefulness, not only for industry but for planes, ships, trains, and automobiles. *Direct* conversion of atomic energy into electricity—a principle already demonstrated experimentally by RCA—will be a fact. Atomic batteries, based on low-cost waste products from nuclear reactors and operating for many years without recharging, will supply energy for industry and for the home.

264 2. *Solar energy.* The energy of sun rays will be effectively harnessed and in worldwide use. It will prove of special value to tropical and semitropical parts of the globe, where the sun's energy is immense but where underdeveloped nations cannot afford fully to utilize present-day fuels and power sources.

3. *Communications*. Television, in full colors, will be completely global, so that man will be able not only to speak and hear all around this planet but to see the entire world in natural colors. Individuals will be able to hold private two-way conversations and see each other as they talk, regardless of the distances separating them. Moreover, the beginnings will have been made in the automatic and instantaneous translation of languages, enabling people to understand one another at once across the barriers of Babel.

4. *Transportation*. Jet-propulsion and rocket-type vehicles, using nuclear fuels, will travel at speeds as high as 5,000 miles an hour with greater safety and comfort than in today's aircraft. The world's leading cities will be only hours apart, many of them virtually within commuting distance. Inexpensive personal planes, flivvers of the skies, will fill the air. Automatically piloted aircraft for passenger service will be far advanced. Guided missiles will transport mail and other freight over vast distances, including oceans.

5. *Automation*. Already well launched, automation will reach a crescendo under the impact of cheap and abundant power. It will increase production, decrease costs, and make more goods and services available to more people. The transition will create problems of adjustment, but ultimately it will free millions of people from arduous and hazardous work. It will increase employment, reduce hours of labor, and increase leisure.

6. *Materials*. Chemistry will make spectacular strides in providing ever new materials tailored to meet almost any specifications man can imagine. A tremendous array of new plastics, ceramics, lubricants, and categories of substances that as yet have no name will become available for personal and industrial uses.

7. *Electronic light*. Electroluminescence, or "cold light," now emerging from the research laboratories, will bring into being startling new types of illumination. It will change the appearance

265

of our factories, streets, stores, highways, and homes. Providing light without heat and almost without shadow, its glow will be subject to easy control for volume and color nuances to suit any taste or decor. Being light without glare, it will eliminate many of the perils of night driving and flying. It will also give us brighter and bigger TV pictures and will ultimately replace the TV tube altogether with a thin, flat-surface screen that will be hung like a picture on the wall.

8. *Computers.* The era of electronic computers, already begun, will reach fruition. Recording and accounting will be taken over by robots, freeing for other work the great majority of the 9 million Americans now engaged in clerical tasks. Business procedures, industrial operations, and fiscal data will be gathered and analyzed automatically. New products will, for the most part, have their performance predicted by computers, removing the need for building actual working models. High-speed writing and reading will be as familiar as high-speed arithmetic is today.

9. *Food.* Striking developments in irrigation and flood control, more efficient use of solar energy, the electronic acceleration of germination and growth, as well as new chemical and biological discoveries, will greatly expand mankind's food resources. At the same time, the oceans will be efficiently "farmed" for nutritive products. Thus all the food needed by all the people of the world will become available, despite the fact that the population will continue to grow. These developments will enable famine to be eliminated in all parts of the world.

10. *Health.* The close ties now developing between biology, chemistry, and physics, applying the new tools of electronics and atomics, will bring an avalanche of improvements in preventive medicine, diagnosis, and treatment of human ills. Biochemistry will furnish disease-controlling and health-sustaining drugs at an accelerated rate, especially in meeting the physical problems of old age. Man's life-span will be further extended, probably within hailing distance of the century mark.

11. *The home.* The housewife's dream of an all-automatic home will be realized. The day's chores in the home will be prescheduled, with each of the tasks performed electronically. The tem-

perature, humidity, and velocity of the air in each part of the
home will be automatically kept at the desired levels day and
night, and the air will be purged of bacteria and other contam-
inating matter. Electronic appliances will do the cooking and the
dishwashing and will dispose of waste. Fortunately, we shall continue to do our own eating.

12. *Climate.* Not only will the prediction of weather for months
and even years ahead be perfected, but major steps will have been
taken to make and control weather as desired. Ports now ice-
bound will be unfrozen, and icebergs rapidly melted. Progress
will have been made in dissipating storms even of hurricane intensity or in diverting them from a destructive course.

Thus far I have dealt mainly with technological progress. It is an
area where we can tread with some assurance. The shape of things to
come already can be discerned in the research laboratories at home
and abroad.

I wish I had the same degree of assurance with respect to developments in the social and political areas, where the most unpredictable force of all—human conduct—tells the story. But social sciences
are deeply affected by changes in physical environment since environment greatly influences human conduct.

So I venture to go on with the listing, perhaps in an overly optimistic spirit, yet with faith in the ultimate good sense of our race of
men.

13. *Communism.* Within the next twenty years, Soviet Communism will collapse under the weight of its economic fallacies, its
political follies, and the pressures of a restive, discontented population. These pressures will increase with the rise and spread of
education amongst the Russian people. Practical ways and means
will be found by the free world to pierce the Iron Curtain and
bring home to the Russian people the facts and the truth. The
Soviet empire will fall apart as one satellite after another attains
its own liberation. The Communist hierarchy will destroy itself
by internal struggles for power and will be displaced by a military
dictatorship, which, in turn, will give way to representative
government.

267

14. *People's capitalism.* The prestige of the Marxist solution of social problems will decline as its limitations and errors become increasingly apparent in a rapidly developing world of technology. It will be more generally realized that centralized state economy is incompatible with human freedom. As socialism is stripped of its popular appeals, the dynamics of a people's capitalism within a democratic framework will be intensified.

15. *Living standards.* The sum of the technical developments already listed will usher in an era of relative economic abundance. Slowly but surely, the waters of wretchedness now covering so much of the earth will recede, and levels of well-being without past parallel will be attained all over the world. The most pressing problems will not be the use of labor but the intelligent and beneficent use of leisure.

16. *Education.* As a by-product of economic progress and expanding leisure, man will enter upon a period of universal education. Not only will general levels of knowledge rise, but the intellectual climate will be favorable to development of special talents and individual genius. Highly geared technology will put a premium on brains: the ever more skilled scientists, engineers, designers, technicians, and others. This mounting demand for mental competence will tend to enlarge educational facilities and promote the arts and sciences.

17. *Entertainment.* Every form of art and every type of entertainment will be readily accessible in the home. Talent—both live and recorded—will be available by television, radio, the phonograph, and electronic photography. The opportunities for creative and interpretive talents will be greater than ever before. The range and variety of programs will embrace everything created by the human mind.

18. *Government.* Because of unprecedented access to information, public opinion will be a more decisive element in the political life of nations. Prevailing sentiment on any issue will be quickly and accurately registered by electronic means. Government and people will thus be brought into closer correlation, so that popular government and democratic processes will tend to become more and more effective.

19. *War.* Universal communications and speedy transportation will shrink the world to a neighborhood. Technological developments in weapons of mass destruction will leave no doubt that the choice is between survival and annihilation. All nations will find it imperative to develop and adopt practical means for disarmament based on effective inspection, control, and enforcement. War as an instrument of international policy will be outlawed.

20. *Science and religion.* As a reaction against current cynicism and materialism, there will be an upsurge of spiritual vitality. The gradual elimination of physical hungers will deepen the more elemental hunger for faith and salvation, for age-old values beyond the material and temporal, that gnaws at the heart of man. . . .

(Book: *Radio and David Sarnoff*, by E. E. Bucher, part 38, pp. 5734–5864. Printed booklet: "David Sarnoff Golden Anniversary.")

Electronics and Biology

Address before World Congress of Gastroenterology
Washington, D.C., May 25, 1958

The impact of electronics upon biology, medicine, and related disciplines is far greater than many practitioners, let alone the public, realize. A great array of electronic tools and techniques is today in use or available for use by physician and surgeon, anesthetist and radiologist. And even more promising devices are now in various stages of gestation in electronic laboratories.

. . . Television, for instance, is thought of primarily as a mass medium of information and entertainment. Yet closed-circuit TV, both in black and white and in color, is becoming a vital adjunct to medical education. Electronic computers, to cite another instance, are thought of primarily in relation to industry and business. Yet their capabilities are multiplying the effectiveness of every man and woman engaged in biological and medical research.

The researcher in biology and the diagnostician in medicine depend largely upon the tools at their disposal. They need electrome-

SCIENCE,
TECHNOLOGY,
AND SOCIETY

269

chanical, electrochemical, and electrothermal equipment; acoustic devices; high-speed apparatus for measuring, recording, and analyzing data; methods of high magnification. In all these respects, electronics is increasingly at their service.

. . . For example, Dr. Vladimir Zworykin and his colleagues recently have produced a startling instrument that has come to be called a *radio pill*—a miniscule radio transmitter which can actually be swallowed. Because the frequency of its signals is governed by the variations of pressure on the capsule, a receiver outside the body gathers telltale information from inside the stomach.

Without doubt, this boldly conceived device represents a breakthrough in biological research and diagnostics since it is the forerunner of a multitude of coming adaptations. They should enable us to study various conditions in the body with a minimum of surgery and, in some cases, without recourse to surgery. At other times, they will provide the diagnostic data that, when surgery is indicated, will make it more accurate.

The surgeon, in fact, has a particularly large stake in enlisting the electron in his service. The most spectacular development in this area is electronic mechanisms acting as temporary substitute organs in the human body while the natural organ is being worked upon.

Substitute Human Organs

. . . The most dramatic of the substitute organs is the *artificial heart*. Here we have an electrically driven and electronically controlled device which bypasses blood flow around the heart and carries out the normal effects of the heartbeat while maintaining a pace adjusted to the needs of the patient. When one reflects that the blood must not clot within the artificial heart, that temperatures and pressures must be maintained with the utmost precision, it is clear that . . . medical science is stranger than science fiction.

Paralleling the artificial heart, we have the development of an *artificial lung* and an *artificial kidney*, each bypassing the natural organ while it is being examined or repaired, each made possible by electronic sensing and control devices.

. . . In theory, at least, it is conceivable that one day compact electronic substitutes will be provided on a permanent basis to replace organs that have become defective through injury or age.

Artificial kidneys, lungs, and even hearts may then become as familiar as artificial teeth or hearing aids. Indeed, one may imagine a man walking around in apparent good health with several of his organs replaced by the refined electronic substitutes of the future. Admittedly, the idea is fantastic, but as the marvels of electronics unfold, the line between fantasy and fact is ever harder to define.

. . . In the field of orthopedics, electronic methods are not yet at the point of major utility, but important possibilities are in evidence. Electronic apparatus for systematic and automatic exercise of any part of the body—in cases of partial paralysis, for instance—are already far advanced.

More important, electronics promises sensational improvement **The Promises of** of prosthetic devices. At the heart of this promise is the electronic ca- **Electronics** pacity to amplify the minutest muscular efforts and impulses to almost any desired magnitude. The outlook—though as yet only a hope—is for equipment which, when attached to the stumps of an amputated limb or to some other part of the anatomy, will actuate and control movements of an artificial leg, arm, or even fingers with acceptable precision.

For the nearly deaf, the bone-conduction receivers and compact electronic equipment for large audio amplification now in use are being constantly improved, and other expedients under study show encouraging prospects. . . .

Among the most humanly exciting potentials now at the experimental stage are devices that in some measure "see" for the blind. Interesting beginnings have been made, for example, toward electronic detection of obstacles in the path of the blind or sudden changes in the ground or pavement levels. Progress is being registered, too, in electronic equipment for translating ordinary type into audible signals, thus enabling the blind to "read" conventional printed matter.

. . . Anything that the human eye can see can be transmitted by television in true color. . . . The details of an operation or the appearance of a lesion can now be sent to any desired point for examination. Any malfunctioning area can be studied without actually visiting the patient. We can envisage a time when the individual **271** patient, in a hospital or at home, can be viewed and advised by a physician from any distance. Microscopic slides and x-ray pictures can be studied at places remote from their physical location. Any picture in motion—let us say of an operation in progress—can be viewed directly, in normal size or greatly enlarged, at any desired point of reception.

. . . Equally important is the ever-expanding contribution of electronic computers to biological, medical, and related sciences. Every physician, every researcher, every hospital struggles with the burden of rapidly accumulating data requiring classification, analysis, and storage for instant availability for reference or study. An even larger share of that burden is being assumed by modern electronic data-processing equipment, with tremendous economies in time and gains in precision. Electronic performance provides almost instantaneously the kind of statistical and probability findings which would, by conventional methods, have required days or weeks of tedious work.

. . . We can say that the youngest of sciences, electronics, and one of the oldest, biology, are converging. The very complexity of man's structure and its electrochemical aspects point up the natural relationship between these sciences.

Of course, it is dangerous to push affinities and analogies to excess. We must never forget that the stuff of life transcends, in its complexity, the most ambitious inventions man can imagine, let alone construct. Even the most elaborate man-made apparatus is primitive when matched against a living creature. The largest electronic computer, for example, may have 1 million storage elements, whereas the human brain has perhaps a hundred billion cells. . . . Man, in the final analysis, invents nothing that is more than a pale shadow of nature, from which he draws his inspiration and his material.

Yet the new science of cybernetics has shown that somewhat similar controls, feedbacks, and methods of operation prevail in man's electronic handiwork and in man himself. It is too early to judge the ultimate meaning and utility of these affinities. It is premature, too, to speculate in any detail on what the skilled electronic designer may accomplish in the future. Let it suffice for our time that electronics and biology are now treading a common path of inquiry, thrilling in its possibilities.

. . . The time may well come when science will have fully uncovered the nature and functioning of both the energy-packed atom and its combinations on the one hand and the living cell and its aggregations on the other. At that point, knowledge of the nature of life itself—the ultimate unity under the appearance of infinite diversity—may be revealed to us.

(Printed pamphlet: "Electronics and Biology," an address by David Sarnoff.)

The Control of Satellite Weapons

Memorandum to Vice President Richard M. Nixon
June 17, 1960

The swift advance of missile and space technology points toward the technical feasibility within the next few years of weapons systems designed to launch missiles against ground targets from orbits several hundred miles above the earth.

Recently, it has been reported in the press that studies of such weapons systems are now being conducted in this country under government sponsorship. It is logical to assume that similar studies are under way in the Soviet Union. . . .

Furthermore, it is evident that such projects must be explored on the basis of both known and unknown potentials, which may turn out to have vital military significance. So long as the present international situation persists, the potentials of this development must not be overlooked.

There is little doubt that both the Russians and we now have the ability to place in orbit a satellite large enough to carry a weapons system. This might consist of one or more nuclear or germ bombs and the electronic devices for their release from the satellite to targets on the ground. From the standpoint of size and weight, it should be noted that missiles designed for launching downward from a satellite in orbit would not require the large, heavy launching rockets that are needed to lift into space our present long-range missiles. **273**

Furthermore, both the United States and the Soviet Union have demonstrated their ability to develop systems which permit the control and command from the ground of certain basic satellite operations in a manner that could be made applicable to the launching of weapons from a satellite at any given point in its orbit. An example is the Tiros television weather satellite, which is now being programmed from the ground and is taking pictures at any point in its orbit and, upon command, transmitting these pictures to the ground.

While the capability thus exists for launching satellites armed with warheads and for causing the warheads to be released by various means of remote control from the ground, it is not believed that either we or the Russians have solved the problems of accuracy and reliability that such systems require.

Much further development is required to achieve weapon-launching platforms with a reasonable probability that the weapons will be able to hit specific ground targets. It should be noted, however, that extremely rapid progress is being made in navigational and missile-guidance techniques and in electronic computing and data-processing capabilities.

The matter of reliability emphasizes the likelihood that any missile-launching satellite, whether American or Russian, is likely to be a Damoclean sword. Once a satellite is placed in orbit with its store of weapons, those who launched it no longer have the degree of control which they retain while the weapons are held on the ground. Instead, they become dependent upon the long-term reliability and security of a complex system whose components cannot easily be repaired or replaced in case of failure, malfunction, or destruction.

Two serious evils are apparent in this situation. The lesser of these is the loss of the weapons, either through a failure which causes the system to become a dud or through enemy countermeasures resulting in its destruction.

The greater potential evil is the . . . accidental discharge of a warhead through a malfunction in the system. A system failure which caused the release of a warhead over another's territory could touch off a full-scale war, and a similar failure over home territory could cause a major catastrophe. In addition to these perils, dependence upon remote control by signals transmitted from the ground involves the danger that an enemy might seize control of the system by using similar signals and thus gain the power to employ the weapon against those who had launched it.

There is no question that scientific effort should continue to be expended to solve these problems of reliability and security. At the same time, it should be clearly recognized that some residual risks will always remain. The degree of these risks and their possible consequences will have to be soberly evaluated before any decision is made in the future to launch a weapons-carrying satellite.

The foregoing would seem to point up the need for the most careful consideration of these potential and terrifying perils. In any plans for nuclear disarmament, we must recognize the possibility that, as navigation in space develops and improves, warheads may be stored in orbiting satellites, instead of underground, and released by the controlling hand on the ground.

We may find ways to remove the present perils, but we must not ignore those in the making, for we cannot disarm the human mind.

> (Copy of memorandum and covering note in bound volume: *Correspondence between Vice President Richard M. Nixon and David Sarnoff, 1954–1961*; David Sarnoff Library, Princeton, N.J.)

Science, Technology, and National Policy

Memorandum to Vice President Richard M. Nixon
August 10, 1960

Within this generation, to a larger extent than ever before in the history of our free society, the affairs of science and the affairs of nations have become inseparably bound in determining our major public policies at home and abroad.

This is a direct consequence of sweeping and revolutionary advances in science and technology, compressed largely into the few brief years since the end of World War II. Because of these advances, and because of the speed with which they have come upon us, every adult American today lives in a world far different from the one into which he was born.

275

In this new world, old concepts of time and distance have been utterly demolished, problems of military defense and strategy have been enormously complicated, patterns of production and distribution have been vastly expanded, and the door has been opened to man's first venture beyond the limits of the planet to which he has been confined since the dawn of time.

For the first time in human history, it has become possible either to extinguish civilization or to raise all of mankind to unprecedentedly high levels of health, prosperity, and personal freedom.

The age in which we now live thus offers the two extremes of bright promise and dark threat, each of them based equally upon the astonishing powers made available to us within the past two decades by science and technology. Never before have we been challenged so directly and so urgently by the need for learning how to live with what we have created.

A first essential for all responsible citizens under these circumstances is a clear understanding of science and technology as the dominant material forces which shape our environment today and influence all of our planning for the future. . . .

It is questionable whether many of us realize fully the extent to which science and technology . . . have opened new frontiers for the satisfaction of basic human needs and desires. . . .

Because of this accelerated material progress, the average American today enjoys a diet of greater variety and quantity than did his compatriots of only twenty-one years ago; he has a life expectancy of nearly seventy years; he has more goods to buy, more leisure, less routine drudgery in his work; he can travel to any country in the world within hours and can see or hear the world in his home. Throughout his environment, at home and at work, the forces of science and technology exert an influence unprecedented in human history.

This astonishing progress in the brief span of two decades is the result of a vast burgeoning of scientific research and engineering development during and since World War II. Formerly, a scientist who formulated a new theory was unlikely to see its useful application within his lifetime. Today, under the impetus of large-scale research and development programs sponsored by industry, the government, and universities, scientists and engineers work together in teams capable of formulating concepts and carrying them to application within a short time. The scope of our present total effort in science and technology is unparalleled in history.

What needs to be understood is not only the magnitude of this material progress but its unprecedented tempo. Those closest to the world of science have no doubt that the next twenty years will see an even more radical change in our physical environment than that of the last twenty years.

Even if there were no other consideration, the increasing dependence of our own society upon science and technology would therefore demand more widespread public understanding of these forces, to ensure the proper direction of the nation through the years immediately ahead.

A full understanding of the new age involves even more than this. It is evident that science and technology now offer the possibility of raising all of mankind to far higher standards of life. But the way is beset with dangers, which spring jointly from man's technological prowess and from his apparent failure to comprehend the change which it has brought to his world.

Consider the advances in medicine and public health, for instance. These have added years to human life expectancy, but they have at the same time contributed to the explosive growth of world population. Our planet has been shrunk by improved transport and communications, but this has eliminated the barriers of distance which once blurred national, economic, and racial inequalities. The increased flow of goods and ideas, penetrating to all parts of the world, has encouraged widespread ferment among millions in Asia, Africa, and Latin America, who rightly demand a greater share of political and economic opportunity. In today's world, Cuba and the Congo are our next-door neighbors and India lives just across the street.

The physical conquest of time and distance has also fostered the grouping of mankind into ever-larger communities bound together by common traditions and values.

Our own nation has become a leader of one of the two major opposing groups and has assumed an inescapable responsibility for

277

promoting and defending the concept of human dignity and freedom against the determined assault of those who would hold man in subservience to the state.

Over a world thus divided hangs the menace of incalculable devastation, born of the same science and technology to which we look for the greater well-being of all men. It is here that the fateful historic dichotomy is most apparent. We rely upon science and technology for the betterment of man's lot in a world at peace. Yet it is the threat of science and technology misdirected which places the most deadly obstacle in the way of this great objective. . . .

While the maintenance of deterrent strength is a matter of vital necessity, this alone accomplishes little more than the creation of a stalemate—literally, a balance of terror. To progress toward the goal of bettering man's lot, positive steps are essential to reduce the threat posed by these weapons, to encourage by democratic means the aspirations of the millions in underdeveloped regions of the world, and to strengthen at home the heritage which we shall leave to future generations of Americans.

These objectives have been generally accepted by Americans as essential national goals. In this new age, national policies to attain these goals must be framed in full awareness of the incalculable potentials inherent in science and technology.

As a means toward reducing present threats, science and technology play a role which already has become evident to us. In reaching decisions relating to nuclear weapons, whether military or political, the advice of the scientist has become indispensable. The same is true in the matter of agreement on any inspection plans involved in proposals for disarmament. At the same time, we must continue to look to science and technology for constantly improved defenses and for deterrents which will avoid apprehension or misunderstanding among nations who are encouraged by our adversaries to distrust our motives. . . .

Our science and technology are fully as vital to the affirmative programs which we contemplate for supporting the upward march of the millions who have yet to share in the dynamic changes which have brought such vast benefits to our own society. The urgency of

such programs has been sharpened by recent and growing Commu-

nist moves to secure economic and political domination of these regions through projects deceptively clothed in the prestige of Soviet
science and technology.

Throughout the new nations and underdeveloped lands of
Africa, Asia, and Latin America, the economic strength essential to
freedom requires an increase in the production of food and goods at
a rate faster than the rate of population growth. In many cases, the
problem initially is one of providing trained experts and knowledge,
drawn from our large store of scientific and technological talents.
Subsequent stages probably would involve material aid in the form
of equipment and capital.

From our science and technology are coming devices and techniques which seem to relate directly to the most urgent needs of these
less privileged nations—new methods of harnessing energy from the
sun, from the atom, and from conventional fuels; advanced systems
of communication for educational as well as general use; improved
chemicals, implements, and conservation methods for expanding
food production.

Against this background of progress and problems, it is apparent
that both our own future needs and the hostile actions of world
Communism challenge us to cultivate our scientific and technological resources and to employ them with understanding and wisdom,
at home and abroad. . . .

The means for satisfying the thirst for knowledge and for applying the fruits of science to man's service through technology are today greater than ever before. At the same time, the vast outpouring
of scientific progress in the past two decades has transformed our
material environment with such swiftness that we appear generally
to have been unable to comprehend its full sweep and significance.

Within this great and swift advance are continuing and accelerated trends and discoveries which promise even more remarkable advances during the years just ahead. Immense gains in knowledge and
understanding will be achieved through intensified exploration beyond the horizons of the known, throughout the spectrum of nature,
from the atom to the universe. Inexhaustible energy for man's use
may be won through the harnessing of nuclear fusion. A substantial
rise in man's intellectual level and greater mutual understanding can **279**

result from new techniques of education and world communication. An end to hunger in the world will be brought closer through achievements in biology and agricultural science.

To move steadfastly toward these inspiring prospects through the dangers of the present, a free society must rely upon the will of a people who can look beyond the dangers to the promise which science and technology hold for the fulfillment of human aspirations. For people everywhere, there must be a growing awareness of science and of what the combined forces of science and technology can provide. In this new age, there must be understanding and affirmation of the intimate relationship between science and technology and national and world policies.

(Copy of memorandum and covering note in bound volume: *Correspondence between Vice President Richard M. Nixon and David Sarnoff, 1954–1961*; David Sarnoff Library, Princeton, N.J.)

Four Memorable Trips

Remarks at 55th-anniversary luncheon
Given by the United States Senate
Washington, D.C., August 30, 1961

During the years I have spent in the electronics industry, which is worldwide in its scope, I have had to travel widely both at home and abroad. Of all my trips, four stand out in my memory, and they will remain with me so long as I live. I would like to say a word or two about each of these four trips—not because I would presume upon your patience to indulge in reminiscence, but because I think that these trips, together, symbolize the spirit, the meaning, the purpose, and the opportunities of America.

My first trip was made in 1900, when I left with my mother and two brothers the country of my birth, Russia. I was then nine years old and the oldest of the children. We sailed across the Atlantic Ocean in a small and slow ship. We traveled in the steerage, and it took us more than a month to arrive in the United States—the wonderful new land of opportunity. When I arrived in New York, I was unable to speak or understand a word of English. I was in a new world, in a new society, among a new people. However, it didn't take me very long to reap all the advantages of America's fine and free public school system—nor did anybody interfere with me when I worked as a newsboy before and after school hours in order to help support myself and my family.

That was trip number 1 in my memory.

Trip number 2 came only nine years later. As a boy of eighteen, I sailed on the steamship *New York*, of the American Line, from New York to Southampton, England. This time I traveled as the Marconi wireless operator on the ship. I was the only operator aboard, for it wasn't until the *Titanic* disaster in 1912 that a law was passed by Congress requiring each passenger ship to carry a complement of wireless operators who could serve around the clock. So there I was, nine years after arriving in this country, serving as the Marconi wireless operator on a first-class passenger liner, with a first-class cabin all to myself, with a uniform and gold braid, classified as a ship's officer, messing with the captain and the other officers, and entertaining and being entertained by the first-class passengers.

That was another trip for my memory.

My third trip, twenty years later, in 1929, was on the steamship *Aquitania*. I left New York for Paris as an assistant to Mr. Owen D. Young, who was chairman of the United States Reparations Commission. In addition to Mr. Young, I accompanied Mr. J. P. Morgan, Mr. Thomas Lamont, and Mr. Nelson Perkins, all members of the Commission. Our mission was to reach final agreement with the Germans on the debts and other problems left by World War I and to replace what was then the Dawes Plan with what later became the Young Plan. In the company of these financial and industrial giants and working as Mr. Young's assistant, I was selected to negotiate on behalf of our Allies with Dr. Hjalmar Schacht, who represented the Germans. I carried on these negotiations with Dr. Schacht for some six weeks. Of course, we thought then we had solved the pressing problems of that time, but we found out very soon thereafter that our plans and our hopes were all dashed to the ground by Adolf Hitler, who repudiated the agreement that was signed in Paris.

However, the impressive and human part of that trip to me was not only the companionship of these important men, who were   **281** much older and wiser than I, but the fact that I was a member of that group and that we were met at Cherbourg by high officials of the French government. This time, no passport problems, no baggage problems, no customs problems. Our reception was conducted with the pomp and protocol that the French are so expert in providing. We were taken from a special tender to a private train supplied by the French government, which whisked us to Paris and the comforts of the Ritz Hotel.

I shall never forget the moment, during this third trip, when I stood on the deck of that tender, reflecting upon this novel experience. The picture that flashed through my mind then was my first crossing of the Atlantic in the steerage. I thought of the contrast between the two trips and the fact that this could happen only in America. For it is as true today as it was then that no other country in the world provides such vast opportunities to develop and to express whatever talents an individual may possess.

On that occasion, I remember saying to myself, "God bless America." Surely, I am no exception, for there are many, many others in the United States who have also developed, advanced, and prospered. I have tried to convey this message to the rising generation of Americans and to point out to them that in my view there are more opportunities in our country today than there were when I arrived in New York in 1900. There are more people in the world, more wants to satisfy, and more resources and tools to employ today than there were then. No American boy or girl needs to weep with Alexander that there are no more worlds to conquer.

Now I come to my fourth trip, and that occurred only today. From New York, I have come to the capital of this nation to be received and honored by the distinguished members of the United States Senate—the greatest deliberative body in the world. I am not sure that any man deserves so great an honor as you are bestowing upon me, but I do want to express to you, Mr. Chairman, and to your distinguished colleagues, how deeply moved and profoundly grateful I am for the friendship you have shown me, for this handsome tribute, and for this wonderful reception.

(Printed booklet: "Fifty-fifth Anniversary Testimonial to David Sarnoff.")

Man and Space

Address at Oklahoma City University
Oklahoma City, Okla., May 27, 1962

For the first time in human history, it is possible to foretell with some degree of exactitude the shape of things to come. In no way that I can identify are we more intelligent than our ancestors, but we are vastly more knowledgeable. What we have done is to organize our knowledge into a coherent pattern, view it in terms of clearly visualized objectives, and utilize it for specific results. Moreover, we are doing this on a scale that in science, at least, dwarfs the sum of all man's previous efforts.

. . . In the fifth year of the Space Age, we know that much of the information we have long sought lies in the vastness beyond the atmosphere. We have reason to hope that as we penetrate and explore this void, we may at last find answers to profound secrets that have always tantalized man: the origin of our world, the nature of gravity, the riddle of life, and whether we are members of a cosmos in which there are, perhaps, millions of inhabited planets in solar orbits such as our own.

. . . What happens in space will affect and, in some instances, dominate our lives on earth. Even now we can see the outlines forming. Man's ways—his modes of work and habits of living, the scope of his thinking, his means of communication and transport, his techniques of learning, his health, life, and outlook on life—all will be fundamentally altered by space. He will be less subject to the whims of nature, for he will be able to foresee and to an extent control some of these whims. Both space and time will be radically shrunk and in some respects virtually eliminated. As the most intrepid of his fellows venture further into the universe, he will have the universe brought within closer reach. Man's concepts of himself and his place in the cosmos will be profoundly revolutionized.

Space will become a vital factor in the national economy, perhaps the dominant one. Already, more than 5,000 companies and research organizations are engaged in civilian and military space ac-

Space a Vital Economic Factor

283

tivities, producing some 3,200 different products related to space enterprises. They range the spectrum of major industries—electronics and communications, metals and fuels, machinery and instruments, chemistry, plastics, ceramics, textiles, and scores of others —whose technology will penetrate every corner of the economy.

We will see new materials, devices, products, power sources, and control and communication systems, designed originally for space purposes, changing our methods of production, distribution, and consumption. They will be lightweight, compact, durable, and reliable in the extreme. Many will operate themselves or other systems for long periods, over great distances, frequently without supervision, repair, or replenishment—in factories, offices, homes, and remote places.

With other nations, particularly in Western Europe, speeding their economic development at an unprecedented rate, our space technology may well be the means of keeping this nation in the competitive forefront. As automation gains momentum, space activities will generate new jobs and careers for the craftsman, technician, and professional. If—as we all ardently hope—the millennium of true disarmament ever arrives, space may be the instrument for diverting the energies devoted to weaponry to a new and higher economic effort.

. . . This ancient world of ours is stirring with fresh vitality. It will call for all the audacity of your mind and spirit and all the learning you have acquired. It will bring out the finest in your pioneering heritage—to seek and find new ways and, if need be, to make them. . . .

(Printed booklet: "Man and Space," by David Sarnoff;
David Sarnoff Library, Princeton, N.J.)

Science and the Future

Article in *Fortune*
Issue of May, 1964

Science and technology will advance more in the next thirty-six years than in all the millennia since man's creation. By the century's end, man will have achieved a growing ascendancy over his physical being, his earth, and his planetary environs.

The primary reason is man's increasing mastery of the electron and of the atom from which it springs. Through this knowledge, he is capable of transforming everything within his reach, from the infinitesimally small to the infinitely large. He is removing the fetters that for more than a million years have chained him to the earth, limited his hegemony over nature, and left him prey to biological infirmities.

By the year A.D. 2000, I believe our descendants will have the technological capacity to make obsolete starvation, to lengthen appreciably the Biblical life-span, and to change hereditary traits. They will have a limitless abundance of energy sources and raw materials. They will bring the moon and other parts of the solar system within the human domain. They will endow machines with the capacity to multiply thought and logic a millionfold.

Food. The Western nations by the turn of the century will be able to produce twice as much food as they consume, and—if political conditions permit—advanced food production and conservation techniques could be extended to the overpopulated and undernourished areas. New approaches—the protein enrichment of foods, genetic alteration of plants and animals, accelerated germination and growth by electronic means—will be widely used. The desalinization of ocean waters and the tapping of vast underground freshwater lakes, such as the one some believe to underlie the Sahara, can turn millions of desert acres to bloom. The ocean itself, covering seven-tenths of the earth's surface, will systematically be cultivated for all kinds of plant crops and fish—floating sea farms. Man's essential nutrients are reducible to chemical formulas, and ultimately the laboratory will create highly nutritive synthetic foods, equaling in palatability and price the products of the land. As that happens, his total dependence upon the products of the soil will terminate.

Raw materials. Technology will find ways of replenishing or replacing the world's industrial materials. The ocean depths will be mined for nickel, cobalt, copper, manganese, and other vital ores. Chemistry will create further substitutes for existing materials, transmute others into new forms and substances, and find hitherto

285

unsuspected uses for the nearly 2,000 recognized minerals that lie within the earth's surface. Oil and coal will be used increasingly as the basis for synthetics. Long before we have exhausted the existing mineral resources, the world will have developed extraction and processing techniques to keep its industries going largely on raw materials provided by the ocean waters and floor, the surface rocks, and the surrounding air. The rocks that crust the earth contain potentially extractable quantities of such basic metals as iron, copper, aluminum, and lead. The ocean abounds in a variety of chemicals.

Energy. The energy at man's disposal is potentially without limit. One pound of fissionable uranium the size of a golf ball has the potential energy of nearly 1,500 tons of coal, and the supply of nuclear resources is greater than all the reserves of coal, oil, and gas. Increasingly, electric-power plants will be nuclear, and atomic energy will be a major power source, particularly in the underdeveloped areas. Small atomic generators will operate remote installations for years without refueling. Electronic generators, converting energy directly to electricity, will light, heat, and cool homes, as will solar energy. Many areas of the world also may draw power from thermal gases and fluids within the earth's crust. Ultimately, even more powerful energy sources will be developed—thermonuclear fusion, the tapping of heat from deep rock layers, the mutual annihilation of matter and antimatter.

Health. Science will find increasingly effective ways of deferring death. In this country, technology will advance average life expectancy from the Biblical "three score and ten" toward the five-score mark, and it will be a healthier, more vigorous, and more useful existence. The electron has become the wonder weapon of the assault on disease and disability. Ultraminiature electronic devices implanted in the body will regulate human organs whose functions have become impaired—the lungs, kidney, heart—or replace them entirely. Electronics will replace defective nerve circuits and will substitute for sight, speech, and touch. Chemistry will help to regenerate muscles and tissues. Laser beams—highly concentrated light pulses—operating inside the body within needle-thin tubes will perform swift, bloodless surgery. By the end of the century, medical diagnosis and treatment will be indicated by computers, assem-

bling and analyzing the latest medical information for use by doctors anywhere in the world.

Genetics. Before the century ends, it will be possible to introduce or eliminate, enhance or diminish, specific hereditary qualities in the living cell—whether viral, microbic, plant, animal, or human. Science will unravel the genetic code, which determines the characteristics that pass from parent to child. Science will also take an inanimate grouping of simple chemicals and breathe into it the spark of elementary life, growth, and reproduction. When this occurs, man will have extended his authority over nature to include the creative processes of life. New and healthier strains of plants and animals will be developed. Transmitted defects of the mind or body will be corrected in the gene before life is conceived. If cancer proves to be genetic or viral, it may be destroyed at the source. There appear, in fact, to be few ultimate limits to man's capacity to modify many forms of living species.

Communications. Through communications satellites, laser beams, and ultraminiaturization, it will be possible by the end of the century to communicate with anyone, anywhere, at any time by voice, sight, or written message. Satellites weighing several hundred tons will route telephone, radio and television, and other communications from country to country, from continent to continent, and between earth and space vehicles and the planets beyond. Participants will be in full sight and hearing of one another through small desk instruments and three-dimensional color-TV screens on the wall. Ultimately, individuals equipped with miniature TV transmitter-receivers will communicate with one another via radio, switchboard, and satellite, using personal channels similar to today's telephone numbers. Overseas mail will be transmitted via satellite by means of facsimile reproduction. Satellite television will transmit on a worldwide basis directly to the home, and a billion people may be watching the same program, with automatic language translation for instant comprehension. Newspaper copy originating on one continent will be transmitted and set in type instantly on another. Indeed, by the year 2000, key newspapers will appear in simultaneous editions around the world.

Travel. From techniques developed for lunar travel and other **287** purposes, new forms of terrestrial transport will emerge. Earth vehicles riding on air cushions and powered by nuclear energy or fuel cells will traverse any terrain and skim across water. Forms of personal transportation will include such devices as a rocket belt to carry individuals through the air for short distances. Cities at opposite points of the globe will be no more than three to four hours apart in travel time, and individuals will breakfast in New York, lunch in Buenos Aires, and be back in New York for dinner. Indeed, the greatest problem will be the adjustment of time and habit to the tremendous acceleration in the speed of travel. As rocket systems are perfected and costs are reduced, it is possible to foresee the transport of cargo across continents and oceans in tens of minutes. Within and among cities and countries, the foundation will be laid for the movement of freight through underground tubes, automatically routed to its destination by computers.

. . . *Air and space.* Around earth, a network of weather satellites will predict with increasing accuracy next season's floods and droughts, extremes of heat and cold. It will note the beginnings of typhoons, tornadoes, and hurricanes in time for the disturbances to be diverted or dissipated before they reach dangerous intensity. Ultimately, the development of worldwide, long-range meteorological theory may lead to the control of weather and climate. Space will become hospitable to sustained human habitation. Manned laboratories will operate for extended periods in space, expanding our basic and practical knowledge about the nature of the universe, the planets, and earth. Permanent bases will be established on the more habitable planetary neighbors, and from these a stream of televised reports and radioed data, inanimate and conceivably also living matter, will flow to earth.

Despite these enormous changes, the machine in the year 2000 will still be the servant of man. The real promise of technology is that it will release man from routine drudgeries of mind and body and will remove the final imprint of the cave. In doing so, science will give new validity to Alfred North Whitehead's profound observation that civilization advances "by extending the number of important operations we can perform without thinking about them." Man's mind will then be free for the creative thinking that must be

done if the impact of science is to be harmonized with man's enduring spiritual, social, and political needs.

(Mimeographed text: David Sarnoff Library, Princeton,
N.J.)

A World Patent System

Address before the Patent, Trademark and
Copyright Research Institute conference
George Washington University, June 16, 1966

More than 3 million American patents have resulted from the government's encouragement to "science and the useful arts." Taken as a group, they have contributed profoundly to America's technological, economic, military, and political leadership and have reshaped the course of history.

The patent procedures which made possible this early flow of inventiveness were attuned to the requirements of individual artisans and inventors who worked independently on their own inventions. With their limited resources, they sought to create for a market that extended no farther than the boundaries of their region or nation, and the device or product they created could nearly always be clearly defined as their own.

Today, the character and scope of the inventive process have changed profoundly. The application of new ideas to practical uses has created new industries and stimulated the growth of old ones, giving new impetus to a growing economy.

The search for new ideas commands the resources of government, education, and private enterprise. Under the stimulus of new concepts, vast and complex facilities have been constructed and industries have grown up almost overnight. The development of new products, processes, and systems has engaged hundreds of thousands of our finest minds, and the fruits of their interlocking efforts are evident wherever civilization extends.

Against this background of extraordinary technological growth, it is ironic that the very instrument designed to advance this progress has not kept pace with the progress it has stimulated. In this age **289** of mass invention, which has produced deep space probes, supersonic flight, and satellite communications, the patent structure of most nations is no longer capable of meeting the requirements imposed by technological change and economic growth.

The United States, for example, is the world leader in quantity and variety of invention, but an average of three years is still required for passage from patent application to patent issue. In some instances, both here and abroad, this time period is even longer. These delays have, in some cases, retarded the progress of an idea from the mind to the marketplace.

When we can transmit an idea around the world in less than one-seventh of a second, why must years elapse before that idea can be validated within or outside the country of origin? Why must an inventor still make separate application in every country where he wishes to protect his idea? Why should some countries make no provision at all for patent filings or impose severely restrictive conditions upon the inventor?

The answers lie in the fragmented array of national patent systems, most of them working in isolation from the others. This condition inhibits the swift and equitable worldwide distribution of patent benefits—through new technology, new industry, and expanded markets. The consequences are unfortunate enough in the industrialized nations, but they are even more damaging to the underdeveloped members of the world community.

**Patents and the
Underdeveloped
Countries**

As technology becomes more complex, the problem of sharing it with others becomes more difficult to solve. Today, material wealth is largely concentrated in a group of nations with only one-third of the world's population. The remaining two-thirds account for less than one-tenth of the world's industrial production, generate less than one-quarter of the world's energy, and produce little more than one-third of the world's food.

To help overcome this disturbing situation, I believe there must be a more equitable distribution of technical know-how and stronger encouragement of inventiveness in the nations that have been left behind in the wake of modern technology. . . . One of **290** today's principal challenges is to design an international patent structure that can accommodate the revolutionary changes in technology and spread its benefits more evenly around the world. Through the tremendous advances that have been made in one aspect of this technology—in communications—the physical means are available to accomplish this purpose. It is now technically feasible to establish a universal patent system, utilizing the latest communications devices and concepts, to bring swiftness, order, and reasonable uniformity to the entire patent structure. . . . A global patent system could now be accommodated technically in a worldwide communications service just as readily as global television, global weather reporting, and global computer services.

A World Patent Center

. . . A world patent center could receive and process applications from inventors everywhere. This center would be the focus of the world patent system, linked to all countries by high-capacity satellite communications and built around a large data-processing and information-storage system.

Incoming data on inventions, appropriately coded in the country of origin, would be compared with key data on prior patents in the same field, retrieved from the computer memory. The novelty and patentability of the idea could be determined within an infinitely shorter time than is now the case—and this could be determined on a worldwide rather than simply a national basis. In addition, the means of instant access to all data could speed immensely the comparison and adjudication of conflicting claims.

Since vast amounts of data accumulate over a short time in this era of growing invention, it has become increasingly difficult to keep track of the progress being made and the patents being issued. Therefore, the patent center also could serve as an international reference source of invention and technology. It could, upon request, provide copies of patents and distribute technical data to interested parties.

In a project of such magnitude, with its many potentialities for service, we cannot expect universal operation to begin overnight. Practical experience suggests that nations will move slowly toward the concept of a single world patent system. But it should be possible to begin applying such a concept on a limited scale among a few

291

major patent countries, sophisticated in the use of technology and conscious of the need. Later, as its advantages became evident, other nations could join the project, and its services would correspondingly expand.

Assuming that such an international agreement can be achieved, it is possible within the next several years to foresee an inventor, patent attorney, or other interested party sitting in his office and submitting a patent application and the accompanying designs through a desk instrument linked by satellite to the central or regional computer of the world patent office. Should there be no problems, the inventor would be informed within a matter of days that his patent had been approved and registered in as many countries as requested.

With this transformation in the world patent process, we could expect many advantages to emerge. Among them would be:

1. A basic simplification of the total process. By providing quick and complete access to all of the relevant information in a patent search, the resolution of conflicting claims could be expedited. The result should be less costly and less time-consuming and should produce a greater respect for the patent system.

2. The ready availability of know-how to people in all countries through a swift and orderly system protecting the interests of inventor and user alike.

3. A spur to improved education in the underdeveloped nations, in order to take maximum advantage of newly available technology.

4. A greater incentive to intellectual investment by the governments and enterprises of the industrialized nations, leading to a climate more conducive to invention and innovation everywhere.

5. A narrowing of the gap created by today's imbalance in technology between the have and have-not nations. . . .

The great challenge of our time is to match the capabilities of technology to the needs of humanity. A world patent system, functioning as I have suggested here, could play an important role in meeting that challenge.

(Printed booklet of text reprinted from *Idea*, vol. 10, published by the Patent, Trademark and Copyright Research Institute, George Washington University.)

Patents and Progress

Address before the Interindustry Conference on International Patents
Frankfurt/Main, Germany, June 7, 1967

Invention and innovation must flourish in an atmosphere free of national and regional restrictions if we are to stimulate economic growth and world trade. This was uppermost in my thoughts a year ago in Washington when I urged the application of advanced information technology to a new world patent system.

Such a system would combine the great capacity of satellite communications and the immense data storage and processing capabilities of computers. It would permit determination of the novelty and patentability of an idea on a worldwide basis and with infinitely greater speed than is now possible.

I hesitated at that time to predict just how soon such a system might become practical, because of the magnitude of the project. But so swift is the pace of scientific and engineering progress that that which seemed distant a year ago has now entered the realm of imminent reality.

By 1975, it should be possible to establish an electronic world patent-search system containing instantly available data on every existing patent and patent application, accessible to every inventor or his agent as well as to every potential user of his invention. Such a center would be the vital heart of a workable global patent system.

In three major areas—communications, information storage, and electronic printing—advances and research breakthroughs in recent months have converged to bring this goal within early reach.

New generations of communications satellites with vastly increased capacities are on the drawing board, and new cable facilities are also being expanded. At the same time, a revolutionary discovery has opened the way to an all but limitless capability for the central storage of information in easily accessible form.

This advance is based upon the use of lasers, which generate controlled light beams for the transmission of information, and a new lensless picture process known as *holography*. In the laser hologram, a standard typewriter-size page of copy and pictures can be

293

reduced to a pinpoint of light—a minute fraction of the space required by microfilm.

As the system is developed, it will be possible to transfer all of the information on 100,000 standard typewriter-size pages to a single card approximately the area of an automobile license plate.

There is parallel progress, too, in the development of computer circuits and memories to keep pace with the vast external storage capacity offered by the laser hologram. Computers now in planning will be able to store up to 100 million bits of information in their main memory units and retrieve them at the rate of a millionth of a second per bit.

New electronic techniques are also becoming available to eliminate any significant delay in printing the rising torrent of information from the computer. High-speed electronic printers currently in development will be able to reproduce data flowing directly from computers at thousands of lines per minute—far more rapidly than the most advanced mechanical printers now in use.

Electronic systems now coming into use can compose images, diagrams, and text a hundred times more rapidly than conventional manual and mechanical methods. With the latest of these, a 600-page book could be made up in any desired typeface in only an hour.

All of these new electronic printing methods use memory systems that store a wide variety of type symbols. This arrangement would allow us to print out patent data in any one of many desired languages with different alphabets or characters—Roman, Cyrillic, Japanese, Arabic, or even Sanskrit.

With all of these elements as building blocks, we can envision a working world patent-search center that would be the nucleus of a unified system for determining the originality of an invention anywhere in the world.

The search system would comprise a network of national and regional patent offices linked by satellite, cable, and overland circuits to a central computer. Each of the national and regional offices would maintain laser-hologram files of all existing patents and patent applications in its area.

Whenever an inventor filed a patent application in any country

in the system, the information would be flashed via the world network to the computer. From the computer, an automatic call would
go to all offices in the network for any information in their hologram
files needed to determine the novelty of the invention.

The whole process, from start to finish, would be automatic and
practically instantaneous, and the inventor filing the application
would know within hours whether he could obtain a world patent
on his idea.

While the technical feasibility of such a system is imminent, this
does not mean that it can start operating the moment it is delivered
—like a toaster or a television set. An essential requirement for a
global system of any type is prior agreement on basic standards and
procedures. . . .

Beyond this, there are important operational questions to be re-
solved. Who should have access to the data in the search system
and under what conditions? What procedures should be followed in
adding new information to the files? How will outdated material be
eliminated?

The answer to these and other crucial questions can only come
within the framework of a broad international accord. We can give
birth to great concepts in our scientific laboratories, but they must
be brought to fruition in the parliaments of nations. While technology forges the means, political agreements among nations must
delineate the ends.

We must resolve conflicts of attitude, tradition, and law. We
must smooth differences in procedure and reconcile our varied policies and practices. We must cease, for example, to characterize the
identical employment of patents as a privilege in one country and
an abuse in another. Certainly, no global system worthy of the
name can be built on the restricted foundations of nationalism.

Those of us who represent industrialized nations should be particularly responsive to the value of a universal patent system that is
reliable, fast, simple, and reasonably priced. For the great preponderance of invention in the world today continues to take place
within our borders.

Nevertheless, whatever patent system evolves must also reflect
a deliberate concern for the progress of the developing nations. It **295**

must recognize—as a resolution of the United Nations' General
Assembly has set forth—that access to knowledge and experience in
technology is essential to the enlargement of their economic produc-
tivity.

. . . We must assist the emerging countries in mastering technology rather than simply offering them its fruits. It is both en-
lightened self-interest and good business for the industrialized third
of the world to seek advancement for the other two-thirds. If it does
not, advancing technology will simply serve to magnify the already
perilous imbalance between the have and the have-not nations.

This international conference in Frankfurt will seek and undoubtedly find agreement in many areas bearing on the problems of
patents. But if it achieves agreement on one subject alone—the need
for immediate development of an electronic world patent-search system—it will have taken a major step forward toward the realization
of true universality in the process of invention. In doing so, this
conference can contribute significantly to man's long and continuing search for world peace and progress.

(Printed booklet: "Patents and Progress," by David
Sarnoff.)

Sixtieth Anniversary—Reflections on
the Social Responsibilities of Technology

Address at 60th-anniversary dinner
New York City, September 30, 1966

We have come together, in the final analysis, to salute six decades of
electronics history and the countless men and women whose brains
and labors and courage have woven the tapestry of that history. I
have been cast as a symbol of our common dedication and purpose,
and in that spirit I not only accept the salute in humility but join it
in pride. . . .

Through electronics we have telescoped space and time and conquered isolation. We have probed the heavens and oceans, con-
296 nected the continents, manipulated instruments across millions of

miles of space, informed and entertained mankind, and stored for instant use vast accumulations of human knowledge.

We have become a new band of explorers, impelled by what Albert Einstein called "a holy curiosity." We have shared the same great moments of anticipation and eagerness that men of an earlier age experienced when they sailed with Columbus or Magellan or Drake. And this adventure, far from diminishing with time, has taken on new dimensions. Every discovery and invention has been simply a prelude to new challenges and fresh opportunities.

You and I, and our colleagues throughout the world, sit at the focal center of forces which are reshaping civilization. The next five years will bring more dramatic technological progress than any comparable period we have known. The opportunities facing our youth are, if anything, more challenging and promising than those that we of the pioneering generations enjoyed.

This is what keeps us all moving steadfastly in the electron's orbit. Because it is so dynamic, so alive with change and promise, electronics has from the beginning attracted men of exceptional creativity and daring, impatient of the static and routine. Together they have built this great industry under the creative spur and challenge of competition.

Competition, of course, is the ally of freedom and progress, but it can sometimes put a strain on human relationships. Indeed, at one time or another over the years, some of us in this hall have been adversaries, and our confrontations have occasionally been spirited. Yet, here we are gathered in friendship and mutual esteem. This, it seems to me, speaks volumes for the bonds that join us in scientific and industrial fraternity.

In the months and years ahead, we will come to grips again, no doubt, but this is a logical and necessary accompaniment of the change and growth that serves our progress. We can wear our competitive scars with the pride of veterans, for they have been earned on a great battlefield for a common cause—the advancement of the electronics art and sciences for the public benefit.

There is no reason to doubt that the continuing progress of science and technology can provide solutions to most of the material problems that face the world. Our chief concern must be with the

SIXTIETH
ANNIVERSARY—
REFLECTIONS
ON THE SOCIAL
RESPONSIBILITIES
OF TECHNOLOGY

297

spiritual, social, and political progress of mankind. In the final analysis, it is the use to which the new invention is put, and not the invention itself, that determines its value to society.

In the past sixty years, our attentions have been focused primarily on the means to translate scientific knowledge to practical ends. Now I believe we must involve ourselves in the social applications of technology with the same energy and devotion that we give to its development. As the creators of progress, we share a new and fundamental responsibility to the purposes it serves. This is a challenge to us as individuals and as electronics pioneers facing the world of tomorrow. It is worthy of our finest talents. . . .

I am grateful to the very depths of my being for sixty years of challenge and adventure such as few men have been privileged to enjoy. . . . It is my humble prayer that we may march together toward a future that will continue to demand the best in each of us —that will help to better the lot of our fellow man and advance the cause of world peace.

(Printed booklet: "Salute to David Sarnoff by the Communications and Electronics Industries.")

Research—A Quarter Century of Change

Address at RCA Laboratories 25th-anniversary dinner
Princeton, N.J., September 28, 1967

. . . The accomplishments of the RCA research staff over the past quarter century are written in large letters upon the history of the new art and industry of electronics. To them and to their able co-workers in these laboratories belongs a major share of credit for RCA's progress during the years we commemorate today. . . .

Their explorations and applications, with those of their contemporaries in many other laboratories, have lighted the way into realms of science and technology which were but dimly perceived or entirely unknown a quarter century ago.

This combined effort has transformed electronics and communications beyond recognition. It has brought forth color television, the transistor, solid-state computers, integrated circuitry, the laser, super-conductive devices, and communications satellites. The familiar instruments of yesterday—the Morse key and the audion tube—now seem as remote as the spark-coil and coherer used in the early days of wireless telegraphy.

The end of this process defies prophecy, for it has in truth only begun. When our laboratory opened here in 1942, only a handful of companies sponsored research programs of significance. In electronics, the list included Bell Laboratories, General Electric, Westinghouse, RCA, and few (if any) others.

In that era, the quest for scientific knowledge was still felt to be largely the province of the university. The popular concept placed the scientist in a remote and separate sphere of life divorced from the practicalities of commercial enterprise and the pursuit of profitable business.

Today, research is every man's concern. Scientific exploration engages government and industry as well as universities, and the scientist is recognized and respected as a man of the world.

Princeton has become the nucleus of one of the nation's foremost scientific communities. Since RCA settled its research facilities here, scores of other private and commercial laboratories have moved into the area and the research activities of the university itself have been vastly enlarged. The region centering upon this campus has become a major fountainhead of new knowledge and technology, ranging across a spectrum from improved tiling to the exploration of means to control thermonuclear fusion.

The Princeton experience of the past quarter century has its parallel in other parts of the nation. Today, there is no viable industry which does not recognize the need for science to nourish its growth and secure its future. Research and development have become industries in themselves, responding to an insistent demand for new technology everywhere. They inspire and feed upon scientific progress, and the momentum that has been generated can carry us upward to unprecedented material achievement in the years ahead.

In communications, for example, I believe we now command such immense capabilities that we shall soon be able to do anything that the mind can visualize in linking people with people, people

299

with machines, and machines with machines. The rate of advance henceforth is more likely to be determined by economic, social, and political influences than by scientific or technical limitations.

What is true of communications is almost as true of all major technologies nourished by progress in research—medicine and public health, information and education, agriculture, energy, transportation.

Never have we been confronted with so many opportunities to better the lot of mankind or with so pressing a need to do so. Never have we been so well endowed with the physical means. During the past quarter century, there has been great progress in delineating major areas of scientific conquest and exploring their potentialities. Now the time has come to press ahead with their development and concerted application to some of our most urgent problems. . . .

These advantages, however, are not simply to be had for the taking. Oliver Wendell Holmes once remarked, with his homely wisdom, that "science is a first-rate piece of furniture for a man's upper chamber if he has common sense on the ground floor."

There is all too abundant evidence that the human race is still generally more gifted with ingenuity than with foresight and that common sense and common purpose may be more uncommon than we care to admit. We have failed to anticipate and prevent unwanted effects of technology, such as noise and pollution. We have been deficient in extending technology as widely as we might to the alleviation of poverty and the assault on illiteracy and ignorance.

Yet as I view the progress of science and technology today, I see more opportunities than ever before. I am not blind to the shortcomings in human nature which hinder the timeless quest for a better world based upon understanding, mutual respect, and freedom of choice. But I have an abiding faith in the ultimate determination of man to survive and benefit from his growing ability to master the forces of nature rather than to be destroyed by them. This faith is reinforced through the contacts which I have been privileged to maintain with the men of science, most of whom believe, as I do, that it is not the Creator's purpose to lead man toward destruction of this world.

300 I deeply believe that so long as men and their science are free to follow the truth wherever it leads, we shall find solutions to our problems and continue to progress. Then all that has happened here in these past twenty-five years, and all that has happened in the thousands of other research centers that have grown or come into being, will be far surpassed by the achievements of the years that lie ahead.

(Mimeographed text of an address by David Sarnoff.)

The Management of Environmental Forces

Address at the Freedom Award Dinner of the
International Rescue Committee
New York City, October 31, 1967

Every age has its distinctive and often contradictory hallmarks. Ours has been characterized by acts of exceptional cruelty, but it has also seen the human spirit reach new summits of courage and compassion.

For more than thirty years, the International Rescue Committee has responded to these twin developments—as an implacable enemy of tyranny on the one hand and as a dedicated agency of human freedom and dignity on the other.

It would indeed be man's finest hour if we could achieve a world in which the IRC might close the books on its work of human salvage—a world cleansed of mass inhumanity. But this day has not yet come. Against the somber background of Vietnam, Hong Kong, the Berlin Wall, the Middle East, and Cuba, there is unhappily little prospect that the enterprises on behalf of freedom can or should be relaxed.

Human lives are still to be rescued from tyranny and chaos, and this must be our immediate task. But beyond this, it is even more mandatory that we diagnose and treat the conditions which give rise to tyranny.

. . . Most of the unrest and violence that have shaken the structure of human society have arisen from the persistence of poverty,

301

hunger, disease, and ignorance among a majority of the world's people. Moreover, the pressures continue to rise as population growth outstrips the slow pace of economic development on the most impoverished continents.

By the end of the century, there will be four times more people living in the underdeveloped nations than in those with advanced industrial economies. Unless present trends are reversed, they may be even hungrier, poorer, more disease-ridden than the inhabitants of the most backward areas today.

Along with political oppression, these conditions represent further forms of tyranny from which men must be liberated. Accomplishing this will require a massive and organized offensive against poverty, scarcity, and ignorance, mobilizing human talents and resources everywhere on an unprecedented scale.

Until recently, such an ambitious effort would have been beyond our capabilities. Today, science and technology have called forth a host of powerful allies to aid us. Because of the astonishing burst of discovery, invention, and innovation during the past few decades, we have now within our reach the means to raise all of mankind to much higher levels of prosperity, health, and education before this century ends. . . .

Why, then, cannot man look forward to a future free of harassment and deprivation? The answer is that he does not yet know how to use or to control the enormous forces at his command. For all the vast benefits that it bestows on civilization, technology has also demonstrated that it can inflict deep and lasting social injuries on man and physical injuries on nature.

The carbon energy which runs our civilization also corrodes the atmosphere which gives us elemental life. The insecticides which produce our agricultural abundance pollute our waters and decimate our fish and bird life. The uncontrolled growth of the city and suburb scars our countryside and creates intolerable tensions in our communities.

Much thought has been given to the dangers of technology slipping away from human control, and some corrective measures have been proposed. The Department of Health, Education and Welfare has been a leader in this area, as have been many universities. Bills have been introduced in the Congress to deal with various aspects of the problem. One excellent proposal is to create a National Social Science Foundation and to give the social sciences a degree of support comparable to that which the physical sciences now enjoy.

These steps are all to the good, but they are not enough. We must implement our thoughts with suitable action. The technological dichotomy of today compels us to look to new approaches if we are going to keep this earth both tranquil and habitable.

We must begin to think of a new relationship in which our technology, our society, and our physical environment are considered as one organic unity. The physical sciences, the social sciences, and the humanities must plan their efforts in unison.

A New Profession

I believe we must have new forms of education, new learning disciplines—indeed, an entirely new profession—to reflect in practice the fundamental unity of man's life on this earth. We need a new type of professional—a manager of environmental forces.

His profession would deal with technology in its total relationship to the human and natural environment. His primary function would be to anticipate the possible effects of a new technology or a major technological innovation and to recommend practical and timely corrective actions.

The manager of environmental forces would serve governments and industries at the levels of decision, counseling them on broad problems involving technology and environmental and social change. He would work with the United Nations and its specialized agencies where the problems called for regional or international consideration. He would draw up plans for coping with problems already in existence and destined to reach crisis levels in the future. He would hold these plans in readiness, maintaining them on a current basis for use at the appropriate moment.

This new discipline would draw initially upon the elements of other major disciplines and professions. In time, it would acquire its own distinctive qualities and its own centers of professional instruction. Eventually, it would become a major new force in education, bridging the physical and biological sciences, the social sciences, and the humanities. Into each of the other disciplines it would also

303

help to instill a new sense of unity and purpose in relation to other fields—from medicine and the law to the sciences and arts.

The development of such an educational force could begin in the United States, but parallel centers of environmental management should also develop abroad since the success of the concept depends, in the long run, on universal acceptance.

It should be a lifetime profession to which the youth of the nation could aspire from their earliest years and which would require formal preparatory education leading to a doctorate. Indeed, the process of breaking down the barriers among the disciplines and creating an entirely new area of study should extend into the colleges and high schools and even the elementary schools.

Whether or not students ever entered the profession of environmental management, as adults they would be able to render more constructive judgments on the range of issues which affect technology, the nation, and the world. For these are the concern not only of the specialist but of every thinking inhabitant on earth.

Despite the world's chaos, human beings everywhere are endeavoring to build or renew their societies. They are struggling to provide the means to satisfy their elemental needs. They are trying to develop political and social institutions responsive to new and changing times.

This age, which has witnessed so much turbulence, has also seen a stirring affirmation of new loyalties to ancient human values—to justice, compassion, human responsibility, the eternal sanctities of life, liberty, and personal dignity. For more than a third of our century, the IRC has been the symbol of these loyalties in action. Today, on the threshold of immense new challenges and opportunities, we are called again to renew our dedication to our fellowman—not only in the act of rescue but also in the service of prevention.

With vision, concentration, and faith in mankind, we can bring enormous forces of support to these goals. Technology, properly guided, can satisfy every material human requirement—feed and clothe the world's multitudes, shelter them, give them work, and guard them from disease. The Western nations have shown that it is possible to meet man's political aspirations to govern himself and to

304 determine his own destiny.

If we can muster the wisdom to use the tools which technology has given us, the generosity to devote them to the benefit of all men, the humility to live in harmony with nature, there is little in the spectrum of human progress that is not within our grasp.

Indeed, with reason and will we can achieve for humanity what no civilization has thus far been able to provide—the basis for a truly enduring peace on earth.

(Printed booklet: "The International Rescue Committee
Freedom Award to David Sarnoff.")

THE
MANAGEMENT
OF
ENVIRONMENTAL
FORCES

305

307

308

311